MODERN
WEED
CONTROL

Modern mechanized weed control. Elimination of weeds on rights-of-way provides good visibility and prevents spread of weeds to adjacent farms. Many of our serious infestations of introduced weeds have come from railroads.(Photograph courtesy of Washburn Agricultural Service.)

MODERN WEED CONTROL

by

Alden S. Crafts

UNIVERSITY OF CALIFORNIA PRESS
BERKELEY · LOS ANGELES · LONDON

University of California Press
Berkeley and Los Angeles, California

University of California Press, Ltd.
London, England

ISBN 0-520-02733-7
Library of Congress Catalog Card Number: 74-76383
Printed in the United States of America

Designed by Henry Bennett

3 4 5 6 7 8 9 0

CONTENTS

PREFACE

Since the publication of the first edition of *Weed Control*, in 1942, the science of weed control has developed from a relatively insignificant practice to one of the major techniques of modern agriculture. Workers in this field, who numbered only a few in 1942, now include chemists, agronomists, plant physiologists, taxonomists, and weed researchers totalling several thousand. And weed-control technology, centered in Western Europe and the United States, has spread to encircle the globe. Weed control has become one of the major activities of agribusiness.

Herbicides, as listed in the appendix of this volume, now number over 200 and, in spite of the greatly increased cost of researching and developing new chemicals, are still being introduced in great numbers. Many of the older chemicals such as 2,4-D, the ureas, triazines, and uracils are finding new uses. And new chemicals of increasing selectivity and toxicity are appearing. One, glyphosate, represents a new approach to herbicidal action, namely the use of substituted amino acids as toxicants.

With the new concern for our environment brought on by air, soil, and water pollution, and by overuse and misuse of pesticides, much greater restrictions are placed on the use of our current arsenal of herbicides, and on the registration of new herbicides. In spite of these restrictions and the attendant increased costs, new herbicides are appearing and chemical weed control is on the increase. One of the newer developments is the combination of herbicides, insecticides, and fertilizers into a single liquid for simultaneous application. Thus, agriculture marches on in its attempt to feed and clothe the increasing millions of our population.

Many people have contributed to the publication of this new volume. My close associates in the Department of Botany at Davis, my many friends in the Weed Science Society of America, associates in the United States and in countries abroad, and the management and staff on the University of California Press. I hope that this book will continue, as have the previous three editions, to meet the needs of all who are interested in the basic principles of the botany of weeds, as well as the techniques used in their control.

A. S. Crafts

1

Plants and Man

Primitive man, with a population much smaller than ours today, was able to obtain his food by hunting and fishing and by collecting berries, fruits, and seeds. Agriculture, the domestication of animals, and the development of industry permitted population increases, which in turn, put greater and greater pressure upon food and fiber supplies.

Given our present population of over three billion, one third to one half of whom are always hungry, food production must have top priority among the needs of the people. And food production, despite a 36 percent rise in the current decade, has barely kept up with population increase (Hannah, 1972). While population control must become effective if the human race is to survive the twenty-first century, time is required to educate people the world around to the practices required. Meanwhile food production and distribution must be increased to stave off starvation and violence.

Modern agricultural technology could provide adequate food for many more people than those who are adequately nourished today, but time, education, and resource development will all be necessary. Vegetation management must be improved to eliminate inefficient tools, low-yielding crops, and pest-ridden fields and storage facilities. When all of the up-to-date, efficient, cultural practices, including pest control, processing methods, and distribution, are put into use, most of the world's population should be adequately nourished until birth control can level off population numbers and a stable condition can be attained.

When man first started to deliberately grow plants for food he soon learned that production was greatest when single crop species were grown alone, free from competition. Thus monoculture, contrary to nature's way, was developed, and the concept of weeds as unwanted plants that, through competition, reduced yields was born. And with the growing of plants in monoculture, insects and plant diseases became of much greater consequence. Scourges of grasshoppers, locusts, blights, and rusts became common, and weeds, pests since the earliest development of agriculture, took on new vigor as they became adapted to individual crops through selection. Cruciferous weeds such as the wild radish and the mustards plagued cereal production around the world; poppies became a common pest in Europe, and many other species became adapted to the growth requirements of specific crops.

As weed infestations began to seriously limit the production of crops, methods were devised to combat them. Crop rotations were devised in which winter weeds were controlled by tillage in summer crops, alternating with summer fallow and winter crops. In this way progressive farmers were able to keep their serious weeds under control while producing adequate crops. Leguminous crops were introduced into the rotations to enhance the fertility of the soil; alfalfa and clovers were grown in rotation with cereal and forage crops.

Row-crop culture, introduced to England in the eighteenth century by Jethro Tull, became a standard practice. Turnips and beets in Europe and maize in the Americas were successful crops; they could be rotated with cereals and, in the hands of industrious farmers, these methods sufficed to maintain food and fiber production at levels commensurate with the population, at least in the Western world. Even in the eighteenth and nineteenth centuries when the early mechanization of agriculture enabled man to keep up with population increases in the West, populations in India and China were outgrowing the food supplies and famines became common.

Concerning the role of weeds in the life of man, Holm (1971) has said, 'I have chosen to begin with the proposition that more energy is expended for the weeding of man's crops than for any other single human task" (Fig. 1–1). Holm has extensively surveyed the world's weed problems for the Food and Agriculture Organization of the United Nations. He tells of women and children working day after day in fields at the never-ending job of hoeing weeds, and he makes a plea for modernization of weed control so that women may have time to keep their homes and that children may have the privilege of going to school (Fig. 1–2). These opportunities which are taken for granted in the Western world, Holm explains, are available, in most tropical countries, to only a favored few.

In 1969 Holm listed what he and many of his associates consider to be the world's worst weeds (Table 1-1).

Eight of these weeds are grasses or sedges and five of them are perennials; all occur in some parts of the United States. Holm presents a map showing that these ten weeds are distributed rather uniformly around the world, and he goes on to describe ways, in addition to competition with crops, that weeds harm agriculture. Weeds harbor

FIGURE 1-1. "The man with the hoe," the traditional symbol of agrarian life before the introduction of herbicides.

insect pests and plant diseases, parasitic weeds cannot be controlled by traditional hand methods, and purple nutsedge and several perennial grasses have such regenerative powers that hand methods are ineffective. When one adds to this the difficulty of controlling aquatic weeds in lakes, drains, and irrigation ditches, the costs of holding weeds in check along highways and railroad and power rights-of-way, and the innumerable problems involved in industrial weed control, it is obvious that weeds pose a very serious and costly problem the world around.

FIGURE 1-2. Top left, pigweeds in young alfalfa. Bottom, women weeding young alfalfa; (top right) alfalfa weeded with diuron.

Weeds are plants growing where we don't want them. In our modern urbanized world they interfere with our activities and we have developed many ways to suppress or eradicate them. These methods vary with the type of weed, the nature of its weedy habit, the means available, and the relation of the method to the environment (Fig. 1-3).

Table 1-1. The World's Worst Weeds

Purple nutsedge (*Cyperus rotundus* L.)
Bermudagrass (*Cynodon dactylon*(L.) Pers.)
Barnyardgrass (*Echinochloa crusgalli* (L.) Beauv.)
Junglerice (*Echinochloa colonum* L.) Link
Goosegrass (*Eleusine indica* (L.) Gaertn.)
Johnsongrass (*Sorghum halepense* (L.) Pers.)
Guineagrass (*Panicum maximum* Jacq)
Waterhyacinth (*Eichhornia crassipes* Mart.) Solms
Cogongrass (*Imperata cylindrica* (L.) Beauv.)
Lantana (*Lantana camara* L.)

For financial reasons, methods used on a golf course or a public park cannot be applied on range land or in a forest. And chemicals sprayed on a roadside to eliminate unsightly weeds which constitute a fire hazard are not proper for use on cropland.

FIGURE 1-3a. Applying a contact herbicide in sugar cane with knapsack sprayers.

Thus weed control in the twentieth century has become a highly specialized activity. With over two hundred available herbicides and innumerable weed situations, thousands of highly trained personnel are employed in the practice of weed control. Universities and agricultural colleges teach courses in weed control. Many of our major chemical companies provide the necessary herbicides. Federal, state, and county agencies and private individuals are engaged daily in the practice of weed control. The growing of food and fiber crops depends on weed control for current levels of production. Within a half century weed control has become a multimillion-dollar industry and much of the advance in agricultural technology is in some way dependent upon

FIGURE 1-3b.   Applying a preemergence chemical by duster.

it. Highly developed in the Western world, weed control is slowly moving into the underdeveloped countries (Fig. 1-4). When fully established as an essential part of vegetation management, weed control will enhance the efficiency of agriculture and release millions of people from the drudge of hand methods, enabling them to proceed with modernization of their way of life (Fig. 1-5).

ALIEN SPECIES AS WEEDS

Weeds have developed and spread with the introduction of agriculture in new lands around the world. In the United States and Canada, a large percentage of the most pernicious weeds are aliens, introduced from Europe or from other countries in which the crops were grown before introduction. Weeds growing in the United States have come in from Europe, Asia, South Africa, South America, and Australia; their introduction has been related to the movements of people.

FIGURE 1-4. Left, corn field recently weeded by machete. Right, corn weeded with simazine.

The westward migration of people in the United States and Canada, the reclamation and settlement of new lands, the growing of useful crop plants and the development of the livestock industry have all contributed to the establishment of many undesirable alien species of plants. And this process is still going on in Alaska and in other regions where new lands are being opened for farming.

Many species of weeds have been present in the United States and Canada from the pioneering days; others have been introduced more recently; some have spread slowly, others with alarming rapidity. Giant foxtail, witchweed, Kikuyu grass, musk thistle, Dalmatian toad flax, and skeleton weed are recent introductions into various parts of the United States.

Major (1960), following studies in the Mediterranean countries and Near East, reported a number of weed species not now present in the western United States that are potentially noxious. A description of a few well-known weed species should serve to emphasize the need for rigid seed inspection, for vigilance in detecting incipient introductions, and for prompt eradication of all limited infestations of potentially noxious weeds.

FIGURE 1-5. Top, hand weeding is still a common practice in India—a field of young cotton. Bottom, a cotton field in Venezuela weeded with chemicals.

NUTSEDGE (*Cyperus rotundus*)

Nutsedge has the dubious honor of being named the world's worst weed by Holm (1969, 1971). It is an Asiatic perennial found around the world in the tropics and present in the temperate zones in most agricultural countries. It reproduces by seeds and by vegetative nutlets that are produced in great numbers at various depths in the soil. Although Day and Russell (1955) have shown that this weed may be controlled by dessication in the field, this method is not possible in the humid tropics where nutsedge causes its greatest losses (Fig. 1–6).

FIGURE 1-6. Vigorous young plant of *Cyperus rotundus*. Note the mother tuber, the mass of fibrous roots, and the young white rhizomes. These will bear new nutlets. (Photograph by courtesy of the California State Department of Agriculture).

JOHNSONGRASS (*Sorghum halepense*)

Johnsongrass, a native of southern Europe and Asia, was brought into this country from Turkey in about 1830 as a forage plant. It soon spread throughout the southern states and now occurs in the mid-Atlantic states, throughout the Mississippi Valley, and along the west coast from California to Washington.

Johnsongrass was introduced to California in about 1884, probably for forage, and has been supplemented by innumerable importations in commercial seeds (Sudan grass, for example). It is a serious pest in orchards, vineyards, alfalfa, open croplands, and along roadsides and in irrigation and drain ditches (Fig. 1-7). Its control has recently been greatly enhanced by the introduction of new grass killers such as organic arsonates and glyphosate (Crafts and Robbins, 1962).

FIGURE 1-7.   Johnsongrass, a vigorous weed.

BERMUDAGRASS (*Cynodon dactylon*)

Bermudagrass is a native of the tropics of the Old World. It is now distributed throughout tropical, subtropical, and semi-arid regions of the entire world. It does not survive where the soil is frozen during winters.

Bermudagrass is used as a forage crop, and certain selected varieties are important pasture and turf crops. It is also used as a soil binder on ditch and canal banks. Bermudagrass is listed by Holm (1969) as one of the world's worst weeds, and this stems from his experience in poorly developed tropical countries. It is prevalent in many sugar-cane-growing countries and is a pest in most plantation-grown crops where poor management prevails. Bermudagrass can be controlled by dry plowing and subsequent desiccation. It is susceptible to competition and to shading, and several modern herbicides may be used to keep it in check.

BARNYARDGRASS (*Echinochloa crusgalli*)

This grass, also commonly called watergrass, cockspurgrass, or cocksfoot panicum, is widely distributed throughout the warmer countries of the world, particularly in irrigated regions. It is a serious pest in rice, being the principal reason for flooding in some countries. It is also a nuisance in orchards, vineyards, in many irrigated row crops such as potatoes, tomatoes, and other vegetables, in sugar beets, young sugar cane, alfalfa, and seed crops. It is a vigorous, stout annual and produces great quantities of seeds; barnyardgrass seed screened out of rice in California is sold as feed for poultry and wild birds.

Barnyardgrass occurs in many varieties differing in stature, in germination, and in time of maturation. Propanil, a chemical used postemergence to kill barnyardgrass, has proven to be extremely toxic to prune trees in northern California. Propanil and preemergence materials are now available to handle this pest in rice.

JUNGLERICE (*Echinochloa colonum*) AND GOOSEGRASS (*Eleusine indica*)

These two annual grasses are common weeds in rice, sugar cane, cotton, and a host of other crops growing in the humid tropics and in irrigated regions. Introduced into the United States from the tropics, they have adapted to rice culture and in certain situations are very troublesome. In plantation agriculture in the tropics they have proven difficult to control. In the Western countries where they are a problem in turf, they have proven susceptible to preemergence herbicides and so are not considered noxious.

WATER HYACINTH (*Eichhornia crassipes*)

Water hyacinth, a native of tropical America, has seriously hampered navigation in lakes and rivers in many parts of the world. Holm (1969) terms it "the most massive, the most terrible and frightening weed problem I have ever known." Troublesome since 1890 in the Saint Johns River in Florida, this weed is present now in the tropics around the world. In developing countries it prevents people from fishing and hence denies them protein in their diets. In the Far East, floods cause great masses of the weed to crash through fences kept in the rivers for fish culture. In the tropics water hyacinth harbors insects that are vectors of animal and human diseases; snakes and crocodiles hide in the masses of vegetation. Many lakes in the world's tropics are covered with such dense mats of hyacinth that birds and small animals can walk about on them.

Huge amounts of money have been expended on opening up rivers for navigation; saw boats, dragline dredgers, and a host of other devices have been used. Efforts have been made to convert macerated hyacinth into livestock feed or fertilizer. The herbicide 2,4-D is effective in controlling hyacinth but it cannot be used in many situations because of the hazards of drift to valuable crops.

COGONGRASS (*Imperata cylindrica*)

This vigorous stout grass is the bane of farmers in India, Africa, and much of the Far East. It is a deep-rooted perennial that regrows rapidly when cut off and so far it has not proved particularly susceptible to grass killers such as dalapon and glyphosate.

HALOGETON (*Halogeton glomeratus*)

This plant, which occupies several million acres of arid sheep range in the western United States, is a relatively recent introduction from the Near East. Unnoticed for many years it came to the attention of sheep growers when large numbers of sheep died while being driven across infested areas. Studies proved that the plant is high in oxalates which precipitate calcium and cause tetany. The U. S. Department of Agriculture has spent large sums of money in studies on the life history and habits of this weed. So far no satisfactory methods of control have been found (Crafts and Robbins, 1962).

DUDAIM MELON (*Cucumis melo* variety *Dudaim*)

Dudaim melon is an annual cucurbit related to the cantaloupe. This newly recognized weed is a threat to asparagus. In 1955 it was observed as a pest in the Imperial Valley of California and in the Mexicali Valley of Mexico; in the latter area it escaped into pasturelands and became widespread. It has also been reported from Louisiana and Texas. At present its most dangerous site is the south bank of the All American Canal from whence floating fruits could be distributed to any field in the Imperial Valley; new infestations have been discovered near Holtville and west of El Centro. It already covers about 3000 acres in the Imperial Valley and it threatens alfalfa, sugar beets, and other crops used in rotation with asparagus.

Dudaim melon is a hardy, fast-growing weed which produces hundreds of fruits per plant, each containing an average of 276 seeds.

Viable seeds are produced from March until the first freeze; major production is in midsummer. Germination takes place whenever the temperature is above freezing. The plant is resistant to diseases and insects; seeds pass through animals intact. The fruits are eaten like cucumbers by the Mexican field workers in the area.

An eradication project has been initiated with a target date of 1982. Cooperation by the Agricultural Commissioners of Imperial County and the California Department of Food and Agriculture should be effective in the elimination of this potentially hazardous pest (Dixon and Kreps, 1973).

BIOLOGICAL CONTROL

St. Johnswort (*Hypericum perforatum*), puncturevine (*Tribulus terrestris*), prickly pear (*Opuntia sp*), lantana (*Lantana camara*), gorse (*Ulex europaeus*), tansy ragwort (*Senecio jacobaea*), and Scotch broom (*Cytisus scoparius*) are among the weeds being attacked by methods of biological control. Prickly pear and St. Johnswort have been brought under practical control; some of the others give promise of ultimate control; none will be eradicated, because biological control, to be successful, must reach an equilibrium between the host weed and the parasitic insect so that both may survive but with the weed at a low population level (Crafts and Robbins, 1962).

LOSSES CAUSED BY WEEDS

That weeds cause losses to farmers has been recognized for a long time, but few people recognize the multiple interrelations of weeds with our modern industrialized, suburbanized culture. There are many reasons for controlling weeds and these become more complex with time. Sunflowers, Johnsongrass, telegraphplant, horseweed, and a host of other tall, vigorous weeds were no problem in the horse-and-buggy days. Today they obscure vision on roads and make death traps of intersections. Foxtails and ripgut grass are nuisances to animals in a cow pasture; when the area is converted to a golf course or a public park they become insufferable. Poison oak is rather a pleasant shrub on a sunny hillside in the open country; in a military reservation or a boy scout campground it is a definite health hazard. And nothing is more pleasant than the waving heads of grass on a hillside in spring; but when the hillside becomes a tank farm for storage of oil, the fire hazard becomes serious in summer and the grass must be eliminated. Examples can be multiplied to cover every aspect of agriculture, forestry, highway, waterway, and public-land management, arboretum, park, and golf course care, and home landscape maintenance.

Weeds compete with crop plants for water, light, and nutrients. Weeds of rangelands and pastures may be unpalatable to animals;

they may cause injuries as with lodging of foxtails in horses' mouths; they may lower values of animal products as in the case of cockleburs or clotburs in wool; they may add to the burden of animal care as when horses graze in tarweeds and become covered with a black sticky mess; many weeds such as water hemlock, larkspur, halogeton, common groundsel, and locoweeds are poisonous. Many weeds are hosts of plant pathogens. Examples are prickly lettuce and sowthistle that serve as hosts for downy mildew, Johnsongrass, a host for sugar cane mosaic, wild mustards that host clubroot of cabbage, and saltbush and Russian thistle, in which curly top virus overwinters to be carried to sugar beets by leaf hoppers. And many weeds are the favorite hosts of insects; examples are *Lactuca* species that harbor bean thrips, nightshade that hosts pepper weevil, and jimsonweed that nourishes red spider, cotton aphid, and potato flea beetle (Crafts and Robbins, 1962).

Table 1-2.   Losses to Agriculture, National Annual Average 1942-1951

Soil losses—erosion, deterioration, floods	$1,512,000,000
Plant—insect losses, all crops	1,065,727,000
Plant—disease losses, all crops	2,912,601,000
Livestock diseases, all losses	1,847,904,000
Weed losses, agricultural land only	3,747,036,000

Competition from weeds can reduce crop yields in several ways. For example, if fifteen surface inches of water are necessary to mature a crop of barley and only half this much is available to the crop because of use by weeds, yield may be seriously reduced, even though mineral nutrients and light are available in abundance. On the other hand, in regions of abundant rainfall or irrigation where water is not limiting, utilization of minerals and shading by rank weed growth may ruin a crop.

While irrigation of arid western lands has been recognized as necessary, recent studies have shown that many crops in our midwestern and Atlantic-coast states also suffer water deficits, often as harvest time approaches in late summer; if these crops are infested with weeds, losses may be serious. While losses in quantity may be readily measurable by yield weights, often in seed, vegetable, and fruit crops, quality as well as quantity may be affected.

Losses from weeds to agriculture in the United States have been estimated to run between three and five billion dollars annually. Table 1-2 gives the average annual losses to agriculture from erosion, insects, diseases of plants and livestock, and weed losses confined to agricultural lands only. Table 1-3 gives losses caused by weeds (Crafts and Robbins, 1962) in the United States.

REGULATION OF HERBICIDE USE

Although the losses from weeds are serious, some aspects of the use of herbicides require restraints and regulation. The use of 2,4-D, while greatly relieving the farmer of the losses from weeds, had another side; in some places and in certain crops, drift of spray or vapors from the light esters of 2,4-D caused injury. The earliest signs of danger came from the drift and volatilization of 2,4-D compounds as they affected neighboring crops. Very soon after its introduction as a selective spray, 2,4-D-growth-regulatory symptoms were noted on grapes, cotton, tomatoes, alfalfa, melons, and other susceptible crops. Almost immediately lawsuits appeared in the courts, there were public hear-

Table 1-3. Losses Caused by Weeds

Source of loss	Acreage	Percentage reduction in potential value	Value of products	Annual loss from weeds
58 crops	357,835,000	10.2	$15,714,777,000	$1,789,175,000
Pasture and ranges.	1,020,000,000	9.1	4,715,100,000	471,510,000
Tillage costs .	977,520,000	7.4	18,579,387,000	1,486,351,000
				$3,747,036,000

ings in the Departments of Agriculture in many states, and in 1950 hazardous areas were set up by law in California where spraying with 2,4-D was prohibited between March 15 and October 15. Many hearings since this date have altered the shape and size of the hazardous areas but there have been few modifications of the original intent of the law, namely to prevent injury of susceptible crops by prohibiting the use of 2,4-D. Even in areas where this herbicide is allowed, all commercial applications on a field scale come under the jurisdiction of the county Agricultural Commissioners. Similar laws exist in many other states.

Since the problems with 2,4-D, a number of other types of herbicides have brought on difficulties. The substituted urea and symmetrical triazine materials, when used on roadsides or drain ditches, have caused injury or death of roadside ornamentals and orchard trees. A problem in California involves the use of propanil to control barnyardgrass in rice. After this chemical had come into general use in rice-growing areas of the northern Sacramento Valley, many prune trees in the district began to decline and prune production has fallen off.

Meanwhile it has been found that certain chlorinated hydrocarbon insecticides, including DDT, dieldrin, and chlordane, are stored in body fat and bone marrow of man and animals. These and other pesticides enter food chains and build up to high levels in some members of the chain resulting in injury or death.

This matter was brought to a head in 1962 with the publication of Rachel Carson's *The Silent Spring*. Since that time tons of publications on the pros and cons of pesticide usage have appeared. Let us look into some of the controversial aspects of this problem and some of the public-policy actions that are in practice to safeguard public health.

Pesticides first became a subject for legislative action by the federal government of the United States when Congress passed the Federal Insecticide Act. Regulation has been strengthened from time to time to protect both the users and the consuming public.

1. The Federal Insecticide, Fungicide, and Rodenticide Act of 1947 requires that manufacturers prove to the U.S. Department of Agriculture that these pesticides are effective, and that they are safe for the user and the public when applied according to instructions and warnings on the label. Labelling must indicate what pests the chemical will control, the crops or livestock it can be used on, the quantities to be applied, and any necessary safety precautions.

2. The Miller Pesticide Residue Amendment to the Federal Food, Drug, and Cosmetics Act of 1938 was passed in 1954. It requires manufacturers to provide detailed scientific reports of how much residue, if any, will remain on a crop, and how much could be tolerated in a crop. This information is used by the Food and Drug Administration to set tolerances for the trace amounts of pesticides that may be allowed on market produce which would not prove hazardous to the consumer.

Unless a tolerance has been established, any residue is illegal, and the food is subject to confiscation. Unless a tolerance has been set for a given chemical, the USDA, under provisions of the insecticide act, will refuse permission for sale of the product. Many states have similar laws governing chemicals not involved in interstate commerce.

Congress assigned the USDA the responsibility for registration of safe, effective agricultural chemicals. No pesticide can be sold in interstate commerce unless it and its label have been registered by the USDA. State laws require registration of pesticides produced and sold within a state. The label must carry safety warnings and necessary instructions for safe handling, for antidotes, and for first aid in case of accident.

If there is any possibility that a residue remains on food following application of a pesticide, a tolerance limit from the Food and Drug Administration is required. This tolerance is set below the amount of a pesticide which scientists have determined can safely remain as a residue without injury to the consumer, and is no more than is necessary for control of the target pest. Often hundreds of pages of documents, proving that residues left on each crop are perfectly safe, are submitted before a tolerance is established. Toxicological tests proving safety and chemical tests measuring the quantities of residue that are left on crops when directions for use are followed, are included in applications for registration. Pharmacologists and chemists of the Food and Drug Administration study each petition for registration carefully. If satisfied with the evidence with respect to residues and safety, a tolerance is set at a level that provides a wide margin of safety. As a rule a safe dosage for humans is set at about one one hundredth of that considered safe for rats. In some foods, such as milk, no residue of any chemical at any level is permitted. Agricultural chemicals are kept under constant surveilance by the Food and Drug Administration. It spot-checks food on a regular schedule, analysing for pesticides in excess of tolerance. If above-tolerance amounts are found, the food is seized and may be destroyed. The famous cranberry case in 1959 is an example.

Manufacturers of pesticidal chemicals have tested to determine safe practices for many years. Today, these tests are required by laws which represent recognition by state and federal governments of the economic necessity of pesticides and of their hazards. These laws also set standards by which manufacturers are required to prove that a new chemical is effective and that warnings on the label will protect the user. The laws recognize that residues will appear on crops, and they establish procedures by which the amount of residue may be limited to a level that will safeguard the consumer.

The types of questions asked by federal and state agencies in registration procedures are as follows;
1. What happens if the chemical gets on the skin or is inhaled?
2. What amounts are left on crops for how long?
3. Does it show up in milk or meat of animals that are fed treated crops?
4. What laboratory procedures prove these findings?
5. What amounts may occur in foods?

The pesticide manufacturers state that from one to five years may be required to answer these questions; it may take as much as 5 million dollars to satisfy the demands of the agencies supervising registration. In spite of this situation many of the leading chemical and pharmaceutical companies in the United States and Europe are continuing the search for new, more effective herbicides.

There can be no doubt concerning the need for the present high levels of agricultural production made possible by the use of modern pesticides. Table 1-4 shows world statistics on Population, Income, and Food Consumption taken from a report of the Foreign Agricultural Service. Of the nineteen areas reported, seven are below the minimum daily calorie consumption level; these seven areas have a total population of 1,638,926,000 people. Thus about two-thirds of the world's population live in countries with national average diets that are nutritionally inadequate.

Table 1-4. **World Statistics on Population, Income, and Food Consumption**[a]

	Population 1,000	People 100 acres	Income per capita	Food consump. per capita	Calorie consump. per capita
United States	179,900	16	$2,342	$109.2	3,190*
Canada	17,900	12	1,482	104.0	3,100*
Oceania	12,700	1	1,256	117.2	3,260*
North Europe	211,283	88	1,093	93.2	3,060*
South Europe	96,967	70	445	67.1	2,720*
Japan	93,200	527	395	51.2	2,360 Std[c]
River Plate	22,753	6	365	97.2	3,200*
South Africa	17,619	4	360	57.4	2,670*
Mexico	34,934	15	281	43.7	2,580*
South America	51,549	25	263	49.4	2,260
Central America[b]	32,328	61	227	47.5	2,240
Brazil	70,551	23	211	55.5	2,710*
West Asia	79,391	16	193	42.4	2,350
North Africa	84,813	19	112	35.4	2,210
East Africa	48,563	10	86	40.9	2,390*
Other E. Asia	246,238	154	82	35.8	2,150
W. Central Africa	108,907	17	81	31.3	2,460*
Communist Asia	712,907	100	69	23.5	1,790
India	431,700	100	69	29.8	2,060

[a]From the world food budget: 1970, Foreign Agric. Econ. Rept. No. 19.

[b]Includes the Caribbean area.

[c]Japan is considered to have the minimum daily requirement. Those marked with asterisk (*) are above this level.

Registration of pesticides first fell within the jurisdiction of the Food and Drug Administration of the U.S. Department of Agriculture. As the pressure by the public increased and the work of administering the Insecticide, Fungicide, and Rodenticide Act, and the Miller Pesticide Residue Amendment became a burden, a move was made to simplify the organization and activities related to the regulation of pesticides.

INTERDEPARTMENTAL AGREEMENT FOR PROTECTION OF THE PUBLIC HEALTH AND THE QUALITY OF THE ENVIRONMENT IN RELATION TO PESTICIDES

On January 28, 1970 the Secretary of Agriculture, the Secretary of Health, Education, and Welfare, and the Secretary of the Interior affixed their signature to the Interdepartmental Agreement fixing statutory authority and responsibility relating to pesticides in the environment, as set forth below;

DEPARTMENT OF AGRICULTURE (USDA)

USDA has the statutory authority under the Federal Insecticide, Fungicide, and Rodenticide Act for registration of pesticides.

It is also responsible for research, education, information, regulatory, and action programs designed to protect the well-being of man, crops, livestock, forests, ranges, habitats, products, structures, and premises against arthropod and other invertebrate pests, weeds, and fungi with equal concern for the protection of beneficial nontarget organisms and the quality of the environment.

DEPARTMENT OF HEALTH, EDUCATION, AND WELFARE (DHEW)

DHEW has the statutory authority and responsibility under the Federal Food, Drug, and Cosmetic Act for establishing safe tolerances for pesticides in or on raw agricultural commodities, processed food and potable water. The department also has responsibilities for protecting the public from health, occupational, and environmental hazards related to the use and disposal of pesticides, and for other public-health aspects such as the control of diseases and their vectors.

DEPARTMENT OF INTERIOR (USDI)

USDI has statutory authority and responsibility under the Federal Water Pollution Control Act to carry out programs to protect and enhance the quality of the nation's waters, including determining the effects of pesticides in water on health, welfare, and aquatic life. These responsibilities include establishing water-quality standards for interstate waters. The department also has statutory authority for the conservation of wild birds, fish, mammals, their food organisms, and their environment as affected by pesticides and the appraisal of effects of pesticides on fish and wildlife.

THE ENVIRONMENTAL PROTECTION AGENCY (EPA)

On July 9, 1970 the office of the White House released to the Congress of the United States, Reorganization Plan No. 3 of 1970 providing for an Environmental Protection Agency. This became law 120 days from July 9, 1970.

On December 2, 1970 EPA was established to mount a front-line attack on environmental problems of air and water pollution, pesticide regulation, solid-waste management, and radiation and noise abatement.

The new agency, so far as pesticide registration, regulation, and research is concerned, has assumed most of those duties from the secretaries of Agriculture, Health, Education and Welfare, Interior, and the Atomic Energy Commission, Federal Radiation Council, and the Council of Environmental Quality. With this broad-powered agency in charge of registration of all pesticides there should be no problem of pesticides in our food or in any other part of our environment. Already DDT is banned from use in the United States and 2,4,5-T has been withdrawn from use around homes and water courses; many other materials have been taken off the market and others will be in the future.

One possible result of entrusting the permission to use pesticides in the hands of such a broad-powered agency is that, through public pressure by uninformed people, through prejudice or lack of knowledge, or through just plain ignorance, many safe and important chemicals may never pass the multitude of requirements and thus never reach the market. In the case of 2,4,5-T a contamination in the formulation, dioxin, is teratogenic, not 2,4,5-T itself. And one of the leading manufacturers is able to synthesize and market 2,4,5-T relatively free of dioxin and hence safe. Instead of taking this very useful chemical off the market, it would seem more logical to prohibit its sale if it contained more than a minimum permissible amount of dioxin. Some environmentalists would remove many more agricultural chemicals from the market; they don't explain how we could continue to feed an already hungry world with the consequent reduction in food production.

REFERENCES

Crafts, A. S., and W. W. Robbins. 1962. *Weed Control, a Textbook and Manual.* New York; McGraw-Hill Book Co., 660 pages.

Day, B. E., and R. C. Russell. 1955. The effect of drying on the survival of nutgrass tubers. *Calif. Agr. Expt. Sta. Bul.* 751.

Dixon, D., and L. Kreps. 1973. Dudaim Melon—a direct threat to asparagus. *25th Ann. Proc. Calif. Weed Conf.* Anaheim, Calif.

Hannah, J. A. 1972. SALT—an opportunity. *War on Hunger* VI(8):1–2, 15 U.S. AID Washington, D.C.

Holm, LeRoy. 1969. Weed problems in developing countries. *Weed Sci.* 17:113–118.

_____. 1971. The role of weeds in human affairs. *Weed Sci.* 19:485–490.

Major, J. 1960. Private communication.

2

Reproduction and Spread of Weeds

One of the most pernicious habits of weeds is their vigorous reproduction. Annual weeds reproduce mainly by seeds; perennial weeds reproduce both by seeds and vegetatively. Some annuals may reproduce vegetatively, principally in humid situations. In general annual weeds are characterized by the production of very large numbers of seeds. Whereas a single barnyardgrass plant may produce from one to five hundred seeds, depending upon its size, a Russian thistle plant may produce twenty to fifty thousand seeds, a single rough pigweed may produce one million seeds, and a tumbling pigweed several million. In general, annual, biennial, and perennial weeds may produce about the same numbers of seed (Stevens, 1932). Such "escapes" as horseradish, spearmint, peppermint, commelina, and day lily rarely produce seeds.

Some weed species are dioecious; that is, there are male plants having stamens only and female plants bearing pistils only. Some examples are Canada thistle, sheep sorrel, and willow. Seeds are produced on the female plants if they have been pollinated. Although any population of a dioecious plant may be composed of about equal numbers of male and female plants, in the case of perennials such as Canada thistle and willow, if the weed has spread vegetatively, whole patches may consist of only male or female plants and the female plants will not produce viable seeds unless they receive pollen. A few weeds, notably dandelion, may set seed parthenocarpicly, without pollination.

WEED-SEED POPULATION OF SOILS

One of the most difficult aspects of weed control is the huge accumulation of seeds in most soils. Several factors account for such weed-seed populations: (1) accumulation in place from weeds allowed to grow to maturity, (2) movement of seeds into an area by wind or water, and (3) the sowing of weed seeds as contaminants in crop seeds. Losses of weed seeds result from feeding by birds, rodents, and ants, and from natural decay in the soil. The use of preemergence herbicides results in the death of many weed seeds both in row cropping and in nontillage practices. Harper (1960) cites three examples of buried weed-seed populations in British soils (Table 2-1).

Table 2-1: Typical Buried Weed-seed Population Expressed in Terms of Viable Seeds per Square Foot (from Harper, 1960)

(a) A sandy soil; 8 years' cropping, 7 cereal, 1 root crop plus 1-year ley at Wellsbourne; cited by Roberts, 1958

Species	No. seed	Species	No. seed
Poa annua	2,948	Matricaria chamomilla	262
Polygonum aviculare	563	Anagallis arvenis	234
Capsella bursa-pastoris	480	Veronica persica	232
Arabidopsis thaliana	302		

(b) Rothamsted heavy clay; continuous wheat; cited by Brenchley and Warington, 1933

Species	No. seed	Species	No. seed
Papaver rhoeas	2,122	Polygonum aviculare	54
Alchemilla arvensis	269	Veronica hederaefolia	44
Alopecurus agretis	259	Arenaria serpyllifolia	18
Veronica arvensis	153	Capsella bursa-pastoris	10
Veronica buxbaumii	56		

(c) Woburn light sand; continuous wheat; by Brenchley and Warington, 1933

Species	No. seed	Species	No. seed
Alchemilla arvensis	215	Poa annua	138
Spergula arvensis	404	Polygonum aviculare	50
Matricaria indora	152		
(old name for M. maritima)			

Harper (1960) has found that the type of cultivation and cropping has a definite effect on the weed seed population of a soil; the moldboard plow buries many seeds deep in the soil where they may lie dormant until returned to the surface; discing and chiseling may also bury weed seeds.

Migration of seeds may play a major role in the maintenance of weed-seed populations. Mass migrations may be brought about by flooding, by birds, and, in the case of such species as *Typha, Lactuca, Taraxacum, Sonchus, Salix*, etc., by wind.

Probably one of the most serious problems in the dissemination of weeds is the careless planting of crop seeds contaminated with weed seeds. Harper (1960) cites the following examples: sowing 1.5 hundredweight of cereal per acre with 1 percent contamination by *Galium aparine* results in 5 *Galium* seeds per square foot; if the weed were *Raphanus raphanistrum* 2 seeds would be planted per square foot; with *Polygonum aviculare* it would be 2 or 3. A grass-seed mixture sown at 16 lb. per acre having a 1 percent contamination with *Cerastium arvense* would give 16 seeds per square foot; with *Plantago major*, 8; and with *Holcus lanatus*, 6. The writer observed a farmer in Mendocino County, California sowing wheat so contaminated with cheat (darnel) that more cheat seeds than wheat were going into the field.

DISSEMINATION OF WEED SEEDS

Wind, water, and animals, including man, are largely responsible for spreading the seeds and fruits of weeds. Probably no other means of dissemination is so effective as the sale and distribution of farm and garden seeds and farm products containing the seeds of various weeds; unsterilized farm manure is an example. Where man is the agent there is the possibility of control; where wind, water, and animals are concerned, once weed seeds have matured there is no easy means of control.

WIND

Structural features of weed seeds may aid in their distribution by wind: thistles, cattails, willow, and milkweed are examples. Winged fruits and seeds are modified so that wind may promote their movement. Some docks (Figure 2–1) have winged fruits like those of maple trees; tree-of-heaven has winged fruit of the samara type. Comate seeds are covered with long silky hairs, capillary hairs, or bristles. They occur in the milkweed family (*Asclepidaceae*), in willows, willow herbs, and cattails. Parachute fruits are common to the family Compositae; examples are dandelion, prickly lettuce, salsify (*Tragopogon*), and many thistles. Plumed fruits occur in the Clematis family. They have the style modified into a long, branched plume.

Wind scatters seeds by blowing them over the surface of soil or snow; light seeds may drift for miles. Tumbleweeds are specially adapted for seed dispersal by wind. Russian thistle and tumbling pigweed, for example, are globose in form; when mature the plant breaks off at the soil line and rolls over the earth scattering seeds as it goes. The seeds of Russian thistle are so attached that they do not all break loose immediately. They are held in place by twisted hairs that prevent scattering so that the plant may be blown about for months before all

of the seeds are freed. Buffalo bur, winged pigweed, and Russian pigweed are also tumbleweeds.

Stinkgrass and witchgrass have inflorescenses that abscise at maturity and travel with wind.

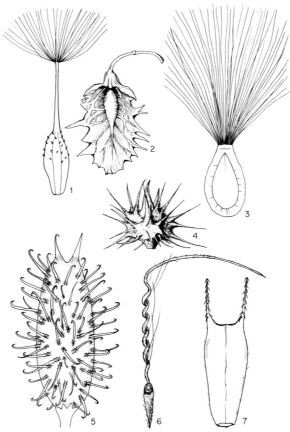

FIGURE 2-1. Structural modifications which aid in dissemination of seeds
and fruits of: (1) common dandelion, (2) fiddle dock, (3) Mexican whorled
milkweed, (4) sandbur, (5) cocklebur, (6) redstem filaree, and (7) beggarticks.

WATER

Most weed seeds will float on water if they fall on the surface of
streams, lakes, drain ditches, or irrigation canals. Flood waters, running streams, and irrigation water are all important in the spread of
weed seeds. Millions of seeds may pass a given point on a river or an
irrigation canal in a single day. Early in the season when irrigation

ditches are first filled, they often carry heavy loads of weed seeds; flood waters may likewise move large quantities of seeds.

Various adaptations enable seeds to float. Fruits with membranous envelopes containing air are found in the sedges; fruits of docks have corky callous grains; the seeds of arrowheads have a corky wing that makes them buoyant.

When the polders of Holland were reclaimed from the Zuider Zee, coltsfoot (*Tussilago farfara*) was a prominent weed in the first growing vegetation. Many seeds had been deposited prior to reclamation. Such infestations were soon replaced by crops under the intensive cultivation that has been carried on since.

ANIMALS

Animals, both wild and domestic, assist in the dispersal of seeds. The viability of many seeds is unaffected by passage through the digestive tracts of animals. Rosenfels (1940) found that the seeds of whitetop are unharmed by their passage through cattle and that this weed is commonly spread by grazing animals. Viable seeds of camel's-thorn frequently occur in horse manure.

Tests show that the droppings from birds seldom contain viable seeds; the grinding action in their crops fractures seeds rendering their contents available as food. Some birds regurgitate certain seeds contained in fruits and thus aid in their dispersal; an example is the spreading of the seeds from berries of *Pyracantha* by robins. Poison oak, poison ivy, pokeweed, elderberry, mistletoe, and toyon are additional examples.

Many seeds, such as those of cocklebur, spiny clotbur, sandbur, and beggarticks , have beards, awns, or hooks that enable them to cling to the hair of animals or to clothing. Some small seeds such as those of St. Johnswort, crabgrass, or Bermudagrass simply lodge temporarily in the hair or on the legs of pasturing animals. The spread of St. Johnswort and medusa head from the coastal hills inland to the upper Sacramento Valley and thence southward along the Sierra Nevada has followed cattle and sheep trails. The rapid spread of Bermudagrass and oxalis from lawn to lawn in residential areas is undoubtedly brought about by the movements of pets.

MAN

Man is probably the most active agent in the dissemination of weeds. Weed seeds have been transported from one part of the world to another in the ballast of ships, in agricultural products such as seeds, hay, feed stuffs, and in nursery stock. The great numbers of imported weeds found in all agricultural areas result from importation, usually due to man's indifference or carelessness in the importation and planting of contaminated crop plants or seeds.

Most states have seed laws that conform to the general provisions of the Federal Seed Law. The movement of commercial seeds has become recognized as a most important means of weed-seed dispersal. These seed laws are designed to prevent, as far as possible, introduction of foreign weed seed into the agriculture of the United States.

Other sources of weed seeds that are often overlooked are imported dried-plant bouquets for home decoration, the exchange of seeds to plant "peace gardens," and the agricultural wastes often used as packing material. Plant explorers warn that there are still many potentially noxious weeds that have not yet been brought into our country. Only by constant vigilance can we keep these out.

Weed seeds often occur in screenings from threshing machines and seed cleaners. Too often these screenings find their way to feed lots or livestock farms. Here they may pass through animals and be scattered in manure, still in a viable condition. And they may adhere to wool, hair, or to the animals' feet to be carried to farm land or the pasture or open range.

Agricultural officers have made many tests on the weed-seed content of screenings. They always contain some weed seeds; often they are composed mainly of weed seed of many species. Even ground screenings contain viable weed seed; steam treatment is about the only method for killing weed seeds, but this has to be prolonged; treatment in boiling water is a common method for making hard seeds germinate.

Weed seeds are often carried in packing about nursery stock; in soil and sand or gravel used in construction; in mud on animals' feet or the wheels of vehicles; in soil adhering to plows, cultivators, or other farm implements; in threshing machines, hay balers, and portable seed cleaners; and, now, on rubber tires of bicycles, automobiles, and airplanes.

GERMINATION

The viability of weed seeds, the conditions that affect their vitality, dormancy, and germination, concern reproduction of weeds. The vitality of seeds is influenced by such factors as vigor of the parent, conditions under which the seeds develop, maturity, and environmental conditions such as temperature and humidity, age, and presence or absence of herbicides in the soil.

In order to germinate, seeds must have: (1) available water, (2) a favorable temperature, and (3) a supply of oxygen. In some cases germination is increased by exposure of the seeds to light after they have absorbed water. Many seeds show increased germination if KNO_3 is included in the germination medium; Fulwider and Engel (1959) used 0.2 percent in their trials. Fluctuating temperatures increase germination in some cases; 20° and 30°C or 35°C are commonly used. Wild oats seed, which becomes dormant when immersed in water, germinated when the seed coats were punctured and KNO_3, $NaNO_3$, H_2O_2, or gibberellic acid was included in the germination medium (Hay and Cumming, 1959).

Many seeds, though viable, may be incapable of germination immediately after they mature even when placed in favorable conditions. This characteristic is termed dormancy. Some seeds germinate soon after favorable conditions occur, others from the same plant may germinate in succeeding years. Delayed germination may result from dormancy, or from lack of oxygen or light; in the latter case, seeds may germinate and produce a weed population if returned by tillage to the soil surface. The light requirement for seed germination may be met by irradiation with red light and reversed by far-red radiation. Borthwick and Hendricks (1960) have found that a pigment called phytochrome, a bluish-green protein, is responsible for this reversal; the absorption maximum of phytochrome is 660 millimicrons in the far-red. A number of weed species have been found to respond to the red-far-red reversal of germination; these include members of the *Lactuca*, *Xanthium*, *Lepidium*, *Epilobium*, *Hypericum*, and *Rumex* genera (Isikawa and Fujii, 1961).

Some seed dormancy may result from impervious seed coats; treatment with concentrated H_2SO_4 or boiling water may render them pervious. Prechilling and use of KNO_3 in the germinating water may aid in certain weed species; scarification is useful for promoting germination of seeds with hard coats.

Thurston (1961) found the maximum survival for *Avena fatua* to be 61 months and for *A. ludoviciana*, 33 months in field plots at Rothamsted. *A. fatua* germinated in spring and fall, *A. ludoviciana* in winter; more seedlings of *A. fatua* grew in the second spring than at any other time; 80 percent of those of *A. ludoviciana* appeared in the first autumn and winter.

Tingey and Allred (1961) found that acid treatment or scarification were not effective in breaking dormancy of small-seeded alfalfa dodder (*Cuscuta approximata*). Chilling the seeds at 35° to 45°F for two to three weeks after acid treatment or scarification induced germination.

Cocklebur seeds exhibit dormancy. Each bur contains two seeds, one slightly above the other (Fig. 2–2). Usually the lower seed germinates first, the upper seed one or two years later. Experiments showed that dormancy in cocklebur results from restriction in the oxygen supply to the embryos by the seed coat. Burs of cocklebur in moist soil do not germinate during the summer but the dormancy is broken by low temperatures of winter.

Germination of many weeds is prevented by their hard, impervious seed coats. These are acted upon by temperature, moisture, bacteria, fungi, and insects in the soil. They eventually become thin, worn, and permeable and then the seeds will germinate. This is one reason for the long survival of weed seeds in agricultural soils.

Thurston (1960) points out that seeds of most weedy species germinate at definite times of year, generally in the spring or fall and sometimes in both; temperature is probably the predominating factor.

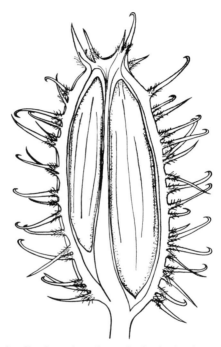

FIGURE 2-2. Longitudinal section through the fruit of cocklebur showing the two seeds. The lower seed usually germinates the first spring after maturation, whereas there is often a delay in the germination of the upper seed.

Seedlings from one year's crop will appear at about the same date for several successive years provided the soil is cultivated; in undisturbed soil the deeply buried seeds remain dormant until they are brought to the surface.

LONGEVITY OF BURIED SEED

Seeds of many weeds retain their viability for years when buried in the soil; weeds cannot be controlled by plowing seeds under because many seeds may outlive the crop rotation. Most agricultural soils in the past were well-stocked with weed seeds; however, at present with the common use of preemergence herbicides, soils may be gradually depleted of such stored seed. The best way to rid the soil of weed seeds is to till shallowly to keep the seeds near the soil surface where they will germinate and can be killed.

Dr. W. J. Beal's seed-viability test has become well-known. In 1879 at Michigan Agricultural College, he buried freshly gathered seeds from 20 different species. Twenty pint bottles of each species, containing fifty seeds mixed with sand, were buried to a depth of about 18 in. below the soil surface. Every five years up to 1920 one bottle of each species was dug up and the percentage germination determined; after 1920 the interval was lengthened to ten years. Table 2–2 from the report of Kivilaan and Bandurski (1973) gives a summary of the tests to date.

In a test by the USDA in 1902, 32 sets of seeds of 107 species were buried 8, 22, and 42″ in depth. After twenty years some seeds of 51 species were still viable. Whereas seeds of most crops will live only a few years when buried, this experiment proves that seeds of many weed species will germinate after twenty years burial. Likewise weed seeds in storage under cool, dry conditions remain viable for many years; seeds of field bindweed so stored have germinated after fifty years.

Submergence under water will kill many seeds; in some, however, germination is improved if submergence is not carried on too long. Submergence is important in relation to weed control by flooding and in and along irrigation canals. Bruns and Rasmussen (1953) stored seed of whitetop, Russian knapweed, Canada thistle, field bindweed and povertyweed in a canal of running water at depths of 12 and 48 in. for periods up to 22 months; germination tests were run each month up to 8 months and bimonthly thereafter. Figure 2–3 presents their results. An inverse relationship between germination of Canada thistle, Russian knapweed, and field bindweed seeds and water temperature is shown. Germination of all but whitetop increased after the warm water temperatures of July, indicating that the warm water had temporarily increased dormancy but had not killed the seed. All seeds but whitetop maintained sufficient viability after 22 months in fresh water to produce seedlings when placed under suitable conditions.

In a later report (1957), Bruns and Rasmussen stated that freshwater storage increased the germination of field bindweed seed over a five-year period. Canada thistle and Russian knapweed seeds did not germinate after 54 months; poverty weed did not survive after 48 months; all seeds of whitetop were destroyed after 14 months.

In 1958 Bruns and Rasmussen reported work showing that less than 1 percent of the seeds of barnyardgrass and halogeton germinated after 3 months of water storage; none after 12 months. One percent or less of yellow bristlegrass and no more than 3 percent of quackgrass

Table 2-2. Viability of Buried Seeds in the Beal Buried-seed Experiments; Results of all Tests to Date[a]

Name of species tested	Duration	5th year 1884	10th year 1889	15th year 1894	20th year 1899	25th year 1904	30th year 1909	35th year 1914	40th year 1920	50th year 1930	60th year 1940	70th year 1950	80th year 1960	90th year 1970
Agrostemma githago	1	0	0	0	0	0	0	0	0	0	0	0	0	0
Amaranthus retroflexus	1	+	+	+	+	+	+	0	+	0	0	0	0	0
Ambrosia artemisifolia	1	0	0	0	0	0	0	0	+	0	0	0	0	0
Anthemis cotula	1	+	+	+	0	+	+	0	+	0	0	0	0	0
Brassica nigra	1	0	+	+	+	+	+	+	+	+	0	0	0	0
Bromus secalinus	1	0	0	0	0	0	0	0	0	0	0	0	0	0
Capsella bursa-pastoris	1	+	+	+	+	+	+	+	0	0	0	0	0	0
Erechtites hieracifolia	1	0	0	0	0	0	0	0	0	0	0	0	0	0
Euphorbia maculata (nutans)[b]	1	0	0	0	0	0	0	0	0	0	0	0	0	0
Lepidium virginicum	1	+	+	+	+	+	+	+	+	0	0	0	0	0
Malva rotundifolia	1 or 2	+	0	0	+	0	0	0	0	0	0	0	0	0
Plantago major	per.[c]	0	?	+	+	0	0	0	+	+	0	0	0	0
Polygonum hydropiper	1	+	+	+	+	+	?	0	0	0	0	0	0	0
Portulaca oleracea	1	+	+	+	+	+	0	0	+	0	0	0	0	0
Setaria glauca	1	+	+	+	0	+	+	0	0	0	0	0	0	0
Stellaria media	1	+	+	+	+	+	+	0	0	0	0	0	0	0
Trifolium repens	per.[c]	+	0	0	0	0	0	0	0	0	0	0	0	0
Verbascum thapsus[d]	2	+	+	+	+	+	+	+	19(38)	19(38)	12(24)	7(14)	5(10)	0
Oenothera biennis	2	+	+	+	+	+	+	0	9(18)	26(52)	2(4)	4(8)	1(2)	0
Rumex crispus	2	+	+	+	+	+	+	+	0	0	0	0	0	0
Verbascum blatteraria[d]									31(62)	34(68)	37(74)	35(70)	10(20)

aThe + signs following each species, both in the upper and in the lower parts of the table, indicate that one or more seeds of that species germinated for the year shown. The number indicates the number of seeds germinating, while the number in parentheses indicates the percentage germinating.

bNow named E. nutans.

cPerennial.

dThere is some question concerning the identification of Verbascum plants in the early period (1884–1920) as V. blattaria. (Darlington and Steinbauer, 1961.)

seed sprouted after 3 months; none after 27 months. Less than 10 percent of green bristlegrass sprouted after 15 months; none after 30 months. Nine percent of pigweed still sprouted after 33 months. Water temperature, pH, salt content, and organic matter content must all affect viability of submerged weed seed. Soil sterilants of low solubility are used to kill weed seedlings as they germinate in irrigation ditches.

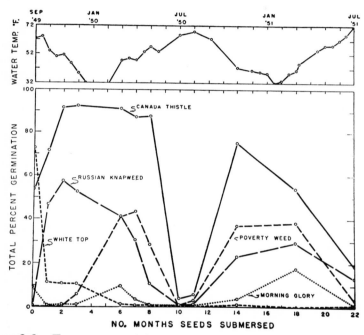

FIGURE 2-3. Temperature of the water and the average total percentage of seeds which germinated after submergence at 12- and 48-in. depths for periods of up to 22 months. (Photograph by courtesy of V. F. Bruns and L. W. Rasmussen.)

The burning of dry weeds has little effect on seeds on the ground. Fire may stimulate germination of the seeds of brush species. In controlled burning tests on manzanita and ceanothus species, seedlings often appear in tremendous numbers during the following winter and spring. Chamise seeds are not prevented from germinating by fire.

HERBICIDES

Early work with herbicides proved that some may affect weed-seed germination. Mature burs of puncturevine were not affected by treatment with crude-acid sludge from oil refining or by moistening with soluble arsenic compounds or sodium chlorate. Diesel oil, on the other hand, penetrates the seed coats and renders them impervious to water. The viability of the embryos may not be impaired, and seeds so treated have been found to germinate as much as ten years after treatment if the coats are cracked so that water may penetrate.

Immersion of weed seeds in a 90 percent sulfonatable fuel oil gave variable effects. Yellow starthistle and artichoke thistle seeds were dead after 1 hour; Western dock and lambsquarters seeds were unaffected by a 7-hour immersion.

Spraying weeds with 2,4-D and 2,4,5-T may actually increase germination of the seeds. Early spraying on scentless mayweed almost doubled the percentage of germination; late spraying lowered germinability. Late spraying of wild oats increased germination from 40 to between 80 and 90 percent.

A number of chemicals are used to inhibit germination of weed seeds in soil and compost; most promising are methyl bromide, chloropicrin, calcium cyanamide, Metham, EPTC, Mylone, the sulfamate and thiocyanate of ammonia, synthetic urea (Uramon), IPC, CIPC, trichloronitromethane, dazomet, GASPA, and vorlex. Solid chemicals of low vapor pressure may be worked into the moist top soil and the surface covered with plastic or compacted by rolling. The more volatile compounds may be injected into the soil and a cover of thin plastic immediately applied. For sterilizing greenhouse and potting soils, the moist soils in flats may be treated, stacked, and covered with plastic. Very volatile compounds like methyl bromide, chloropicrin, and DD may be injected into plastic-covered soil or into stacks of flats after covering with plastic.

Germination of field bindweed and other weeds fails if the plants are sprayed with translocated herbicides such as 2,4-D or amitrole while the seeds are still green and succulent. Seeds that are brown and starting to harden are unaffected.

PERIODICITY OF GERMINATION

Seeds of few weed species germinate freely throughout the year; germination requirements are best met by conditions that exist at some one season. Winter-annual weeds germinate best in the autumn under lowering temperatures and shortening days. Summer annuals respond to increasing temperatures in spring; often there will be successions or flushes of seedling appearance as temperatures reach favorable levels. The seasons during which flushes of seedlings appear are of practical significance in relation to dates of plowing, seedbed preparation, and seeding, and in determining the time and frequency of cultivating fallow land. In nontillage programs, contact sprays are most effectively used after the principal germination of weed seeds has taken place. A few species, including shepherdspurse and common chickweed, have no periodicity; some germination takes place at all seasons if conditions are right.

VIABILITY TESTING

Although the testing of seed viability by germination is reliable, it is very time-consuming. Recently, chemical methods for determining seed viability have been found. One method involves a reduction of

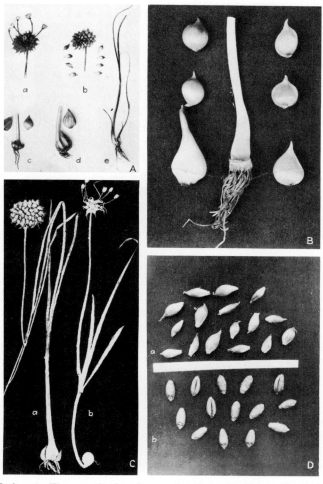

FIGURE 2-4. *A.* Five methods of reproduction of wild garlic: (*a*) flowers (seed), (*b*) aerial bulblets, (*c*) hard-shelled bulbs, (*d*) soft-shelled bulbs, (*e*) secondary bulblets (growing). *B.* Underground part showing central stem, one soft-shelled bulb, and five hard-shelled bulbs. *C.* (*a*) Wild garlic, (*b*) wild onion. *D.* (*a*) Aerial bulblets of wild garlic, (*b*) kernels of wheat. (From Pipal, Indiana Agricultural Experiment Station.)

selenium salts; another, a staining reaction using tetrazolium chloride. There is also a method that depends upon the fluorescense of the germinating seed; another utilizes a test of the acidity of the fat of a seed. A new method uses the dye resazurin (Plaut and Heller-Cohen, 1956). This dye forms a blue color in slightly alkaline solution; in acid solution it is red. The dye is readily reduced, first to red, then to orange; finally it loses color entirely. Germs of viable pea seeds remain white, nonviable seeds turn red or blue; the dye does not destroy the ability of

FIGURE 2-5.   Root and rhizome development of a 4½-month-old Johnson-grass plant at the winter dormancy stage. (Photograph courtesy of L. E. Anderson, Kansas Agricultural Experiment Station.)

the seed to germinate. When seeds of cereals are treated, the germs of dead seeds stain blue; viable seeds are red or pink. After this test the seeds can be germinated as a control on the results.

VEGETATIVE REPRODUCTION

Most perennial weeds and a few annuals reproduce and spread vegetatively as well as by seeds; such weeds are our most persistent pests. Cut pieces of the stems of such annuals as crabgrass and chickweed are able to take root and grow in moist lawns and gardens.

Cut pieces of the roots of such perennials as dandelion are able to strike root and grow. Bulbs produced underground and bulblets that develop in inflorescenses of wild garlic (Fig. 2-4) aid in dispersal. Some creeping perennials such as mouseear chickweed, and oxalis spread by stems that grow along the soil surface; others, like quackgrass and Johnsongrass, spread vegetatively (Fig. 2-5) by rhizomes only; others, like perennial sowthistle, horsenettle, and western ragweed, extend horizontally by roots only; a number of creeping perennials, such as Canada thistle and field bindweed, spread underground by both roots and rhizomes.

DEPTH OF PENETRATION

The depth to which roots of weeds penetrate depends upon soil texture, the depth of the watertable, the nature of the subsoil and the

Table 2-3.   Depth of Root Penetration of Certain Perennial Weeds

Weed species	Depth of root penetration, ft.
Field bindweed (*Convolvulus arvensis*)	20 or more
Hedge bindweed (*Convolvulus sepium*)	6
Canada thistle (*Cirsium arvense*)	8
Pasture thistle (*Cirsium pumilum*)	6
Perennial smartweed (*Polygonum muhlenbergia*)[a]	8 or more
Red sorrel (*Rumex acetosella*)	5
Common milkweed (*Asclepias syriaca*)	8
Indian hemp (*Apocynum cannabinum*)	5
Horsenettle (*Solanum carolinense*)	8
Perennial ragweed (*Ambrosia psilostachya*)	6
Leafy spurge (*Euphorbia esula*)	8–10
Austrian fieldcress (*Rorippa austriaca*)	6–10
Hoary cress (*Cardaria draba*)	4
Camelthorn (*Alhagi camelorum*)	11–13

[a] A synonym for *P. cocineum*.

nature of tillage practices used. Plowing or cultivation is known to induce deep root penetration by Johnsongrass, Bermudagrass, nut-sedges, and other perennial weeds. Field bindweed roots taken from depths of 20′ or more have sprouted and grown in greenhouse trials. In permanent pasture, the major part of the root system of Canada thistle is within the surface foot; in loose, well-tilled soil the roots may extend to 6 ft. or more in depth.

The maximum depth of roots of fourteen common weeds, growing in fertile silt loam of windblown or alluvial origin and having no hard pan, is given in Table 2-3 (Kiltz, 1930).

Creeping perennials may invade new soil and spread laterally very rapidly by vegetative means only. For example Figures 2-6 and 2-7 show 6-week-old and 13-week-old field bindweed plants that have spread for 4′ laterally between the 6th and 13th week. Such rapid spread is common in new orchards and vineyards that become infested with bindweed. The normal spread of a single bindweed plant may be 15 ft. or more. Pavlychenko, et al. (1940) found that a small root cutting of perennial sowthistle only ¼ in. long produced a mature plant with underground runners spreading over an area 15 ft. in dia-

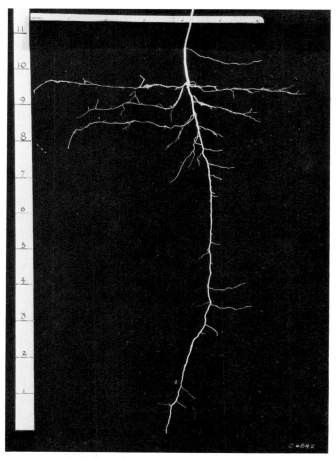

FIGURE 2-6. Field bindweed plant showing 6 weeks' growth after emergence from seed. (Photograph from J. C. Frazier, Kansas Agricultural Experiment Station.)

meter in a single season. A cutting of Canada thistle 1 to 3 in. long produced a patch 60 ft. in diameter in 3 years.

DEPTH FROM WHICH ROOTS AND RHIZOMES REGENERATE

The depth from which perennial weeds may regenerate is important in relation to tillage practices and use of herbicides. The rhizomes

of quackgrass do not regenerate from a depth of 12 in. and field experience has proven that deep plowing may control this weed. Pammel
and King (1909) buried quackgrass rootstocks at depths of 4, 6, 8, 12,
and 24 in. Shoots did not grow to the surface from depths of 12 in. or
deeper, and not readily from 8 in. Most of the rootstocks of quackgrass
are between 2 and 4 in. below the surface. Plowing has also proved
beneficial following spraying quackgrass with herbicides.

Although shoots of field bindweed seldom arise from buds below 4
ft., the writer has found them coming up from that depth through the
channel of the old tap root following summer treatment with the

FIGURE 2-7. Field bindweed plant showing 13 week's growth after emergence
from seed. (Photograph from J. C. Frazier, Kansas Agricultural Experiment
Station.)

acid-arsenical spray; the appearance above ground was in August of
the year following treatment. If 2,4-D application results in penetration and root destruction to depths of 4 ft. or more, one can be assured
of a high percentage of kill. Vertical shoots may arise and grow to the
surface from horizontal rhizomes of camelthorn at depths from 1 ½ to 2
½ ft.

Size of root piece may determine if a root will survive fractiona-
tion. Pieces of Canada thistle roots ¼ in. to 1 in. in length were found
to be capable of regeneration. Bindweed root pieces 1 in. or more in
length will regenerate and produce viable plants if they are maintained
in moist soil.

Arny (1927) found that quackgrass seedlings up to 8 weeks in age
were killed like seedlings of annual weeds by tillage. Beyond 8 weeks
they behaved like perennials. Field bindweed seedlings die when cut off
up to a stage when they have five true leaves; after this stage the roots

regenerate. In greenhouse trials under warm humid conditions, bind-weed seedlings 8 days old would regenerate from roots when the plants were cut off 1 in. below the soil surface.

USE OF CHEMICALS IN CONTROL OF PERENNIAL WEEDS

In any program of perennial-weed control, bud dormancy may be an interfering factor. When infestations of field bindweed or leafy spurge are attacked by a program of frequent tillage, the crowns may become dormant. If this dormancy could be overcome and the plants maintained in an active state, control might be effected more rapidly. Both water deficiency and high summer temperatures may be involved in this lack of growth activity. Shafer and Monson (1958) have shown that gibberellic acid applied as a spray or in lanolin paste will activate dormant buds and maintain active growth. There was a correlation between activity and concentration up to 500 ppm of the applied solution.

More recently a method for applying chemical in a narrow layer under several inches of loose soil by means of a spray blade has been devised, and trial using casoron and trifluralin have given some promising results. By this method a thin, concentrated layer of chemical is laid into the soil by means of spray nozzles placed under a knife blade drawn horizontally through the soil at depths of from 4 to 6 in. When the growing shoots of perennial weeds come into contact with this chemical barrier, they stop growing, swell, and produce a lot of callus tissue. One treatment applied in spring may last an entire season.

REPRODUCTION OF NUTSEDGES

The nutsedges (*Cyperus esculentus* and *C. rotundus*) make up a group of the most serious weed pests in the world (Holm, 1969, 1971). Found worldwide in temperate and tropical climates, they reproduce by seeds and tubers; when disturbed they produce tubers at greater and greater depths; and the tubers, by dormancy, are able to survive intensive tillage programs. A few chemicals are effective in controlling nutsedges; the early ones such as methyl bromide, DD, chloropicrin, metham, and EPTC were volatile and had to be held in the soil by plastic sheeting, rolling, or shallow irrigation. More recent nutsedge herbicides, such as alachlor, atrazine, butylate, cycloate, dichlobenil, pebulate, glyphosate, MSMA, norea, and dazomet, have lower vapor pressures and these may be disced in or layered in with a spray blade; several are effective throughout a cropping season; none can effect eradication because there are always some dormant tubers in the soil.

Day and Russell (1955) have shown that *C. rotundus* tubers may be killed by drying. In irrigated districts where dry fallow can be practiced, this has proved effective in ridding the soil of this pest; it is not effective in the humid tropics. *C. esculentus* produces tubers with hard, drought-resistant coats which cannot be controlled by dessication.

REFERENCES

Arny, A. C. 1927. Successful eradication of perennial weeds. *Ontario Dept. Agr., Agr. and Expt. Union Ann. Rept.* 48:58–63.

Borthwick, H. A., and S. B. Hendricks. 1960. Photoperiodism in plants. *Science* 132:1223–1228.

Bruns, V. F., and L. W. Rasmussen. 1953. The effects of fresh water storage on the germination of certain weed seeds. I. Whitetop, Russian knapweed, Canada thistle, morning glory, and poverty weed. *Weeds* 2:138–147.

————— and —————. 1957. The effects of fresh water storage on the germination of certain weed seeds. II. Whitetop, Russian knapweed, Canada thistle, morning glory, and poverty weed. *Weeds* 5:20–24.

————— and —————. 1958. The effects of fresh water storage on the germination of certain weed seeds. III. Quackgrass, greenbristlegrass, yellow bristlegrass, watergrass, pigweed, and halogeton. *Weeds* 6:42–48.

Day, B. E., and R. C. Russell. 1955. The effect of drying on the survival of nutgrass tubers. *Calif. Agr. Expt. Sta. Bul.* 751.

Fulwider, J. R., and R. E. Engel. 1959. The effect of temperature and light on germination of seeds of goosegrass, *Eleusine indica*. *Weeds* 7:359–361.

Harper, J. L. 1960. Factors controlling plant numbers. In *The Biology of Weeds. A Symposium of the British Ecological Society,* John L. Harper, ed. pp. 119–132. Oxford: Blackwell Scientific Publications, Ltd.

Hay, J. R., and B. G. Cumming. 1959. A method for inducing dormancy in wild oats (*Avena fatua* L.). *Weeds* 7:34–40.

Holm, LeRoy. 1969. Weed problems in developing countries. *Weed Sci.* 17:113–118.

—————. 1971. The role of weeds in human affairs. *Weed Sci.* 19:485–490.

Isikawa, S., and T. Fujii. 1961. Photocontrol and temperature dependence of germination of Rumex seeds. *Plant and Cell Physiol.* 2:51–62.

Kiltz, B. F. 1930. Perennial weeds which spread vegetatively. *Amer. Soc. Agron. J.* 22:216–234.

Kivilaan, A., and R. S. Bandurski. 1973. The ninety-year period for Dr. Beal's seed viability experiment. *Amer. J. Bot.* 60:140–145.

Pammel, L. H., and Charlotte M. King. 1909. Notes on the eradication of weeds, with experiments made in 1907 and 1908. *Iowa Agr. Expt. Sta. Bul.* 105:265–300.

Pavlychenko, T. K., L. E. Kirk, and W. Kossar. 1940. Eradication of perennial weeds by the shallow cultivation method. *Univ. Saskatchewan Col. Agr., Agr. Ext. Bul.* 100:1–8.

Plaut, M., and O. Heller-Cohen. 1956. New methods for testing viability of seeds. *World Crops* 8:311,319.

Rosenfels, R. S. 1940. Spread of white-top seed in droppings of grazing cattle. *Nev. Agr. Expt. Sta. Bul.* 152:1–5.

Shafer, N. E., and W. G. Monson. 1958. The role of gibberellic acid in overcoming bud dormancy in perennial weeds. I. Leafy spurge (*Euphorbia esula* L.) and iron weed (*Vernonia baldwinii Torr*). *Weeds* 6:172–178.

Stevens, O. A. 1932. The number and weight of seeds produced by weeds. *Amer. J. Bot.* 19:784–794.

Thurston, J. M. 1960. Dormancy in weed seeds. In *The Biology of Weeds. A Symposium of the British Ecological Society*, John L. Harper ed. Oxford: Blackwell Scientific Publications, Ltd., July.

_____. 1961. The effect of depth of burying and frequency of cultivation on survival and germination of seeds of wild oats (*Avena fatua* and *Avena ludoviciana* Dur.). *Weed Res.* 1:19–31.

Tingey, D. C., and K. R. Allred. 1961. Breaking dormancy in seeds of *Cuscuta approximata. Weeds* 9:429–436.

3

Cost of Weeds

Anyone who has lived on a farm, worked in a park, or cared for a home knows that weeds are a burden to man. The losses from weeds in farm operations have been a concern of the United States Department of Agriculture for years; it has spent millions of dollars for research on herbicides and weed-control methods. And the agribusiness industry is spending many more millions on research and development of our modern arsenal of weed-control chemicals.

Thus, while the costs of weeds are widely recognized, measuring and evaluating these costs is much more difficult. Many estimates have been made of the losses to crop production caused by weeds. Furtick (1967, 1970) presents the results of thirteen years of research in Colombia, South America as summarized by Lang. Table 3–1 shows that normal hand-weeding practices usually are undertaken too late to prevent substantial yield losses. This is quite understandable since weeds must have some growth before hand weeding can be easily performed. The average increase of 19 percent in yield of crops treated with a herbicide over those of hand-weeded plots represents the losses traditionally suffered before the introduction of chemical control. Additional losses in yield from the effects of weeds on the quality of crops and livestock are difficult to measure and are often ignored.

Table 3–2 shows the percentage decreases in yield in rice in Taiwan caused by five major weeds.

Rice is the most important crop in many countries of the world and yield reductions of these proportions are common where herbicides are not used. (Moomas et al. 1966)

Table 3-3 from Matsunaka (1970) presents changes in weeding costs for growing rice in Japan brought about by the introduction of herbicides. The total savings of $337,500,000 in 1966 gives a measure of the economic advantages of chemical weed control.

Table 3-1.   The Effect of Weed Competition on the Yield of Crops in Columbia (Furtick, 1970, after Lange)

Crop	Percent losses range	Average of losses	Average increase in yield over hand weeded check from herbicide treatments
Rice	30–73	54	24
Cotton	0–39	31	13
Corn	10–84	46	21
Beans	15–88	51	24
Wheat	0–90	29	17
Barley	0–63	19	16
Potatoes	0–53	17	20
Average		35	19

Table 3-2.   Percentage of Yield Reduction in Rice Caused by Five Major Weeds in Taiwan (100 plants/m^2) (Matsunaka, 1970)

Weed species	Crop season	Fertility	
		High	Low
Echinochloa crusgalli	First	85.5	76.1
	Second	87.0	71.4
Monochoria vaginalis	First	31.2	25.4
	Second	84.0	81.2
Cyperus difformis	First	73.6	49.1
	Second	80.9	53.5
Marsilea quadrifolia	First	56.5	45.1
	Second	52.2	54.7
Spirodela polyrhiza	First	8.5	10.6
	Second	5.2	0

Figure 3-1 graphs the yield reduction in wheat caused by four common weeds of the wheat belt evaluated on the basis of the numbers of weeds per square yard. Heavy infestations of wild mustard and wild oats brought yields down nearly 50 percent; foxtail and wild buckwheat, two less competitive plants, reduced it by 15 percent (Nalewaja and Arnold, 1970).

Table 3-3. Changes in Weeding Costs in Japan (Transplanted Rice Culture) (Matsunaka, 1970)

Year	Hand-weeding cost cent/hr (1)	Weeding labor hr/ha (2)	Cost of weeding cost $/ha (1) × (2) (3)	Cost of herbicides $/ha (4)	Weeding cost in total $/ha (3) + (4) (5)	Weeding cost without herbicides $/ha (1) × 505.6 (6)	Saved money by herbicides $/ha (6) – (5) (7)	Total area transplanted 1,000 ha (8)	Total saved money million $ (7) × (8) (9)
1949	7.4	505.6	37.2	0.000	37.2	37.2	–	2,875	–
1952	8.9	357.0	31.6	0.38	32.0	44.8	12.8	2,872	36.7
1954	10.9	310.7	33.8	0.49	34.3	55.1	20.7	2,888	59.8
1956	11.9	331.5	37.2	0.72	37.9	59.9	22.1	3,059	67.5
1958	12.7	309.8	39.2	0.83	40.1	64.0	24.0	3,080	73.8
1960	14.2	267.6	38.1	1.72	39.9	72.0	32.2	3,124	100.5
1962	20.2	208.7	42.1	4.61	46.8	102.0	55.3	3,134	173.4
1964	27.4	175.7	48.2	6.61	54.8	138.6	83.8	3,126	262.0
1965	30.7	174.4	53.6	6.92	60.5	155.4	94.9	3,123	296.4
1966	34.0	164.2	55.8	8.22	64.0	171.9	107.8	3,129	337.5

Potatoes are an important food crop in temperate regions around the world. Dallyn and Sweet (1970) discuss losses due to weeds in this crop; they reduce the value of the crop through yield suppression and quality defects. One estimate of the annual loss per year for the United States is $25,000,000. The Agricultural Research Service in their 1965 Agr. Handbook 291 indicated an annual loss in the potato crop at 3 percent, or a value of $28,272,000 annually for the period 1951–60. (Anon. 1965)

Reports were made of losses of up to 50 percent in the efficiency of mechanical harvesting with as much as 20 percent of the tubers lost in

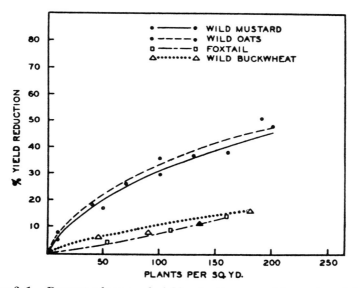

FIGURE 3-1. Percent wheat seed yield reduction caused by various infestations (1 sq yd = 0.8 sq m) of wild mustard, wild oats, foxtail, and wild buckwheat. Values for some weeds are an average of locations, crop seeding density, and fertility variable (Nalewaja and Arnold, 1970).

masses of rootbound soil. Losses as high as 70 percent are reported (Isleib, 1960) where quackgrass infestation was dense. The writer has seen barnyardgrass infestation in potatoes in the Sacramento River Delta so dense that mechanical harvest was impossible; hand harvesting under such conditions is so expensive as to reduce profits to zero.

Table 3–4 from Dallyn and Sweet (1970) gives estimated losses due to weeds in potatoes in 1969 for the four potato-growing regions in the United States. The estimated yield loss, in both quantity and quality, was almost exactly 4 percent; the largest single effect of weeds was to reduce the size of tubers affecting both yield and grade. Quality defects due to quackgrass and nutsedge punctures were reported from all areas. Total loss to the potato industry caused by weeds in 1969 was approximately $65,000,000.

Danielson (1970) reports annual losses in vegetable legumes (beans, peas, lentils) in the United States in 1965 were $110,000,000 resulting from reduced yields and quality of the crops. Average annual

Table 3-4. Estimated Losses Due to Weeds in Potatoes, 1969
(Dallyn and Sweet, 1970)

Item	Region			
	Northeast	South	Central	West
Total acreage (1,000 acres)	301.5	151.1	342.5	608.7
Average reported on :	273.1	80.6	284.1	519.8
Reported losses—Yield	1,462	843	86	4,578
(1000 cwt) Quality	772	422	15	1,627
Total	2,234	1,265	101	6,205
Estimated total loss	2,466	2,366	122	7,260
National average loss per acre:	8.7 cwt			
Water and nutrient loss reported: ($1000)	3,128	400	500	11,611
Estimated total loss	3,453	748	603	13,585
National average loss per acre:	$13.10			
Incr. preharvest costs reported: ($1000)	99.7	0	26.6	180.3
Incr. harvest costs reported	467.9	311.5	34.5	779.9
Total reported	567.4	311.5	61.1	960.2
Estimated total increase	626.6	582.5	73.7	1,123.4
National average loss per acre:	$1.71			

cost of weed control with herbicides was $2,200,000 for vegetable legume plantings.

Since all herbicide costs and much of the tillage cost would not be necessary in the absence of weeds, such costs can be added to the losses due to weeds. Table 3-4 lists costs of weed-control measures in the potato crop of 1969.

The average cost of weed control in 1954 for the United States was $11.83 per acre (Loomis, 1955). The Agricultural Research Service placed the average cost per acre of weed control in potatoes at $14.00

for the period 1951–60. The average cost, given in Table 3–4, for 1969 was $13.56. This shows that, despite rapidly rising costs of labor and equipment, the growers have kept weeding costs relatively stable through increased efficiency and use of herbicides.

Costs for weed control in California deciduous fruit crops are presented in Table 3–5 (Lange, 1970). Savings resulting from using a herbicide on a 6-foot strip down the tree row are given in the last column; these run from $10 in grapes to $90 in walnuts.

Table 3–5.   *Approximate Orchard-Weed-Control Costs in California Deciduous Fruit Crops (Lange, 1970)*

Crop	Cost of weed control/yr.		Years to commercial crop[c]	Total savings $/A[d]
	Cultivation $/A[a]	Chemical and cultivation $/A[b]		
Almond	22	10	6	72
Apples	12	8	10	40
Apricots	21	14	6	42
Bushberries	29	10	1	19
Cherries	17	12	8	19
Grapes	14	12	5	10
Peaches	27	14	5	65
Pears	17	13	9	41
Plums	14	10	6	24
Prunes	13	10	6	18
Walnuts	22	13	10	90

[a]Approximate average cost of weed control by combined tillage and hand hoe per year per acre until crop is commercially selfsustaining.

[b]Estimated cost of 6-ft chemical strip down the tree or vine row and tilling the centers in one direction.

[c]Years until the crop is commercially selfsustaining.

[d]Total savings over the 1- to 10-year period while the orchard is reaching commercial bearing age.

The benefits of hand weeding over no weed control for two situations in rice in the Philippines are shown in Table 3–6. Matsunaka (1970) in his economic analysis (Table 3–3) points out that the use of herbicides to replace hand labor will increase as the profits from such use increase. Low-cost herbicides have a considerable advantage over expensive ones. For example, in the Philippines the cost of enough 2,4-D to treat one hectare will be paid for by a yield increase of 90 kg per hectare, which is less than half the cost of hand weeding of one hectare of transplanted rice.

While it is impossible to evaluate accurately the costs of weeds, the foregoing tables are a sample of the sort of data being presented. From these large-scale estimates it might be interesting to turn to a few individual cases. From a county agent in California comes a report of a grower whose weeding costs in direct-seeded asparagus were $100 per acre. In strawberries the annual cost for weeding is around $150 per

Table 3-6. Benefits from Hand-weeding Rice in Two Situations[a]
(Matsunaka, 1970)

Place and treatment	Yield of rough rice (kg/ha)	Yield loss (%)	Weeding labor (hr/ha)	Net yield increase from weeding[b] (kg/ha)
Laguna, hand-weeded twice	5204	0	616	2515
Laguna, not weeded	1611	69.2	0	—
Iloilo, hand-weeded twice	4032	0	278	752
Iloilo, not weeded	2794	30.7	0	—

[a]Data on yield and labor requirements are from experiments reported by Moomaw et al., 1966.

[b]Total yield increase less an amount of rough rice that was equal in value to the cost of hand-weeding. Values of $0.073/kg for rice, and $0.128 per man-hour of labor were used in the calculations.

Table 3-7. Losses Caused by Weeds and Costs of Control in the
United States (Anon., 1965)

Crop or situation	Losses in yield and quality	Cost of control	Total
Agronomic crops	$1,573,024,000	$1,876,000,000	$3,449,024,000
Horticultural crops	254,281,000	307,000,000	561,281,000
Grazing lands	632,325,000	365,000,000	997,325,000
Aquatic sites and noncropland	53,140,000	55,638,000	108,778,000
Total	$2,512,770,000	$2,603,638,000	$5,116,408,000

acre. In celery the average cost is estimated at $75 per acre. Weeding peppers without the use of a selective spray cost $98 per acre; with a preemergence spray with carrot oil the cost was cut to $45 per acre.

Returning to the costs of weeds nationwide, Table 3-7 reports the losses caused by weeds and the costs of control. The total cost of weeds in the right-hand column presents some impressive figures; the total for the four situations is well over $5 billion per year.

Table 3–8 gives the relative losses from weeds, insects, and plant diseases, and provides information on pesticide sales and research efforts. Despite the frequently stressed magnitude of weed losses, the research efforts on insects and plant diseases far outweigh those devoted to weeds. This shows how difficult it is to get a new idea across to

Table 3-8. Relative Losses from Weeds, Insects, and Diseases Compared with Pesticide Sales and Research Efforts in the United States (Furtick, 1967)

Annual losses and costs of control $ Millions	1965 pesticide sales $ Thousands	Research support USDA and state $ Thousands
Weeds 5,064	201,753	8,707
Insects 4,298	237,317	34,368
Diseases 3,779	48,603	44,164

Table 3-9. Production of Organic Herbicides in the United States (1958-1966) (House, W. B. et al., 1967; Anon., 1967-1970)

| Year | 1000 pounds | | |
	2,4–D and 2,4,5–T acids	Other organic herbicides	Total
1958	34,622	25,295	59,917
1959	34,829	29,756	64,585
1960	42,522	33,201	75,723
1961	50,301	46,367	96,668
1962	51,366	51,913	103,279
1963	55,402	64,626	120,028
1964	65,148	93,909	159,057
1965	74,921	111,127	186,048
1966	83,671	149,352	233,023
1967	91,691	206,759	298,450
1968	96,793	235,541	332,334
1969	52,076	340,924	393,000
1970	48,447	312,553	361,000
1971	44,000	414,849	458,849

government administrators. The present adverse publicity given to all agricultural chemicals will probably further widen the gap between support for entomology and plant pathology and that devoted to weed science. (House, W. B. et al. 1967.)

Because the costs of herbicide production represent one of the major costs of weeds, the data in Table 3–9 show the great increase in herbicide use during the period 1958–1969. With 393,000,000 pounds produced in the United States in 1969, overall costs of weed control should be on the decline for, as shown in some of the above tables, herbicides lower the costs of weed control.

Table 3–10 shows the dollar value of the total consumption of herbicides in 1968 in the six largest agricultural areas of the world.

Because rising expenditures for herbicides indicate increasing profits for agriculture, the data presented in Table 3–9 and 3–10 show that chemical weed control, in addition to alleviating the discouraging burden of hand weeding, has increased the income of farmers around

Table 3–10. **Estimated 1968 World Consumption of Herbicides at the Consumer Level (Furtick, 1970)[a]**

Area	Consumption
North America	$550,000,000
Japan	70,000,000
Latin America	80,000,000
Near East, Southeast Asia, and Oceania	80,000,000
Western Europe	60,000,000
Africa	40,000,000
Total	$880,000,000

[a]Based on figures compiled by the International Plant Protection Center, Oregon State University. From industry, agricultural agency, and commerce agency sources.

the world. And as real as these advances have been, further improvements can be expected to continue for many years as herbicides become available and are used in the less developed countries of the world.

Supporting this new development in agriculture is a broad research effort involved in synthesis, testing, development, and sales of new herbicides. Methods from many aspects of biology have been adopted. Laboratories in biochemistry, plant physiology, and agronomy in universities and federal experiment stations, as well as those of industry, are doing research on the absorption, translocation, mode of action, and fate of new compounds. Studies have been made on the morphological and cytological effects of herbicides. And departments of soil science, microbiology, and pesticide toxicology are studying the fate of herbicides: adsorption, conjugation, chemical breakdown, and biological degradation are under investigation. This work represents the normal study required to understand the action of herbicides in weed killing. And much is being done to aid the ecologists and conservationists in their efforts to protect our environment from pollution and decline.

Practically all modern herbicides are organic compounds that break down in plants and soils to CO_2, H_2O, $SO_4^=$, $PO_4^\equiv$, NO_3^-, Cl^-, Br^-, and natural plant and soil constituents. Many of the intermediate products of herbicide decomposition are compounds that occur naturally in nature; they are no more harmful than salt, soda, or common flavorings and pharmaceuticals. Those that actually present a hazard to human health or to the safety of the environment must be identified and handled in such a way as to avoid any harmful effects; after all, gasoline and dynamite are common materials that are used in tremendous quantities; no one suggests banning their use.

With the increasing interest in and development of weed control, the burden of weed costs and the debilitating effects of hand methods should be alleviated around the world. With the publication of *Weed Science* and *Weed Research*, the means are at hand to rapidly disseminate research findings from laboratories in the developed countries. With weed conferences, not only in the United States and Europe but in Africa, South America, the Pacific Basin, and Asia, there are many opportunities for weed researchers, industrial personnel, and progressive farmers to meet and exchange information. And with the efforts of FAO, AID, the Rockefeller and Ford foundations, and many other educational organizations interested in agriculture, weed-control methods should spread and bring all advancing countries to a common understanding of weed losses and costs and the need for improvement in weed-control methods.

REFERENCES

Anon. 1965. A survey of extent and cost of weed control and specific weed problems. *USDA ARS* 34–23–1. 1965.

Dallyn, S., and R. Sweet. 1970. Weed control methods, losses and costs due to weeds and benefits of weed control in potatoes. *F.A.O. Internatl. Conf. on Weed Control.* Davis, Calif., p. 210–228.

Danielson, L. L. 1970. Losses and costs due to weeds, weed control methods, and benefits of weed control in vegetable legumes. *F.A.O. Internatl. Conf. on Weed Control.* Davis, Calif., p. 245–259.

Furtick, W. R. 1967. National and international need for weed science, a challenge for WSA. *Weeds* 15:291–295.

――――――. 1970. Present and potential contributions of weed control to solution of problems of world's food needs. *F. A. O. Internatl. Conf. on Weed Control.* Davis, Calif., p. 1–6.

House, W. B., et al. 1967. Assessment of ecological effects of extensive or repeated use of herbicides. U.S. Dept. Defence, D.D.C. AD824314, 369 pp. Midwest Research Inst.

Isleib, D. R. 1960. Quackgrass control in potato production. *Weeds* 8:631–635.

Lange, A. H. 1970. Weed control methods, losses and costs due to weeds, and benefits of weed control in deciduous fruit and nut crops. *F.A.O. Internatl. Conf. on Weed Control.* Davis, Calif., p. 143–162.

Loomis, W. E. 1955. Losses from weeds. Mimeo. Rep. on Natl. Res. Council, U.S.A. Survey of Weed Costs.

Matsunaka, S. 1970. Weed control in cereal crops. *F.A.O. Internatl. Conf. on Weed Control.* Davis, Calif., p. 7–23.

Moomas, J. C., V. P. Nevero, and A. C. Tauro. 1966. Riceweed control in tropical monsoon climates: problems and prospects. *Int. Rice Comm. Newsletter* 15:(4)1–16.

Nalewaja, J. D. and W. E. Arnold. 1970. Weed control methods and costs due to weeds, and benefits of weed control in wheat and other small grains. *F.A.O. Internatl. Conf. on Weed Control.* Davis, Calif., p. 48–64.

4

Preventive Weed Control

In weed control, as in medicine, an ounce of prevention is worth a pound of cure. If one could start with a pest-free crop, preventive measures could keep the land free of pests. All land of agricultural value is already populated with plants, even desert soil being brought under irrigation. The farmer always has some plant species to fight. The farmer wants to grow a single crop in monoculture or, at least, a controlled mixture, such as oats and vetch, as a forage crop or a cover crop in an orchard or vineyard. Thus, he is attempting to eliminate indigenous plants on new land or introduced weed species on an old-cropped soil.

Usually the native species in a virgin soil are easily brought under control. Our serious weed problems involve species that have been selected by their resemblance to the crop, and hence are difficult to eliminate in the presence of the crop. Examples are mustards or poppies in cereal crops, bristle grasses in corn, and wild onions or garlic in a pasture. These weeds are able to escape the normal cultural methods of weed control and hence they may survive years of preventive attempts at control.

With the introduction of modern herbicides, many of these traditional crop-weed combinations are being broken up and the crops, free from competition, are producing at unprecedented rates. Table 4–1 from Furtick (1970) shows increases in grain yields per acre in countries the world around. The highest gains are in countries that use modern agricultural technology, especially the use of high-yielding varieties, sufficient fertilizer, and chemical weed control.

A knowledge of the reproduction and dispersal methods of weeds is essential to a program of preventive weed control. Incipient infestations of weeds new to a particular region are constantly occurring on both new and old farms. In most instances one can easily determine the origin of a new weed; it is usually possible to trace it back to a particular purchase of crop seeds, to manure shipped in from another locality, to custom machinery used in harvest, to irrigation water or flooding, or to some other similar means (Fig. 4–1). It should be noted that at the time of initial introduction a particular infestation was small and limited. If preventive methods had been utilized then, much labor and anguish could have been spared. Most of our very serious weeds, especially the pernicious perennials, were introduced by the pioneers who originally broke the sod and planted the first crops.

*Table 4-1. Increase in Grain Yields per Acre 1934–1938 to 1960
(Furtick, 1970)*

Area	Percentage Increase
North America	107
Oceania	68
West Europe	38
Eeast Europe and USSR	20
Africa	20
Latin America	10
Asia	8

Knowledge of weeds, their serious effects, and preventive methods of control was either not developed or not practiced in those early years. Only now, a century or more later, are the losses caused by weeds recognized and methods for their control at hand.

PREVENTIVE WEED-CONTROL METHODS

WEED-SEED LONGEVITY

The great reproductive ability of weeds through seed production is described in Chapter 2. To practice weed prevention, a farmer must know the potentially dangerous weeds of his own locality and of other regions of the world where similar crops are grown. He must be able to recognize the weed seed and the seedlings in their early stages of growth, for at the young stages weeds are easily killed.

Seed dormancy is of great importance, as noted in Chapter 2. Dormancy is a determining factor in weed-seed populations of soils. There are reports in the literature of weed seeds that readily survive for decades in the soil, in some instances for centuries. For this reason the

past history of the farming of a soil may explain the occurrence of
particular weed species, for example mustards in grain fields, dodder in
alfalfa, quackgrass in maize, or bindweed in wheat. The overriding
problem of preventive weed control, then, becomes the knowledge of

FIGURE 4-1. Contrasting view of clean and weedy irrigation canals. Top,
structures where soil sterilization has been used, to eliminate weeds. Bottom,
structures lined with wild oats. Seeds of the latter are carried by water into the
fields where they germinate and grow.

the weeds present in a soil, the recognition of new weed species, and the
prevention of introduction of the new species into the present mixture.
Many of the new, preemergence herbicides can be used in a program of
weed control that envisions the gradual elimination of the stored weed
seed in the soil and, at the same time, prevention of the introduction of

new weed species. Thus, with the new array of selective herbicides, it may be possible to finally get on top of the weed-control problem, something which could not be accomplished when cultural and cropping methods alone were available.

The soil is a tremendous reservoir of weed seeds. Trials in England have proved that there may be over 100 million poppy seeds per acre in a soil that has a long history of cropping and as many as 45 million seeds per acre for 27 other major species (Brenchley and Warington, 1930) (Fig. 4-2).

FIGURE 4-2. Horses grazing in grassland infested with buttercup. The pasture has been sprayed with MCPA except for the strip of flowering plants. This strip illustrates the intensity of weed infestation that may develop under grazing conditions. (Photograph by courtesy of Plant Protection Ltd.).

Brenchley and Warington (1936) found that fallowing for four years reduced the viable weed-seed population in the soil drastically but did not eliminate all weeds. The natural dormancy of most species was four to nine years. Wheat planted after this extensive fallow was dense, but some weeds survived the competition and reestablished the weed-seed population of the soil by the time the crop was harvested. This report emphasizes the importance of modern herbicides in weed control. Fifty years ago, the very best of control practices, such as crop rotation and fallowing, allowed weed seed to mature and disseminate

whenever a seed crop such as cereals, peas, rape, or flax was allowed to
go to maturity.

PREVENTION OF SEED PRODUCTION

The survival of nearly all annual and biennial weed species depends upon seed production. The initial infestation of many perennial
weeds depends upon seed. If seed production could be stopped, most
weeds could eventually be eliminated.

In North Dakota, Stevens (1932) studied seed production by
weeds. He counted seeds and found the average number of seeds per
plant produced by annuals, biennials, and perennials. For 101 annuals
he found 20,832 seeds per plant; for 19 biennials, 26,600 seeds per plant;
and for 61 perennials, 16,629 seeds per plant. Seed production per plant
was, for 23 species, less than 1,000 seeds per plant; for 86 species from
1,000 to 10,000 seeds per plant; for 56 species, 10,000 to 50,000 per plant;
for 9 species, 50,000 to 100,000; and for 9 species, over 100,000 seeds per
plant. When one considers the area taken up by a vigorous, wild oat
plant, a tumbling pigweed, a cheeseweed, or a puncturevine it is easy to
understand how weeds can compete with crop plants.

Mowing is a common practice for preventing seed production by
weeds. This practice is important in croplands, in turf, in hay crops,
and on fencelines, roadsides, canal banks, and non-cropped areas
where weeds abound and produce seeds to infest neighboring crop land.
Mowing may not be completely effective; some plants such as star
thistle will produce lateral branches below the level of cutting and
ripen seed by the end of the growing season. In cutting, the inflores-
cences should be severed very soon after blooming; when they are
allowed to ripen for as much as ten days after bloom, the seeds may be
viable and hence the effort wasted.

Burning after cutting, and burning stubble has been used with the
assumption that the heat kills the weed seeds. However Durrell (1929)
reported that, under Colorado conditions, weed seeds on the ground
are only slightly injured by burning the dead weeds, even after this
ground cover had been sprayed with oil.

Seed destruction by burning depends very much on the location of
the seeds and upon the duration and intensity of the fire. Mercer (1941)
found that weed seeds recovered from the ground after burning had
greatly reduced germination; the species studied were two perennials,
Russian knapweed, whose seeds are located at the top, and field bindweed, whose seeds are in the foliar portion of the plant. Seeds so
located would receive the full impact of the fire and, in contrast to
weeds that shed their seeds on the soil, should give the results noted.
Mature, dry seeds are more resistant to fire than immature ones containing moisture.

Preventive Control Programs

There is an interdependence among weed-control methods and currently much interest is being given to integrated programs involving cultural, cropping, and chemical methods. No weed-control program can be successful unless it is properly conducted and followed vigilantly to note areas where plants have been missed or the possible encroachment of new or different weeds.

Repeated spring tillage is often used to stimulate weed-seed germination and to kill young weeds. However, if the soil has not met the critical minimum temperature for germination of the target species, the work will be in vain. Working the land so as to kill all existing weeds gives the crop and the weeds an even start, and vigorous crops may soon shade out the weeds. Tillage in the absence of weeds prepares the soil for a crop; if temperatures after planting rise above the critical value, large numbers of weeds may appear and form a solid mat of vegetation. In this situation an effective, selective, preemergence herbicide will be of tremendous use in handling weeds that normally germinate after a crop is seeded. Preemergence herbicide treatment can be considered a preventive method because it eliminates the weeds from competition and from producing seeds while the crop is maturing.

Because tillage tends to compact soils, to injure plant roots, and to impair soil structure, non-tillage is becoming practiced in many agricultural areas. Whereas tillage is cheap and effective, where one or more of the above effects are found, chemical control may be substituted and it may prove economical in the long run. A compromise widely used is to apply herbicide over narrow (6–12") bands and to cultivate the weeds out of the middles; this practice is used in many row crops and also in orchards, vineyards, and tree plantings. Controlling weeds around young forest trees may gain several years in bringing the crop to marketable size.

Practices that start with clean, sound, adapted seed planted at the optimum rate and date and at proper depth usually result in vigorous stands of crop plants. There is an inverse relation between crop density and weed competition and many practices that were related to tillage by horse-drawn tools (row spacing for example) are being changed; row crops are being planted in dense rows instead of in hills; row spacings are narrower; and some traditional row crops are being broadcast into soil in which weeds are under chemical control. Optimum rate, placement, and timing of fertilizer application makes for less weed competition. And irrigation, long limited to the more arid soils of the western United States, is coming into use in the regions of summer rainfall, where long dry spells may materially reduce crop yields. Adequate screening of weed seeds from irrigation water, use of pipe instead of ditches, and sprinkling in place of flooding are all practices that minimize weed problems. Application of irrigation water from wells and distribution through pipe is ideal from the standpoint of preventive weed control.

Crop rotation, a system long used to control weeds, is going out of use in our modern, chemicalized, mechanized agriculture. However, as weeds become tolerant of economical herbicides and as fuel prices advance in the face of diminishing supplies of petroleum, crop rotation may return to a place of prominence; it is an ideal preventive method for controlling weeds and maintaining soil fertility.

With the use of improved cropping methods, including chemical weed control, certain common weeds associated with our major crops are becoming scarce and even disappearing. For example, common mustards and wild radish are much less prevalent in our principal cereal-producing areas than they were before the introduction of 2,4-D. Prevalence of perennial weeds, such as Canada thistle, field bindweed, and quackgrass, is decreasing where deeper plowing, thorough cultivation, and optimum growing conditions for crops are found. The writer has seen the production of high yields of tomatoes on bindweed-infested fields in California where the growers have practiced preventive cultural practices and have used effective preemergence herbicides.

However, dodder has made its appearance on tomatoes and this can be a pest of serious consequence. Tests are underway to find a pre- or postemergence chemical tolerated by tomatoes and effective on dodder. Meanwhile it behooves tomato growers to buy only pure, tested seeds, to eradicate small, incipient spots of dodder, and to observe every preventive method available. If dodder seeds should become as prevalent as are the seeds of pigweeds, lambsquarters, milkweeds, and other common annuals, tomato growing would become uneconomical on these soils. The increase of grassy weeds following the wide use of 2,4-D is another problem that faces not only farmers in the temperate regions but farmers and plantation owners in the tropics.

Because of the selection between weeds exhibited by modern herbicides, rotation of herbicides, pioneered on the sugar plantations of Hawaii, is being adopted in many agricultural regions. In modern, integrated weed control, preventive methods, tillage under proper conditions, herbicide rotation, and even crop rotation are seen as useful methods for accomplishing the desired ends, namely crop production free of pests. To make such a system work, the grower must recognize weeds, understand their particular properties and habits of growth, and be able to identify them in all stages of growth. He must be persistent in his operations and vigilant in every way to detect any new intruder on his land. And he must know and use herbicides wherever they are effective in his cropping programs. Under such a systems approach, the grower may eventually hope for a nearly weed-free agriculture.

Production and Use of Weed-free Seed

The history of agriculture is replete with stories of farmers who have purchased crop seeds at bargain prices in the market or over the fence from a neighbor only to find that they have infested their land with weeds that are very difficult to get rid of. It pays therefore to buy certified seed which states on the label the numbers of weed seed present, or to have unlabeled seed tested at a reliable seed-testing laboratory.

Because the life cycle, the size, and the shape of certain crop and weed seeds are similar, the weeds become associated with the crop so that the crop seed is seldom free from weed seeds. One example is the common occurrence of field bindweed in areas where wheat and barley have been grown in California. In the early days of the combined harvester, bindweed seeds, which resemble wheat in size and weight, were widely spread in the straw, in screenings, and in wheat used for seed. This bindweed remains to plague orchardists, vineyardists, and vegetable growers throughout the state.

PRINCIPLES OF PRODUCTION

Production of Weed-free Seed

Production of weed-free, genetically pure, high-yielding crop seeds has become a specialized business in the Western world. Many large corporations are engaged in the seed business and their investment in land, seed stocks, and special seed-cleaning equipment is a large factor in our economy. Seed certification is big business in many states and the growing of certified seed provides work for many men, most of whom have specialized training. Not only plant breeders, but agronomists, fertilizer specialists, and pest-control experts are employed. And the growing practices used are among the most advanced in the world. The seed crops are planted and grown under strict supervision. Rogueing of off-type plants is conscientiously carried out, fertility is managed to produce a maximum yield of pure-strain viable seed, and pests are held in check with insecticides, fungicides, herbicides, and any other pest control measures required. In the case of hybrid seed, pollination is carried out under strict supervision using tested parent stocks. In the case of maize, detasseling is done in time to eliminate the chance for uncontrolled pollination; in some species male sterile strains are used.

Methods of Seed Cleaning

Seed from the field should be carefully cleaned by methods based upon physical or chemical differences between weed and crop seeds. Such differences include size, shape, weight, surface area, specific gravity, stickiness, pubescense, texture, color, and electrical properties. Cleaning also eliminates inert material that adds to the bulk of the seeds and, if moist, may cause spoilage by heating in storage.

Initial cleaning consists of passing the bulk seeds through a cleaner consisting of a blower and sets of screens having holes of different shapes and sizes. This initial cleaning reduces the bulk by discarding straw, clods, and nonviable seeds and enables the cleaned product to flow smoothly through machines used in the final cleaning. For the final cleaning, machines used are air-screen cleaners, specific-gravity separators, indent disc and indent cylinder separators, pneumatic and aspirator separators, velvet rollers, spiral or inclined drapers, vibrators, timothy bumper mills, horizontal disc separators, electronic separators, magnetic separators, buckhorn plantain cleaners, and color separators. By means of these specialized machines the seedsman may separate almost any weed seeds, dirt, or other contaminant from crop seeds. The effectiveness of this array of machines is responsible for the fact that seeds bought from a reliable seed firm can be depended upon to be weed free and to germinate well.

Planting and Cultivation Machinery

Surface and furrow planters, bed or ridge planters, and listers and broadcast planters generally do not drag trash over the planted area. Minimum tillage systems manipulate the soil less than the older methods, and production costs are reduced; less area is made up into seedbeds. Some ridge farmers push the trash between the ridges so that mechanical weed control can be carried on in the middles. Spike-toothed harrows, finger weeders, and rotary hoes are used after planting; these tools may drag trash and spread weeds. Disc cultivators do a clean job of tillage, but sweep and shovel cultivators may spread trash and parts of perennial weeds. A good moldboard plow fitted with rolling coulters and jointers will turn the trash in a field completely under so that subsequent operations go on over clean soil. Such tools avoid spreading trash, weed seeds, and vegetative parts of perennial weeds.

Harvesting Machinery

Combined harvesters, threshing machines, binders, choppers, and hay balers may harvest mature weed seeds and return them to the field or include them with the crop. Crop seed left in the field may volunteer and become a serious weed problem. Harvesting equipment may be moved from farm to farm crossing county, state, and even national boundaries. An example is the army of combines that move from the southern United States northward through the wheat belt and into Canada each summer doing custom work. Nebraska is situated near the center of this wheat-growing area and state officials have examined many combines for weed seed during their migration into the state. During the years 1961 through 1966 an average of 4815 machines per year coming from 20 states and Canada have entered this state. Records show that 13 percent of these combines were infested with weed seeds and had to be cleaned before they could be used. The owners of these combines were aware of the weed-seed inspection but failed to comply until forced. This indicates the problem posed to states that do not have such inspection laws; such moves within state boundaries go without inspection. The responsibility for weed prevention remains with the individual farmer (Burnside, 1970).

SEED-CLEANING MACHINERY

Because most seed-cleaning machinery moves from farm to farm or, if stationary, is used to clean seeds brought in from different farms, great care should be exercised to be sure that weed seeds on the screens, in the elevators, or left in bins and corners are all removed between jobs; otherwise the very machine that is designed to free crop seed of weed seed may itself become an agent in the dissemination of weeds. Truck beds, storage bins, railroad cars, and bags should all be cleaned between jobs so that weed seeds are not carried from farm to farm.

MOVEMENT AND MANAGEMENT OF LIVESTOCK

MOVEMENT BY LIVESTOCK

Many weed seeds attach to or pass through livestock. Weed seeds may have hooks, spines, awns, beards, or resinous substances that cause them to adhere to animals. Other seeds may be carried in mud that lodges in or on the hooves of cattle or sheep. Most important are the seeds that pass through the digestive tracts of animals. In general the viability of large seeds will be destroyed more readily than that of small seeds, but the germination of some seeds will actually be increased by passing through sheep or cattle. Velvet mesquite passes through cattle unharmed and the moist manure provides a favorable medium for germination and growth. Old sheep with poor teeth are less effective in grinding up seeds and destroying their viability. The movement of livestock, whether driven over trails and roads or carried in trucks and railroad cars, is a common means of weed-seed dispersal. Anyone seeking out the weed flora of a particular locality will do well to traverse the railroad tracks across country. All common local weeds and often exotic species will be found along the rights-of-way.

Livestock Management

Overgrazing generally predisposes a range to invasion by weeds, and these may be spread by the grazing animals. Proper stocking rate is very important in vegetation management on the range; even distribution of the stock over the area is also important. Livestock distribution can be controlled by appropriate fencing, proper location of water and salt, and provision of shade. Weed problems are greatest where livestock concentrate and it is in these areas where weed control should be considered.

Rotational grazing of large ranges allows rest periods for desirable forage species to flower and produce seed; usually seed production of annual species takes place in early summer. In pastures where perennial grasses predominate, a rest period in the fall to allow for restorage of root reserves helps to maintain a vigorous forage production. In some areas livestockmen establish cool-season and warm-season pastures and graze each at the most favorable time with respect to feeding the cattle and maintaining a vigorous forage stand. In several western states the cool-season grazing is carried on in the valleys and foothills, the summer grazing is provided in the high mountain ranges. The cattle were herded along trails from valleys to hills and back; now they are carried in diesel-powered trucks. Spread of weeds may be reduced by confining the livestock in corrals and feeding them for a few days before moving them onto a new pasture; some weed seeds may require as much as a week to pass completely through the animals.

Cattle and sheep or sometimes hogs are used to salvage cereals, maize, or sorghum from the fields after harvest, but weed seeds may be spread by this practice. Foxtails, beggarticks, cockleburs, spiny clotburs, sandbur, and puncturevine seeds are examples of weeds whose seeds are readily transported by animals. Grazing animals may spread seeds from isolated weed patches over an entire farm or range. The pasturing of sheep on alfalfa stubble in the autumn has seriously injured alfalfa stands because of introduced weeds; sheep are particularly bad.

Hay and grain concentrates should be selected with care before feeding them to livestock; seeds of new noxious weeds may be introduced in this way and once they become established it may be practically impossible to eradicate them.

Windbreaks, fence lines, roadsides, and waste areas often serve as breeding grounds for weeds. These should be inspected periodically and cleaned up before the weeds move onto valuable crop land or pasture. Skeleton weed, a common pest in Australia and in the Mediterranean, has recently been found in California where it had spread unnoticed along roadsides over a wide area. Such examples of weed dissemination are common and they emphasize the need for eternal vigilance in our fight against weeds.

STORAGE OF FEED AND MANURE

The primary factors for lengthening seed viability are low moisture content, low temperatures, and low oxygen supply. The moisture contents of grain, hay, and straw are reduced for storage and this contributes to the longevity of weed seeds. Weed seeds may remain viable for years in hay stacks, straw piles, and grain bins; some legume seeds are reported to have survived storage for over 100 years in dry hay or grain. Usually livestock feed and bedding are used up and removed rather frequently but old manure piles may harbor seeds of some weeds for years.

Ensiling of corn, grass, and alfalfa is common for storage. In the presence of fermentable carbohydrates, adequate moisture, and anaerobic conditions that encourage lactic acid fermentation, a pH of from 3.5 to 4 is produced; viability of most weed seed is destroyed by this process, but some hard-seeded weeds, such as field bindweed, puncturevine, and some of the legumes, have seed that will survive ensiling. These seeds then undergo the same conditions as those in hay or concentrates that are fed to cattle; some may pass through in a viable state and live to infest land where the animals are pastured or their manure spread.

PASSAGE OF SEED THROUGH ANIMALS

Many weed seeds are spread in the droppings of animals and birds; some seeds that occur in fruits are regurgitated after the fruity tissue has been removed. In regions where Pyracantha species are used in landscaping, the sidewalks may be littered with their seeds in the winter when the robins and cedar waxwings are migrating. Harmon and Keim (1934) found that the percentage of viable seeds that passed through animals varied with the animals and with the weed species. The following animals are ranked in the order of decreasing destructiveness to the seeds: chickens, sheep, horses, hogs, calves. Poultry have gravel in their gizzards which grind on the seeds and only the hardest survive.

Muenscher (1955) presented work on viability of weed seeds in the digestive tracts of animals; 40 weed species survived after passage through cows, horses, sheep and swine. Only 6 of the species were completely destroyed by all of the animals; 19 species survived the passage through all of the animals studied.

Redroot pigweed seeds passed through cows showed 36, 29, 4 and 3 percent survival after 47, 59, 73 and 97 hours in the digestive tract. (Atkeson et al., 1934)

Oswald (1908) tested the viability of 52 different species of weed seeds buried in manure from horses, cows, and a 50:50 mixture of these. The seeds were mixed in the manures, and remained stacked in piles for 6 months. The temperatures in the fermenting piles were recorded over a period of 60 days, at which time they had returned to that of the surroundings. In the horse manure the highest temperature reached was 201°F, the lowest 40°F, the mean 134°F; in cow manure the temperatures were 168°F, 40°F, and 128°F, respectively; in the mixed manure 188°F, 40°F, and 122°F, respectively. After 1 month none of the seeds germinated although some were still firm; after 6 months all were decayed.

Harmon and Keim (1934) buried the seeds of 8 species in horse and cow manure piles and tested their viability after 1, 2, 3, and 4 months. Temperatures in the horse and cow manure reached 158 and 150°F respectively in 2 weeks. Field bindweed seeds were the most durable; they showed 4, 22, 1 and 0 percent viability after 1, 2, 3, and 4 months storage, respectively.

Stoker et al. (1934) stored seeds of several weed species in chicken manure in small and large piles. In one treatment, the seeds were placed in piles consisting of litter and droppings mixed as in the cleanings from a poultry house; in a second, litter alone was used; in a third, water was added to litter and the pile was compacted. Seeds were removed at intervals from 10 days to 4 months. Bindweed seeds were viable through all tests; whitetop and Russian knapweed seeds were destroyed after 20 days in the loose manure, and 1 month in the moistened and compacted pile. In the unmoistened pile some seeds of all three species were viable at the end of 4 months. These tests proved that only by fine grinding or cooking are weed seeds rendered unviable; screenings used for feed should be treated in this way.

From these reports it seems that no one treatment of material fed to, used, or discarded by livestock or poultry is completely effective in destroying weed seeds. Treatments rank in the following order of effectiveness: compost of manure; ensiling; passage through animals; storage in feed, hay or straw. A combination of these treatments, such as ensiling, feeding, and composting the manure, should destroy all weed seeds.

In spite of all of the suggestions made for using preventive methods for controlling weeds, there are at least two means of dissemination against which the farmer has no control: seeds borne in the air, and seeds regurgitated by or passed through wild birds. The encouraging aspect is that modern selective herbicides are being found that enable a grower to control almost all weeds in almost all crops. This brings out a fact that bears repeating, namely that in place of attempting to control weeds by any single method, the grower should use the modern integrated approach applying each method where it fits best into his total operation and combining two or more methods where the problem demands. By integrated control involving all chemical, mechanical, cultural, and preventive methods, practically any weed can now be held in check and, in many cases, with sufficient time and effort, eradicated.

REFERENCES

Atkeson, F. W., H. W. Hulbert, and T. R. Warren. 1934. Effect of bovine digestion and of manure storage on the viability of weed seeds. *J. Amer. Soc. Agron.* 26:390–397.

Burnside, O. C. 1970. Progress and potential for non-herbicidal control of weeds through preventive weed control. *F.A.O. Internatl. Conf. on Weed Control.* Davis, Calif., pp. 464–483.

Brenchley, W. E., and K. Warington. 1930. The weed seed population of arable soil. I. Numerical estimation of viable seeds and observations on their natural dormancy. *J. Ecol.* 18:235–272.

——— and ———. 1936. The weed seed population of arable soil. III. The reestablishment of weed species after reduction of fallowing. *J. Ecol.* 34:18–27.

Durrell, L. W. 1929. Weed control in Colorado. *Colorado Agr. Exp. Sta. Rept.* 1928. pp. 22–24.

Furtick, W. R. 1970. Present and potential contributions of weed control to solution of problem of meeting the world's food needs. *F.A.O. Internatl. Conf. on Weed Control.* Davis, Calif., June 22–July 1, 1970.

Harmon, G. W., and F. D. Keim. 1934. The percentage and viability of weed seeds recovered in the feces of farm animals, and their longevity when buried in manure. *J. Amer. Soc. Agron.* 26:762–767.

Mercer, W. H. 1941. Annual report (1940) on weeds: Control, research and educational program on the Uncompahgre Irrigation Project. U. S. Bureau of Reclamation. (Mimeographed report).

Muenscher, W. C. *Weeds.* 2nd ed. New York: The Macmillan Co., 560 pp.

Oswald, E. J. 1908. The effect of animal digestion and fermentation of manures on the vitality of seeds. *Md. Agr. Expt. Sta Bul.* 128:265–291.

Stevens, O. A. 1932. The number and weight of seeds produced by weeds. *Amer. J. Bot.* 19:784–794.

Stoker, G. L., D. C. Tingey, and R. J. Evans. 1934. The effect of different methods of storing chicken manure on the viability of certain weed seeds. *J. Amer. Soc. Agron.* 26:390–397.

5

Ecology of Weeds

Ecology concerns the interrelations of organisms and their environment; plant ecology treats the role of climatic, edaphic (soil), and biotic factors in relation to plants. The complex termed "environment" determines the distribution of species, their competitive ability, their prevalence, and their intricate interrelations. As contrasted with native plants, the distribution and behavior of weeds are influenced by a number of factors related to man, principally the recency of introduction, the crops or other plants with which they compete, and various planting, tillage, harvest, and pest-control operations to which they are subject. Prevalence of weeds is often determined by agricultural practices, but plant introduction, as in the case of *Opuntia* in Australia, St. Johnswort in Australia, New Zealand, and the western United States, and *Halogeton* in the arid West, may be a dominant factor. Occurrence of weeds, in some instances, may be taken as an indication of soil fertility or soil reaction; however, so many factors enter into weed occurrence and prevalence that they cannot be depended upon as indicators of the agricultural value of land.

Ecologists in the past have been prone to emphasize only "natural" factors in their studies on plant distribution. More recently people studying weeds have pointed out the very important role played by man in both his agricultural and urban pursuits in the incidence of plant species, their movements, and their competitive interrelations. In current times even newer and more subtle influences are present—all related to man and his activities. These influences involve parasites and their conscious introduction, multiplication, and release in the biological methods of weed control. They include new chemicals that are capable of selectively rendering croplands weed-free, as well as those that eliminate all plants. They may combine controlled burning, airplane seeding and fertilizer application, and herbicide spraying to improve pastures and ranges (Love, 1961). They may involve: (1) broadcast spraying of weeds in grain, so successful as to practically eradicate certain annual weeds, for example wild mustard and radish in the Pacific Northwest and poppies in Britain and Europe; (2) broadcast application of chemicals to forests to inhibit weedy trees and release valuable timber species; (3) airplane treatment of forests to eliminate *Ribes* spp. and protect against blister rust; (4) chemical fallow, which eliminates tillage operations in water conservation and, by avoiding compaction from traffic on the land, improves soil structure; (5) sprayblade application of certain benzonitrile and dinitroaniline herbicides to suppress perennial weeds such as field bindweed and nutsedges; (6) chemical spraying of pastures that is effective in establishment of new and improved forage varieties; (7) chemical treatment of irrigation canals which destroys aquatic weeds for miles from a single treatment; and (8) sterilization of soils that prevents spread of weeds on highways, railroads, and airfields. These methods and many more are having profound effects on vegetation, particularly on those species and varieties used for crops and those that are weeds. By and large, man is becoming more and more successful in providing pure-culture conditions for his crops and in limiting the incidence and spread of undesirable weeds.

In spite of these new, improved agricultural techniques, there are some situations that resist progress. For example turkey mullein, a common weed on highway edges in the western United States, tolerates monuron and hence increases in vigor and density. Fennel is resistant to diesel oil; where oil is used for roadside weed control the fennel develops a monoculture of its own. Cocklebur tolerates trifluralin and this creates problems in certain cotton-growing areas; giant foxtail resists atrazine in the corn belt; and where alfalfa is close cut and hauled off the field for dehydrating, groundsel, a weed that thrives in the winter while alfalfa is dormant, is on the increase. Use of mixed herbicides or rotation of herbicides will handle most of these situations.

WEEDS AND CLIMATE

As is true of plants in general, distribution of weeds is related to climate. For example, Canada thistle is common in southern Canada and across the northern tier of the United States; it is less prevalent as one moves southward, and it is not a pest in the southern states. Quackgrass and field bindweed are more common in the central states, the former in the more humid regions, the latter in the drier states.

Johnsongrass and Bermudagrass are both crop plants and serious pests across the southern states; they are not prevalent in regions where the soil freezes during the winter. Nutsedges (*Cyperus esculentus* and *C. rotundus*) are common throughout the humid tropics and in our more southern states; they do not thrive where soils are subject to frost.

Similarly, whereas giant ragweed and burdock are prevalent in the more humid eastern and midwestern states, puncturevine, halogeton, and Russian thistle are more common in the arid west. Some weeds thrive under desert conditions, for example, halogeton; some prefer mesophytic conditions, for example, mustards, pigweeds, etc.; while some, such as certain buttercups, barnyardgrass, *Paspalum distichum*, and curly dock, are most weedy in moist or aquatic environments. Absinth (*Artemisia absinthium*) has recently invaded large areas in Saskatchewan during a succession of moist years; there has been recession in upland areas during dry weather from 1957 to 1959, but it has continued to thrive in mesic habitats (Selleck and Coupland, 1961). Thus weeds, like other plants, seek out the environments they prefer and often may be controlled by changing the environment. Examples are flooding, which will eradicate Russian knapweed and field bindweed in a single season, or drying, which will kill Bermudagrass rhizomes or purple nutsedge tubers in a summer (Day and Russell, 1955).

In contrast with the above weeds, some species may be found wherever agriculture is practiced. This was true of the wild mustards and wild radish before the days of 2,4-D; now these may be hard to find in some locations where spraying has been frequent and regular. Pigweeds, lambsquarters, groundsel, chickweed, shepherdspurse, purslane, foxtail, and a host of other annual weeds may be found almost everywhere that crops are grown. Unlike perennials, these annuals are opportunists; they escape the rigors of freezing and thawing, wetting and drying, and heat and cold by passing the unfavorable seasons in the seed stage. Usually seeds of such weeds are sensitive to moisture and temperature, and they germinate only when conditions are favorable for growth and survival.

Thus we find that weeds are adapted to a wide variety of climates; some weeds thrive under almost any conditions, others are highly selective in their choice of growing conditions. Climate may have profound effects on the structure and composition of weeds. Thus Hull (1958), using controlled environment, found that greenhouse-grown mesquite plants had little cuticle, whereas those growing outdoors had much more. High temperatures yielded more wax than low; nonwax fatty substances were greatest at low night temperatures.

Russian knapweed growing in northern California is quite susceptible to 2,4-D, but that growing in the hot, dry climate of the San Joaquin Valley has proved to be very resistant to 2,4–D sprays. Field bindweed growing in a humid coastal climate is more susceptible to 2,4-D than that growing in an interior valley. These differences, due largely to climate, reflect variations in cuticle development, pubescence, vegetativeness, growth synchronization, and available moisture. More research is needed on the effects of climate on weeds in relation to vigor and competitiveness, susceptibility to herbicides, and response to weed-control practices of all kinds.

WEEDS AND SOILS

Many studies have been made to determine the degree of association of certain weeds with various soils. Also, attempts have been made to judge the agricultural quality of lands by the character of the weed growth; in this latter connection, both rankness of growth and species composition have been considered.

In general, very few species of weeds are definitely associated with any particular soil. Most weeds may be found in soils differing quite widely in physical characters, in moisture content, and even in soil reaction. Their adaptability to the variable factors of the environment explains, at least in part, why they are weeds.

Considerable data are available showing the relation between soil reaction and the nature of weed growth. It is recognized that there are characteristic 'alkali plants'—species that are confined largely to alkali soils—and other species that grow with greater luxuriance on soils containing only very small amounts of alkali. In the arid and semiarid sections of the United States, the following are characteristic alkali plants, some of which may behave as weeds:

Tussock grass (*Sporobolus airoides*)
Salt grass (*Distichlis spicata*)
Fine-top salt grass (*Sporobolus asperifolius*)
Pickleweed (*Allenrolfea occidentalis*)
Saltbushes (*Atriplex* spp.)
Kochia (*Kochia californica*)
Halogeton (*Halogeton glomeratus*)
Saltwort (*Suaeda suffrutescens* and *S. torreyana*)
Samphire (*Salicornia ambigua* and other species)
Sesuvium (*Sesuvium portulacastrum*)
Spurry (*Spergula* spp.)
Nitrophila (*Nitrophila occidentalis*)
Alkali heath (*Frankenia grandifolia*)
Yerba mansa (*Anemopsis californica*)
Common spikeweed (*Centromadia pungens*)[a]
Bushy goldenrod (*Bigelovia veneta*)

---

[a]Now named *Hemizonia pungens*

Under similar climatic conditions, the following species are intolerant of alkali: common sunflower, common sowthistle, cheeseweed, annual yellow sweet clover, common plantain, Bermudagrass, and horseweed.

Cassia species, such as senna and sicklepod, crotalarias, millet, and crabgrass, tolerate acid soils; corn and soybeans are moderately tolerant. Manganese deficiency may occur in some weeds growing in an acid soil. Frequent use of ammonium sulfate as a nitrogen source for crops may shift the soil pH toward the acid side and cause a shift in the dominant weed population. Some weeds respond to phosphorus application. Beggarweed, pigweeds, annual morning glory, jimsonweed, and crowfoot may thrive under high fertility conditions (Hoveland and Buchanan, 1973).

Cords (1960) finds that foxtail barley (*Hordeum jubatum*) is quite tolerant of saline soils, and where it is a weed, use of salt-tolerant competitors, such as tall wheatgrass, is recommended for controlling the pest. Foxtail has a wide range of adaptation to varying water-table conditions, and its prevalence depends largely on competition from other plants. With a surface water table, a hydrophyte such as spike-sedge offers sufficient competition to control the weed; under low water-table conditions, tall fescue and tall wheatgrass are able to reduce its prevalence. Thus, if drainage is to be used in foxtail control, seeding with the latter two species should accompany the operation. Nitrogen fertilization in the presence of fescue and wheatgrass is an additional practice that may pay off.

Under field conditions, it is generally conceded that the prevalence of sheep sorrel indicates a definite need of lime. The fact that this weed seems to flourish on soil deficient in lime has led to the belief that the plant grows best on, or even demands, an acid soil. Numerous field and pot tests point to the conclusion that sheep sorrel thrives on acid soil because of the absence of competition from those plants that are more sensitive to acid soil. The chief value of lime in reducing sheep sorrel is that it brings about chemical and physical soil conditions that favor the growth of other plants, thus increasing their ability to exclude the sorrel. Welton (1931), in plot tests, showed that sheep sorrel made a much better growth in soil of pH 8 than in soil of pH 4.

Hartwell and Damon (1917), in their study in Rhode Island of lawn and other grasses as influenced especially by the degree of so-called 'soil acidity' or 'soil alkalinity,' found that dandelions and plantains are checked by increasing the degree of soil acidity by applications of sulfate of ammonia. So-called 'alkaline' fertilizers, such as nitrate of soda, promote the growth of these weeds. The development of Kentucky bluegrass and clover was also checked by excessive top dressings of 'acid' fertilizers; redtop and bent grasses respond more favorably to acid fertilizers. Physiologically acidic fertilizers are ammonium sulfate, potassium chloride, and potassium sulfate; physiologically basic fertilizers are nitrate of soda and wood ashes. Where single fertilizers or combinations are used for years on grass lands, characteristic flora develop that are related to the soil conditions that result. In the 'Park Grass' field at Rothamsted, distinct herbage types may be seen that have resulted from such long-time use of single chemicals.

From the foregoing discussion, it appears that most weed species are valueless as indicators of the reaction of the soil in which they grow or of the agricultural quality of the soil. A few species, such as sheep sorrel, are frequently indicative of acid soils, but even in this case the plant grows better in nonacid soils if competition from other species is excluded. However, the occurrence in an area of a mixture of certain species may be a rather reliable indication of soil conditions. For example, in England, according to Brenchley (1920), a weed association consisting of sheep sorrel, small nettle, spurry, corn chrysanthemum, and knawel indicates a light or sandy soil, deficient in lime. And a mixture of such weeds as black bent, hoary plantain, corn buttercup, coltsfoot, and quackgrass is usually associated with clay soil.

It is sometimes claimed that a soil which will support a luxuriant weed growth is excellent for cropping purposes and that the prolific weed growth indicates an abundance of mineral nutrients. This may or may not be true. The character of weed growth on a given area is determined by many factors other than the physical and chemical properties of the soil; among these are its cropping history, proximity of sources of infestation, weed-seed population of the soil, available water supply, and seasonal growing conditions. Furthermore, the adaptation of the crop to the soil and to climatic conditions is important. A luxuriant growth of alkali-tolerant weeds might indicate a soil upon which sugar beets could be grown but one entirely unsuited to corn or grass.

WEEDS AND CROPS

Observations and field surveys seem to show that different crops have their characteristic weeds. For example, in various agricultural sections it is fairly evident that there are characteristic weeds of cereal crops, of alfalfa and other forage crops, of grasslands, of orchards and vineyards, etc. Once certain weed species are introduced, their abundance or scarcity in a given crop is determined largely by the degree of competition offered by that crop. The weed's competitive ability depends upon its vegetative habits, readiness of seed germination, rate of seedling growth, and extent and nature of root and top growth. Moreover, the cultural operations associated with the growing of a crop, together with the rotation in effect, may be such as to encourage or discourage specific weeds.

Many factors contribute to the common occurrence of an association of crops with certain weeds. Among these factors are similarity of seed size, time of ripening and germination, and various tillage, cropping, and harvest practices. The association of annual species of the mustard family (Cruciferae) with small cereals (other than rice) is a notable example. The peculiar conditions under which rice is grown naturally encourage weeds that flourish in water or in a very wet soil; the laying by of such row crops as cotton and corn is conducive to growth of grasses such as lovegrass, tickle grass, barnyardgrass, and Johnsongrass. Some other common examples are: weedy *Hordeum* spp. in early cuttings of alfalfa; watergrass in rice, in late cuttings of alfalfa, and often in irrigated root crops, after they are laid by; certain weeds, such as bracken fern, broomsedge, *Plantago* spp., bull thistle, orange hawkweed, and *Rumex* spp., in meadows and pasturelands in regions of summer rainfall; such annual grasses as downy chess, ripgut grass, red brome, common foxtail, medusahead, rattail fescue, and burclover in western range lands; native bog plants such as field horsetail, cinnamon fern, reed grass, and *Dulichium arundinaceum* in cranberry bogs; and a variety of common weeds, such as dandelion, smooth and hairy crabgrass, annual bluegrass, common chickweed, oxalis, and buckhorn plantain, in lawn and turf grasses.

Vengris (1953) made a population study of weeds in the four principal crops of the Connecticut River Valley in Massachusetts. These crops were tobacco, onions, potatoes, and corn. In these crops, crabgrass, barnyardgrass, old witchgrass, lambsquarters, rough pigweed, and purslane occurred in over 40 percent of the fields. Chickweed and Pennsylvania smartweed were also prevalent. The weed flora of onion fields consisted of 34 species; of tobacco, 39; of potatoes, 55; and of corn, 66.

WEEDS OF ABANDONED LANDS

Throughout most agricultural sections, acreages of farmland, large and small, have been abandoned for one reason or another. The *Yearbook of Agriculture*, U.S. Department of Agriculture, 1938, reports that "fifty million acres of farm land have already been abandoned by farmers because they are no longer productive, and 30,000,000 acres more are in the process of abandonment." The chief causes of reduced productivity of farm lands, leading to their abandonment, are soil erosion, depleted fertility, improper tillage and cropping practices, and overgrazing. In some situations weeds have been responsible.

These millions of acres of abandoned farm lands of the United
States become enormous weed-infested areas. The weed population of
abandoned fields varies with climatic conditions, types of crops grown,
and tillage operations immediately preceding abandonment.

Although the trend on many abandoned lands is toward the original flora, the introduction of weedy species into the plant complex
may so disturb it that a new population, often including alien weeds, is
at least a temporary climax. For example, there is no indication that
complete abandonment of St. Johnswort-infested range land in the
northern coast counties of California will result in a return to the
initial state. On the contrary, most of the abandoned areas become
almost completely covered with St. Johnswort and continue in this
condition for many years. Downy chess, broadleaf filaree, and medusahead are three additional introduced species that show tendencies to
become dominant on range lands of the West.

COMPETITION BETWEEN CROP PLANTS
AND WEEDS

Competition between crop plants and weeds is a critical factor in
the growing of useful plants. If crop plants occupy the soil and are
vigorous, weeds are excluded or retarded in their growth. On the other
hand, if the crop stand is thin or lacks vigor, weeds will flourish. Any
environmental condition or any procedure that promotes the growth
of crop plants tends to diminish the ill effects of weeds. Conversely,
conditions or methods unfavorable to the growth of useful plants
permit the invasion and development of a weed population. According
to Timmons (1941), field bindweed growing in competition with annual
crops at Hays, Kansas, averaged only 2.2 ft in radial spread, while 21
patches growing in partially fallowed areas without crop or annual
weed competition averaged 12 ft of annual increase in radial spread.

Competition is usually evident in cultivated fields. Individual crop
plants may compete with each other, or they may compete with weeds.
The keenest competition between weeds and crop plants usually occurs when the individuals competing are most alike in their vegetative
habits, methods of reproduction, and demands upon the environment.
For example, in small cereal crops, the weeds that furnish the greatest
competition are such annuals as wild oat, various mustards, and pennycress, the seeds of which germinate at about the same time as those
of cereals; thus their top growth and root systems develop simultaneously with those of the cereals, coming into immediate competition
with them.

It is obvious that weed species whose seeds germinate in the autumn will establish themselves with a fall-seeded crop and compete
with it, whereas weed species that germinate in the spring in a fall-

seeded crop have little chance to compete with the well-established crop. Hence plants dissimilar in their vegetative habits or in their demands upon the environment are able to adjust themselves without much injury to one or the other.

A principle of plant competition is that the first plants to occupy any area of soil, small or large, tend to exclude others. This principle finds application in practical weed control. Practices should be such that crop plants occupy the soil before weeds. Thus seedbed preparation, depth of seeding, and date of seeding play important parts in making it possible for crop plants to evade competition with weeds. Weeds that appear in a crop after it is well established usually have negligible competing ability.

Williams (1969) found that the earlier wheat was sown the less it suffered from competition with quackgrass. Early defoliation of quackgrass slowed its growth and reduced its competitive effect in wheat. Quackgrass plants suffered from competition with wheat, especially when planting was early. He also found (Williams, 1970) that shading by a screen which excluded 54 percent of daylight halved the rhizome dry weight of quackgrass; shoot dry weight was less affected. Early shading decreased the final percentage of shoots that developed heads; shoot height was increased.

Wicks and Smika (1973) used chemical fallow to control all weeds during the 14-month fallow period from winter-wheat harvest until winter-wheat planting. Their chemical fallow plots had the least weed growth, the most soil water stored, and the highest amount of surface mulch. Also the plots receiving only herbicides had the highest grain yields.

CHIEF ENVIRONMENTAL FACTORS IN PLANT COMPETITION

The chief environmental factors in plant competition are *water*, *light*, and *mineral nutrients*, their importance usually being in the order given. Two plants do not compete if water, light, and mineral nutrients are in excess of the needs of both. Competition begins when the supply of any one of these factors falls below the requirements of both. Thus, if there is an abundance of nutrients and water, light may be a critical factor; or there may be a sufficiency of water and light for the two neighboring plants but a deficiency of nutrients, in which instance the latter becomes the critical factor in competition; or competition may be for water only, in the event that nutrients and light are ample.

Lack of available moisture during critical periods of the growing season was found by Evans et al. (1972) to be the principal deterrent in the establishment of intermediate wheat grass on downy brome range.

Where the brome was controlled, moisture was available for the wheatgrass seedlings and they were able to survive. Seeding in furrows, along with weed control further improved the conditions for wheatgrass establishment.

EFFECT OF WEED COMPETITION UPON CROP GROWTH

The effect of weed competition upon a specific crop is shown by a number of workers. Godel (1935), in Saskatchewan, determined that annual weeds in Marquis wheat reduced the yield as much as 34.8 percent. Pavlychenko and Harrington (1935) give data on the effect of weed competition in wheat in Saskatoon, Canada. Comparing clean and weedy land infested with wild mustard, the difference in yield was 40 percent; wheat containing seven sowthistles per square foot experienced a loss of 71.06 percent in yield compared with wheat free from sowthistle.

Burrows and Olson (1955a) grew spring wheat seeded at 2 bu per acre in 1952 and at 1, 2, and 3 bu per acre in 1953. In some plots they seeded wild mustard. At the five-leaf stage of wheat in 1952 and the four-leaf stage in 1953, some plots were sprayed with the butyl ester of 2,4-D at 6 and 4 oz acid equivalent per acre, respectively. The presence of wild mustard affected adversely the growth, tillering, and yield of wheat. Tillering and yield were reduced in both the sprayed and unsprayed plots in 1952, a year of only 10.53 in. precipitation; but only in the unsprayed plots in 1953 when there were 16.33 inches. The spraying eliminated the weeds at an earlier stage in 1953. Although increasing the seeding rate of wheat increased the yield of grain in weedy plots, this was not the case where weeds were removed with 2,4-D or by hand. The higher seeding rates undoubtedly increased the competition by the wheat.

Similar trials by Burrows and Olson (1955b) with flax gave even more marked increases from spraying and hand weeding. Sprayed plots with a weed density of 10 or more mustard plants per square yard had increased grain yield over unsprayed. Mustard present in the plots while the flax was in the seedling stage reduced its basal branching even when the weeds were killed soon afterwards with 2,4-D. The number of branches on the sprayed plants was greater than on those that were not sprayed. In 1952 (10.53 in. precipitation), the reduction of basal branching in the sprayed plots became more pronounced as the density of mustard was increased, resulting in parallel reduction in seed bolls per plant, weight of straw, and yield of grain. In 1953 (16.33 in. precipitation), the flax in the sprayed plots apparently outgrew the effect of the early reduction in basal branching and produced yields of grain and straw about equal to the weed-free check.

Pfeiffer and Holmes (1961) studied competition between barley and oats as influenced by barley-seed rate, nitrogen level, and barban treatment. Increasing the seed rate of barley resulted in reduction in the initial oat population, in the shoot weight, and in the shoot number per unit area. Application of barban gave an independent reduction in oats of an order of 80 percent; this value was almost constant for all barley-seed rates. Crop competition and barban treatment acted independently; their effects are additive. Nitrogen application stimulated both barley and oats to a similar degree.

COMPETING ABILITY OF DIFFERENT PLANTS

Plants differ in their competing ability. The characteristics that enable a species to be successful in competition are: high germination of seed under adverse conditions; rapid development of foliage in the seedling stage; and rapid development of an extensive root system having both surface and deep roots.

Variability in life cycle may be a competitive advantage. Young and Evans (1969) found, with Scotch thistle, that life cycle is not bound by strict photoperiod or temperature requirements, but can be conditioned by an interplay of environmental factors which allow Scotch thistle to grow and reproduce under a wide array of conditions; this plant can behave as a summer annual, a winter annual, a biennial, and a short-lived perennial under the prevailing environment of Nevada.

Staniforth and Weber (1956) studied the effects of weed growth upon soybean yields. Using both planted weed infestations and natural weed infestations, they determined the role of weed competition under differing stand intensities of weeds and with weed removal at different stages of soybean growth. Results are reported for 1952, 1953, and 1954.

In contrast with competition in cereal crops, these studies with soybeans proved that competition was most serious during periods of ample rainfall when weed growth was vigorous; competition was most marked from the stage when pods developed until maturity. During 1953 when growth of both beans and weeds was reduced by drought, yield reductions were less than when moisture was ample.

Average yield reduction from natural weed infestations from full season competition was 4.7 bu per acre; from planted weed species, 2.7 bu per acre. Reduction from pigweed which topped the soybean plants was 10.3 bu per acre; from other weeds which did not shade the soybeans, it was about half this value. This information indicates that competition from the lower-grade growing weeds (foxtail, smartweed, and velvetleaf) was principally for water and mineral nutrients.

Weber and Staniforth (1957), summarizing results of work with soybeans for 1953 to 1956, report that soybean stands below 9 to 11 plants per foot of row suffered much more from weed competition than did stands having 15 or more plants. Reductions in yield were most severe when the weeds grew throughout the season and when moisture was not limiting. Staniforth (1958) studied the role of competition from foxtail in soybean yield under varying soil moisture conditions. Using supplemental irrigation, he found competition reduced yields most severely when soil moisture was limiting during the late season growth.

Eaton et al. (1973) found that competition from Venice mallow could reduce yields of soybeans seriously. Venice mallow is a low spreading annual that is tolerant to many soybean herbicides and hence it threatens modern soybean production. One Venice mallow plant per 7.5 cm of soybean row reduced yield of soybean seed 632 kg/ha after 25 days competition. A stand of 215 Venice mallow plants per square meter reduced yield as much as 14 percent after 110 days competition.

Buchanan and Thurlow (1972) studied the competitive effects of sicklepod on Bragg variety soybeans growing on two soils, Malbis sandy loam and Chesterfield sandy loam. Weed density proved to be a linear function of bean yield for densities of 0 to 1.5 weeds per 929 cm^2. Densities of 0.72 weed per 929 cm^2 reduced soybean yield 19 to 32 percent on the Malbis soil, 34 to 35 percent on the Chesterfield soil. The weight of weeds at harvest was almost inversely correlated with bean yield. Sicklepod was more competitive when grown 15 to 30 cm from the drill row than when in the drill row. Competition for as little as 4 weeks reduced soybean yields. If weeds were removed less than 4 weeks after emergence of the crop no further weed removal was needed for maximum yield of the soybeans.

Feldman, McCarthy, and Scifres (1968) studied the relations of chemical treatment, grazing, and nature of pasture plants to invasion and establishment of musk thistle on Nebraska pastures. Picloram and 2,4-D were effective in the control of this weed. Competition was also instrumental in controlling musk thistle. More weed seedlings became established in cool-season grass than in warm-season grass when the plots were not grazed. Greater germination was attributed to reserve moisture and accumulation of litter. Only one musk plant survived on the nongrazed pastures one year after seeding; the other seedlings found the previous year succumbed to competition.

Staniforth (1957) studied the effect of competition by yellow foxtail (*Setaria lutescens*) on corn. With this low grass, competition was principally for moisture and nutrients, particularly nitrogen. Corn yield reductions resulting from mature foxtail infestations averaged 14, 10, and 5 bu per acre with applications of 0, 70, and 140 lb per acre of elemental nitrogen on plots having an over-all application of 300 lb of 0-20-20 fertilizer. These yield reductions were 20, 10, and 5 percent.

Corn yields (dry matter) were increased two to three times as much as were those of foxtail by one or two increments of nitrogen. Since yield reductions of this magnitude were obtained in both wet and dry years, Staniforth concludes that corn-yield responses to nitrogen resulted from development of more extensive root systems, enabling this crop to better utilize moisture from lower soil levels as surface moisture became limiting in late season. This might be true of competition with shallow-rooted weeds like foxtail; it would not apply in the case of perennial weeds.

In work continued through 1958 and 1959, Staniforth (1961) used four corn hybrids to study the relation of seasonal adaptation of hybrids to weed competition. The hybrids ranged from early-adapted, through adapted, to late-adapted; three levels of nitrogen fertilization were also included. Differences in corn yield due to foxtail were as follows: late hybrid, 38.0 bu per acre; late-adapted hybrid, 32.6 bu per acre; adapted hybrid, 26.4 bu per acre; early-adapted hybrid, 19.9 bu per acre. Differences were greatest at low nitrogen levels; nitrogen fertilization tended to counteract weed competition; expressed as corn yield reduction per hundredweight of mature foxtail, average values for all four hybrids were: 0 nitrogen, 2.98 bu per acre; 70 lb nitrogen per acre, 2.56 bu per acre; 140 lb nitrogen per acre, 1.06 bu per acre. Reduction in bushels per acre per hundredweight foxtail for the late-maturing hybrid was twice that of the early hybrid. Since competition from foxtail occurs late in the season in Iowa, Staniforth concludes that the early hybrid escaped competition by early maturity of its crop.

Scholl and Staniforth (1957, 1958) studied the effects of weed competition and companion crop competition on establishment of stands of birdsfoot trefoil. While companion or nurse crops reduce weed competition, they themselves offer strong competition. Best stands were obtained by using dalapon to reduce grass growth and 2,4-DB to inhibit broadleaf weeds. The chemicals were applied 4 to 6 weeks after seeding the trefoil.

Shadbolt and Holm (1956) made detailed experiments studying quantitative aspects of weed competition in some vegetable crops. They found many adverse effects, particularly during the early part of the growing season. Weed concentrations as low as 15 percent of normal were capable of inflicting serious crop injury. The period from emergence of the plant until 4 weeks after emergence was the most critical stage for competition. Carrots suffered yield reductions of 30 to 60 percent, measured either at the time of removal of weeds or at harvest; competition during the first 3 to 5 weeks was still evident at harvesttime.

Onions and beets were also inhibited by weed competition; the former exhibited yield reductions up to 90 percent; beets were capable of recovery if weeds were removed early in the season. Weed competition reduced light intensity as much as 85 percent, and this was responsible for much of the injury suffered by these crop plants.

Bleasdale (1959, 1960) studied competition of weeds with vegetable crops. In an experiment on row spacing, carrots were thinned to a constant number per unit area, whereas weeds in the rows were unthinned so that the number per unit area was inversely proportional to row spacing. Bleasdale (1960) found that the weeds did not affect the yield of marketable carrots, but the spatial arrangement of carrots did affect the weight of weeds. Whereas there were twice as many weeds per unit area in 12-in. spaced rows, the weight of weeds was only half that of 24-in. rows. In an experiment with beets there were three treatments: (1) weed-free, (2) cultivation leaving weeds in the rows, and (3) cultivation and hand weeding leaving a band of weeds between the crop rows similar to that in the rows of (2). In this test the presence of weeds significantly reduced the weight of tops, total roots, and marketable roots of the crop. However, treatment (3) reduced the yield more than (2). Weeds coincident with the row were less competitive than weeds between the rows.

In experiments on the competition of different weeds with carrots at two fertility levels, Bleasdale found that *Poa annua* did not affect carrot weight at either fertility level; chickweed and groundsel considerably reduced both tops and roots. Bleasdale found that time of weeding was important with onions and redbeets; delaying the first weeding significantly reduced the yield of marketable crop. Delaying the sowing of weeds in carrots reduced their competitive ability; sown with the crop, the crop yield was 60.7 g; sown 1 week later, yield was 106.3 g; sown 2 weeks later, yield was 126.3 g. Bleasdale concludes that plants compete for nutrients, light, or water either simultaneously or in rapid succession. He feels that, in his experiments, root exudates or other toxic substances are not involved.

Recent studies by Oliver and Schreiber (1973) indicate that competition for CO_2 in a heteroculture canopy may affect the growth of crop plants. Redroot pigweed and giant foxtail, two weeds of high photosynthetic efficiency, were able by highly efficient CO_2 utilization to outgrow and suppress birdsfoot trefoil, a crop plant of lower efficiency.

PLANT TOXINS AS FACTORS IN COMPETITION

It has long been assumed that certain plants are able to affect their neighbors by excreting toxic substances from their roots. However, it was necessary to develop sensitive analytical methods to show that this is true; by the use of chromatography and bioassay it has been proven that plant toxins from both leaves and roots may be involved in plant competition. Bonner (1950) showed that *Encelia farinosa* contains 3-acetyl-6-methoxybenzaldehyde, a compound that is toxic to many plants which normally compete with *E. farinosa* for space in its desert environment.

Butler (1955) found that clover plants excrete nitrogenous compounds from their roots into the culture medium. Rademacher (1959) has reviewed the subject of the mutual effects of the products of plant metabolism upon adjacent plants, and Martin and Rademacher (1960b) have reported experiments demonstrating the liberation of scopoletin from roots of oat plants. Because this liberation starts when the roots are only 1 to 2 cm in length, the authors conclude that it comes from living cells. In addition to scopoletin and scopoletin glycoside, Martin and Rademacher found that leucine, valine, γ-aminobutyric acid, glutamine, alanine, asparagine, serine, aspartic acid, glutamic acid, glucose, and fructose were liberated from oat roots; the compounds were identified by paper chromatography. Liberation was greater from decaying roots than from living ones.

Experiments on the mutual influence of weeds and crop plants were conducted by special apparatus involving water-culture pots connected with glass tubes so that the nutrient solution could be circulated continuously. The two plant species were set alternately so that compounds liberated by one species could influence the growth of that in the next pot. The pots were spaced so that there was no competition for light; all mutual effects were limited to roots.

In these experiments Martin and Rademacher found that oats inhibited *Sinapis arvensis* to the extent of 38 percent; supplementing nitrogen to eliminate competition for this nutrient did not affect the results. Growth of false chamomile was reduced more by rye than by wheat. Oats did not influence shoot development of this weed, but roots were somewhat stimulated. Oats inhibited poppy more than did rye; these crop plants had similar inhibition of *Sinapis arvensis*. Potato and flax were strongly inhibited when grown with ladysthumb.

In studies on the self-intolerance of flax, Börner et al. (1959) used water cultures and found depression of growth if the flax was grown twice in the same solution. Although nutrients were replaced, the length of stems was reduced 11.6 percent; the dry weight of shoots, 32.5 percent; and the number of flowers, 44.0 percent. Under similar conditions rye, which is self-tolerant, was reduced 1 percent in stem length, 15 percent in dry weight, and 18.8 percent in number of heads. Root growth of neither species was affected. As shown by paper chromatography, under sterile conditions flax seedlings in sand cultures exuded aspartic acid, glutamic acid, alanine, and γ-aminobutyric acid. Although the amounts of these were not at a toxic level, the writers postulate that long-term, continuous exposure to such compounds may have a physiological effect. Addition of SiO_2 reduced the inhibition caused by repeated cropping in a single-culture solution.

Martin and Rademacher (1960a) have investigated the effects of substances given off by roots of rape on other crop plants. In a loamy soil, admixture of rape roots improved root growth of wheat, whereas when oat or wheat roots were mixed with the soil, root growth of wheat was retarded. By paper chromatography a mustard oil glucoside was identified in rape roots; β-phenylethyl mustard oil was in greatest amount. Small amounts of mustard oil mixed with soil improved wheat plant growth, but breakdown soon occurred. Phenylethylamine was identified as a breakdown product.

Grümmer and Beyer (1960) confirmed this observation and by chromatography found evidence for p-hydroxybenzoic acid and vanillic acid in leaf extracts of *Camelina*. Ferulic acid is also suspected.

Because Osvald (1947) claimed that the competitive action of quackgrass (*Agropyron repens*) is partially the result of toxin produced by its roots, Welbank (1960) studied the effects of treating young plants of barley, wheat, kale, and tomato with leachings of roots and rhizomes of *A. repens*; also he grew rape and turnip seedlings in close contact with living roots of *A. repens*. He found no evidence for growth inhibition by the living grass; extracts of roots and rhizomes incubated with soil inhibited germination and extension of rape seedlings. He concluded there was no evidence for secretion of toxins but that inhibitors may arise from the decay of quackgrass material in the soil.

Helgeson and Konzak (1950) found that aqueous extracts of field bindweed and Canada thistle inhibited the germination of seeds and growth of seedlings of several crops. Le Tourneau, Failes, and Heggeness (1956) proved that aqueous extracts of plant material of some 23 species inhibited growth of wheat and pea seedlings; Le Tourneau and Heggeness (1957) showed that extracts of leafy spurge foliage and quackgrass rhizomes contained inhibitors effective on wheat and pea seedlings. Engle (1957) extracted leaves of manzanita (*Arctostaphylos manzanita*) and placed the extract on a chromatopile. Certain sections of the pile contained inhibitors that prevented germination of wheat seed.

Kommedahl et al. (1959) have shown that quackgrass is able to inhibit growth of crop seedlings growing in the field in soil previously occupied by the weed, in the greenhouse in potted soils containing ground quackgrass rhizomes, in soil moistened with extracts or filtrates of ground or living rhizomes, and in petri dishes containing water extracts from ground and living rhizomes (Figs. 5-1 and 5-2). Leaves, roots, and even seeds of quackgrass apparently produce a toxic

substance. The inability to establish alfalfa on quackgrass sod is probably related to the presence of toxins in the soil.

In later tests (Ohman and Kommedahl, 1960), extracts from
quackgrass roots, stems, rhizomes, and leaves all inhibited growth of
alfalfa seedlings and germination of alfalfa seeds. Extracts from
quackgrass seedlings taken 2 and 4 weeks after emergence exhibited
about the same toxicity as leaf extracts from older plants. Extracts

FIGURE 5-1. The effect of quackgrass on the growth of alfalfa. The pot on the
left is the control, the center pot was watered daily with water extract from
ground rhizomes, and the pot on the right contained soil mixed with leached,
ground-rhizome residue. (Photograph by courtesy of Thor Kommedahl.)

from soils in which quackgrass had been growing were more toxic than
Canada thistle soils. When passed through activated carbon, extracts
from rhizomes of quackgrass lost all their toxicity, but extracts from
leaves lost only part.

Using dried subterranean organs of Bermudagrass, nutsedge, and
Johnsongrass, Horowitz and Friedman (1971) showed that not only
plant residues, but ethanolic extracts of tissues may contain toxic

substances; inhibition of growth was proportional to the amount of plant material in the soil and was greater in light than in heavy soil. Residues from nutsedge and Johnsongrass caused greater inhibition than those of Bermudagrass.

Kinsinger and Eckert (1961) tested the effects of halogeton leachate on the growth of a number of grasses and forbs that grow on soils favorable for growth of white sage (*Eurotia lanata*), shad scale (*Atri-*

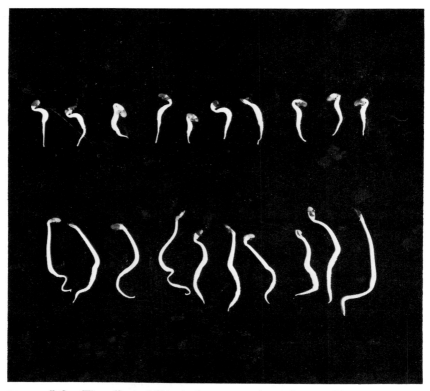

FIGURE 5-2. The effect of filtrate from ground quackgrass rhizomes on germination of alfalfa seed. Top, treated; bottom, controls. (Photograph by courtesy of Thor Kommedahl.)

plex confertifolia), and saltsage (*A. nuttallii*). Sodium and possibly potassium were responsible for reducing emergence and growth of the species tested. One and three inches of mulch (ground halogeton) suppressed emergence and growth of most of the perennial and annual grasses used as test plants. One inch of mulch increased the percent of emergence of most of the forbs. Soils subject to halogeton leachate are more favorable for halogeton and other low-value forbs than for desirable grasses.

Young and Evans (1971) found that the fruits of dyers woad suppress germination of threshed dyers woad seed. The fruits or water used to soak dyers woad fruits inhibited germination and root length of tumble mustard, downy brome, and alfalfa; root length of medusahead was greatly reduced. Washing the fruits of dyers woad for 48 hours greatly increased germination of the seeds; washing for 96 hours almost eliminated the inhibitor.

STIMULATORY SUBSTANCES

Some of the most serious weeds are parasitic upon crops. Two common ones are *Orobanche minor* and *Striga hermonthica*. These are angiospermous root parasites that grow among the tissues of the host plants. They produce very small seeds that germinate and grow only in the presence of substances that escape from the roots of the host plants.

Sunderland (1960a, b) describes studies on the chemical nature of the stimulants produced by corn roots. He has shown that extracts of corn roots and aqueous solutions in which roots are suspended contain a complex of stimulatory substances consisting of one water-soluble component and a number of ether-soluble compounds. Germination of *O. minor* seeds is promoted by the water-soluble component and by one ether-soluble component. Seeds of *S. hermonthica* are stimulated to germinate by a different ether-soluble component. The effects of these three stimulants are greatly enhanced if a trace of a diffusate from linseed roots is included.

Striga asiatica, a root parasite from the Eastern Hemisphere, was discovered in North Carolina and South Carolina in 1956 and is being subjected to a rigorous eradication campaign under the supervision of the U.S. Department of Agriculture (Fig. 5–3). Research conducted in connection with this campaign is being carried out in North Carolina (Worsham, Moreland, and Klingman, 1959). The latter workers have found that kinetin [6-(2-furfuryl) aminopurine] and certain other 6-substituted aminopurines will stimulate the germination of *S. asiatica* seed in concentrations of from 5 to 25 mg per 1. Compounds showing highest activity possess an adenine nucleus with a phenyl, benzyl, phenethyl, or furfuryl radical substituted on the amino group. Seedlings that develop as a result of stimulation by these compounds resemble those that have haustorial connection with the host more than do those that develop in the presence of corn-root substances. Stimulants of parasite-seed germination could be used to induce germination of the myriads of seeds that normally occur in soils where these pests exist. Control of such pests is extremely difficult because the seeds may survive for years in the soil to be stimulated in the presence of host crops whenever these are planted. Robinson and Stokes (1960) have pointed out the potential hazard of witchweed to sugar-cane production. Tests on some 40 varieties showed some to be virtually destroyed by witchweed, some to be quite tolerant.

While experience has indicated that witchweed grows best on light soils, experimental work has proved that it will become established and

FIGURE 5-3.   Witchweed (*Striga asiatica*) growing on a corn plant. Under the soil the witchweed is attached to the corn plant, and it derives a large portion of its nutrients from this host plant. (U.S. Department of Agriculture.)

grow on heavy soils (Robinson, 1960). Apparently, higher temperatures are required for germination on heavier soil types. Witchweed completes its life cycle in 90 to 120 days, and a minimum temperature around 70°F is necessary. From soil and air temperature studies, it seems possible that witchweed could germinate and grow at Lincoln, Nebraska. Robinson concludes from his research that it is improbable that temperatures alone will be a permanent barrier to further spread of witchweed in the United States.

In more recent studies Robinson (1961) has shown that fenac, 2,3,6-TBA, and the alkanolamine salts of 2,4-D may be used to fight witchweed by the preplant soil-incorporation method. Fenac gave the most promising results, but it remained in the soil for at least 12 months and was injurious to peanuts, cotton, soybeans, and tobacco planted in the subsequent year. Corn was not affected.

Eplee (1972) has reported that ethylene gas (C_2H_6) is an effective synthetic germination inducer of witchweed seeds. This gas, when injected into soils was found to diffuse more than 48 " laterally. Under field conditions 85 to 90 percent of witchweed seeds present in a soil germinated in response to ethylene treatment. This offers hope for a control treatment on witchweed-infested land and eventual eradication.

Additional parasites of the type described are *Orobanche hedera*, a parasite of ivy; *Alectra brasiliensis*, a pest on sugar cane; *A. vogelii*, which grows on cowpea; *A. kirkii*, parasitic on tobacco; *Striga lutea*, which parasitizes rice, sorghum, millet, corn and sugar cane; *S. densiflora*, a parasite of many grasses; *S. euphrasioides*, a parasite of rice, sugar cane, corn, and sorghum; and *S. orobanchoides*, which grows on a number of leguminous plants, as well as tobacco, several species of *Ipomoea*, and several grasses.

While only two parasitic plants—*Striga asiatica* in the Carolinas, and *Orobanche ramosa* in Alameda County, California—are known to grow on crops in the United States, all those listed above are potential pests on many of our agricultural crops. There are many indigenous species of *Striga* and *Orobanche* in the United States growing on native plants of no agricultural importance. In the world, over 30 species of *Striga*, around 100 species of *Orobanche*, and over 30 species of *Alectra* have been recognized. Mistletoe and dodder are also parasitic plants. These parasitic plants constitute an ever-present potential source of trouble for farmers in the United States (McGrath et al., 1957).

FACTORS THAT DETERMINE VIGOROUS STANDS OF CROP PLANTS

It seems apparent from plant-competition studies that, in weed control, consideration must be given to the factors that determine vigorous stands of crop plants with high competing ability and that discourage the invasion and growth of weeds. These factors are as follows: variety of crop plant, soil-water relations, soil fertility, soil reaction, tillage, date and rate of seeding, crop rotation, and use of herbicides.

VARIETY OF CROP PLANT

A variety of crop plant not adapted to the soil and climatic conditions of a region will usually produce a poor stand and a weak crop that is unable to compete with weeds. Moreover, varieties susceptible to diseases and insects give noncompetitive stands. Plants attacked by fungi or insects often lose their leaves early, reducing their shading power and thus lowering their ability to retard weed growth. Accordingly, to combat weeds successfully, attention must be given to the selection of varieties that are adapted to the soil and climatic conditions of a region.

SOIL-WATER RELATIONS

Vigor of a crop stand is greatly influenced by soil-water relations. It is a common observation that certain xerophytic weed species establish themselves on high spots in the field where there is insufficient water to support a vigorous stand of crop plants. Meadows and pastures frequently have poorly drained areas, and it is on these areas that species able to thrive in wet soils establish themselves. Among such species are horsetails, rushes, sedges, and buttercups. Accordingly, proper drainage and leveling of arable areas are essentials in weed control.

SOIL FERTILITY

Needless to say, a fertile soil stimulates the rapid growth of both crop plants and weeds. However, if weeds are destroyed by the application of proper cultural operations at the time of seeding and immediately afterward, crop plants that have thereby been given an advantage can more easily maintain a lead if the soil is well supplied with nutrients. An abundance of available nitrogen encourages vegetative growth with resultant increase in the shade produced that tends to suppress weeds.

SOIL REACTION

It is well known that certain weed species tolerate acid soils and others alkaline soils. For example, knawel, corn spurry, and sheep sorrel tend to flourish on acid soils, chiefly because of the failure of other species, including useful ones, to compete with them. The neutralizing of acid soils by liming or by employing alkaline fertilizers may successfully suppress these weeds. On the other hand, high alkalinity of the soil, especially in the arid and semiarid regions of the United States, may so retard the growth of crop plants as to make invasion by halophytes easy.

TILLAGE

The principal functions of tillage are: (1) to control weeds, (2) to create a suitable seedbed, (3) to incorporate fertilizers and crop residues into the soil, (4) to prepare the land for reception of rainfall and/or for the application and distribution of water, (5) to control plant diseases and insect pests, and (6) to maintain proper structural condition of the soil. The evidence in favor of tillage as a *direct* means of liberating plant food and of conserving moisture is not convincing.

Numerous field experiments, using various crops, seem to show that the chief benefit of tillage is the removal of weed competition. This removal makes available for crop plants greater quantities of the principal requirements for which plants compete, namely, water, light, and mineral nutrients. Cates and Cox (1912) tabulated the results of 125 cultivation experiments with corn, conducted in 28 different states during the period from 1906 to 1911. Their conclusion was that the beneficial effect of tillage was the removal of weeds.

DATE AND RATE OF SEEDING

The date of seeding and the subsequent development of seedlings in relation to the growth of weeds determine the degree of competition afforded. Obviously, crop plants should be as far along as possible in their early stages of growth to compete most successfully with weeds. Moreover, it is evident that rate of seeding influences the stand of crop plants and thereby determines the amount of shade and competition provided. Competitive crops are usually those that produce a heavy shade. Among these are rye, winter barley, rape, and hemp.

The shading effect of a crop plant, and hence its ability to suppress the weeds that come with the crop, depends upon three conditions: (1) the time at which shading takes place, (2) the duration of the shade, and (3) the height of the shade.

CROP ROTATION

Crop rotation has been defined as the growing of different crops in recurring succession on the same land, in distinction from a one-crop system or a haphazard change of crops determined by opportunism or lacking a definite plan. The control of weeds is one of the principal reasons for rotating crops.

There are farms on which weeds are of little importance, either in increasing labor costs or in decreasing crop yields. They are often ones on which a definite plan of crop rotation is systematically adhered to. One can expect to have trouble with weeds if he follows a one-crop system or has an improper sequence of crops. A proper sequence of different kinds of crops makes possible variation in the type of implements and soil treatments, which, in turn, assures that each weed association meets with competition or is disturbed in its development.

The principal farming regions of the United States are as follows: corn belt, cotton belt, dairy region, wheat region, dry-land area, and irrigated sections. Within each of these farming regions, there are varied conditions and varied weed problems. Consequently, it is possible to speak in only the most general terms about the rotation systems that are of value in weed control.

With the development of highly selective herbicides adapted to our major crops, and with the production of cheap nitrogenous fertilizers, such as urea and anhydrous ammonia, there has been a tendency to specialize on a single crop or few crops; crop rotation is no longer practiced in many areas. While this may be justified in terms of short-term profits, it may prove disappointing in the long run. In some areas, single cropping is leading to spread of perennial weeds, notably field bindweed. Although the use of dichlobenil and trifluralin by the sprayblade technique is inhibiting growth of this weed it does not eradicate it. Once a crop of bindweed seed is produced on an area and incorporated into the soil, seedlings will be a problem for 20 years or more. Alfalfa is an excellent competitor with bindweed. An occasional rotation with this crop would be useful, not only because of its inhibitory effect on bindweed but also because it tends to restore the fertility of the soil; the channels left by the decaying roots, when it is plowed out, restore the pervious condition of the soil promoting both drainage and aeration.

In planning a crop rotation having as one of its primary aims the control of weeds, chief attention must be given to (1) competitive crops, (2) tillage operations, and (3) use of herbicides. There are numerous rotation systems in the different farming sections of the country. No one rotation can be considered typical, nor is there any one rotation that is of equal value in all cases for the control of weeds.

COMPETITIVE CROPS IN THE CONTROL OF WEEDS

Competitive crops are sometimes known as 'smother crops.' The growth they produce competes successfully with weeds either by excluding light or utilizing large quantities of all three factors available to weeds. The principal competitive crops are as follows: millet, Sudan grass, sweet clover, sunflower, rape, barley, rye, reed canarygrass, crested wheatgrass, sorghums, buckwheat, soybeans, alfalfa, cowpeas, clovers, hemp, Jerusalem artichoke, and ensilage corn. Environmental conditions, soil and climatic, will determine the type of competitive crop to use; also, the weed being combated will be a determining factor.

Alfalfa is a superior competitive crop, of value in weed control because, in addition to its extensive root system and dense top growth, the repeated mowings remove the tops of many weeds before seed can mature. This is particularly true where the alfalfa is cut and removed at once to be dehydrated. Moreover, alfalfa recovers more quickly after mowing than many weeds that infest the crop. Also, as compared with such weeds as Canada thistle and perennial sowthistle, it starts growth earlier in the spring and hence is particularly effective in combating these weeds. However, quackgrass, Austrian fieldcress, hoary cress, and leafy spurge start as early in the spring as does alfalfa, and such weeds cannot be controlled by using alfalfa as a smother crop. Frequent irrigation as practiced in the West is deleterious to the vigor of field bindweed, and alfalfa is very useful in the suppression of this weed.

COMBINATION METHODS

Many combinations of cropping, tillage, and use of herbicides have been developed to handle weed situations. In regions of summer and autumn rainfall, tillage between crops may be used at almost any time of year, and combinations of summer or autumn tillage with winter or spring crops are useful as are uses of winter and spring tillage with summer row-crops. By alternating these practices it is possible to control annual and biennial weeds in many crops. Perennial weeds may present problems, but often even these weeds can be held in check, particularly the more shallow-rooted ones. Herbicides may be used to supplement such programs to eliminate winter and spring annuals in cereal crops or, by preemergence treatments or directed sprays, to control weeds in row crops.

The combination of spring or early summer spraying with a grass killer, followed by plowing, seedbed preparation, and planting of corn or soybeans is proving effective in quackgrass control in the Midwest (Buchholtz, 1955).

Chemical control of Canada thistle with hormone-type sprays has been found more successful if combined with competition from a non-susceptible competing crop.

In the more arid regions, where irrigation is practiced, tillage for controlling annual weeds is effective only when soils are moist enough to bring about germination of seeds; irrigation is often necessary in order to use combinations of tillage and cropping.

Successful use of combination methods against perennial weeds often depends upon special soil or climatic conditions. Where soils remain frozen for several months during winter, a single season of clean tillage often suffices to eradicate an existing stand of Canada thistle or field bindweed; under milder climatic conditions with a longer growing season, more time may be required. Where perennials are present on shallow soils, control is often possible from a single season of fallow; in deep alluvial soils, several seasons may be necessary.

A further aspect of weed ecology is the problem presented by weed seed in soils. Mention has been made of parasitic weeds whose seeds germinate only in the presence of suitable host crop plants. Dormant seed, hard seed, and seed protected by heavy seed coats are known to lie in soils for many years and to germinate when brought to the surface by tillage operations or when seed coats are sufficiently eroded. Any method, whether stressing tillage, cropping, or chemicals, must take into account the possibility of reinfestation by seedlings. Many programs of successful elimination of perennial weeds have failed when crops that allow reinfestation by seedlings were used. Small-grain crops are particularly bad in this way because many perennial weeds become established by the time the crop is ready for harvest.

HERBICIDES IN PLANT ECOLOGY

As experience is gained in the use of herbicides for weed control, it is becoming apparent that these agents are becoming a real factor in plant ecology. Widespread use of 2,4-D for annual-weed control in cereals is bringing about not only distinct changes in the weed flora of large land areas, but also elimination of ornamental plants, shade trees, and native vegetation. An example is the elimination of cotton-wood and willow trees in certain wheat-growing areas of Washington.

Another change is in the development of herbicide-resistant species of weeds. In short times, survival of 2,4-D-resistant weed species have brought about shifts in the species in many areas. Examples are the increase in grass species at the expense of *Commelina* spp. in the cane fields of Puerto Rico; the increase in starthistle in grain-fields where cruciferous species were eliminated in California; the replacement of broadleaf annual weeds by wild oats in Canadian grain-fields; and the succession of changes from cruciferous weeds to chick-weed and *Anagallis arvensis* following the use of MCPA to *Galium aparine* which followed DN (dinitro) sprays in wheat fields in England. Aberg (1958) mentions the ascendency of *Galium aparine, G. mollugo, Matricaria inodora, M. chamomilla, Sonchus* spp., *Vicia hirsuta,* and *Ranunculus* spp. following the use of phenoxyacetic acid herbicides in Sweden. Not only crop rotation but herbicide rotation will be required to control weeds in the future.

A beneficial effect of herbicides on growth and vigor of peanut plants has been noted by Chappell and Miller (1956) in Virginia. Because these effects were found even in the absence of weeds, it was proposed that certain parasitic fungi and nematodes might be inhibit-ed by the chemicals, and tests were run to investigate this theory. Five different fungi were tested using 13 herbicides. DN and PCP inhibited all pathogens at field rates of application; CIPC, CDAA, CDEA, and CDEC prevented growth of some but not all organisms. PCP was the most effective of the group used; DN was second. Against sting nema-todes, CIPC, DN, and PCP were effective at 100 ppm; PCP reduced the growth of nematodes at 1 ppm; dalapon and sesone had little effect even at 10,000 ppm. Field studies with DN and PCP proved that the treated plants showed less *Sclerotium* stem rot and *Cercospora* leaf spot than unsprayed, cultivated plants. Study indicated that the practice of covering the branches of peanut plants in normal weed-control tillage practices was responsible for much of the disease trouble; preemergence spraying with DN and PCP eliminated weeds, and in the absence of tillage the plants were more thrifty.

Another more hopeful aspect of using selective herbicides is the possible broad-scale application of these materials in the improvement of ranges and forests. Already, 2,4-D compounds are being used to release coniferous trees in tree-farming procedures (Arend and Coulter, 1955). Similar sprays are being employed to control brush and other range weeds. It is suggested here that much more wide-scale use of these materials, possibly at very low dosage, might prove useful in rangeland management to achieve more palatable species where normal methods employing managed grazing are too slow or otherwise not effective. This method is used in turf and green management; it might be extremely valuable in improving the billions of acres of range and pasture in the world (Love, 1961).

Some people are concerned that the broad-scale use of herbicides in forest and rangeland management may eventually result in harmful effects on wild life. Experience to date does not substantiate this concern. Schroeder (1972), in reporting on the relationships of range and forest management with herbicides to wildlife, indicates that beneficial effects far outbalanced the harmful ones.

A few cases of loss are reported. Eutrophication in lakes from use of herbicides that kill large masses of aquatic vegetation may change the mineral nutrition and oxygen supply to the detriment of fish and other aquatic animals; instances of this are few. Spraying with 2,4-D may so reduce sagebrush as to reduce the numbers of sage grouse; brewers sparrow populations were also reduced.

The production of pure conifer stands by chemical manipulation is another practice that may seriously affect wild life. In contrast, the suppression of brush in western woodlands and on power and railroad rights-of-way has proved beneficial, increasing the number of rabbits, grouse, deer, quail, and doves. Creation of brush-grass border situations and the increase of plant diversification have greatly improved the habitats for wild life. Opening up of brush areas, establishment of food patches, and stimulation of browse have all proved beneficial; deer use of such treated areas has increased manyfold and small game animals have likewise benefitted. Just as haphazard, unplanned use of chemicals can cause severe loss of feed and cover for wildlife, careful, planned use is a powerful tool in improving wildland use by birds and animals.

INTEGRATED WEED CONTROL

Early in the use of DDT and other systemic insecticides, it was found that, in spite of their great toxicity, they very soon gave diminishing returns in insect control. Research soon proved that two factors were concerned: (1) the insects tended to develop tolerance for the chemicals and (2) the insecticides often killed off insects that were beneficial to the crop because they parasitized the target insect species. This proved true in the case of boll worms in cotton and scales and spider mites on citrus.

Because of these effects, entomologists have been forced to study not only the primary but also secondary and tertiary effects of their insecticide applications. Out of this situation has come the concept of integrated insect control in which all possible factors are determined for each insecticide. Often, combinations of chemical, cropping, biological, and other methods are used, each separate process being used for a specific purpose with the result that the over-all combination keeps the target insect under control. Often two or more agencies act in an integrated way to achieve the end result.

In weed control, because we have cropping, cultural, biological, and chemical methods all available, it seems that integrated approaches may be worked out to handle all of our major weed problems. Highly important are some of the newer herbicides that will kill practically all weeds in single crops. When these are used preplant, preemergence, or early postemergence to handle the great bulk of annual weeds coming from seed in the soil, there is hope of completely eliminating competition with the crop and eventually of eradicating the weeds by depleting the seed reserves in the soil.

We have gradually developed an arsenal of systemic herbicides that are effective in handling a great number of perennial weeds. And now with the sprayblade application of dichlobenil, trifluralin, and other similar compounds, it is possible to suppress many of the most refractive of the perennials, field bindweed and nutsedges for example.

When these new chemical methods are integrated into systems involving cultural, cropping, rotational, and biological methods the outlook for eradication seems more hopeful than at any time in the past. Weed-control research started in the 1930s and 1940s is paying immense dividends.

POISONOUS PLANTS

A feature of weed science often neglected is the fact that plants contain many chemical compounds, some of which are very toxic to man and animals (Binns, 1972). Naturally occurring toxicants in plants may be classified into the following groups: (1) alkaloids, (2) polypeptides, (3) amines, (4) glucosides, (5) oxalates, (6) resinoids, (7) minerals, and (8) organic compounds that are carcinogenic, teratogenic, and photosensitizing agents. Columbia milkvetch, which causes more cattle losses in British Columbia than any other poisonous plant, contains miserotoxin, a nitrosugar (Parker and Williams, 1972).

Plant Factors

Toxic agents vary among plant species, varieties, and structures. Toxicity also is affected by locality, environmental factors, and stage of growth. Toxic compounds may be localized in roots, flowers, young leaves, or seeds. All parts of some plants are toxic; leaves and seeds are most hazardous to livestock. The chemical structure of the toxic agent may differ depending on the environment.

Animal Factors

Plants toxic to one species of animal may be harmless to another. Larkspur causes severe losses in cattle but sheep and horses are not affected. Palatability and hunger are also involved; often, hungry or thirsty animals will ingest sufficient toxic material to succumb while well-fed animals will not. State of health, level of nutrient intake, age, sex, and lactation are additional factors.

Diagnosis of plant poisoning is often difficult. Blood tests and analysis of rumen or stomach contents are of little value. Experience in range management is essential. As many as 8 to 10 percent of range-grazing livestock may become affected by poisonous plants during the grazing season. Treatment of poison hemlock with 2,4-D has been known to render it attractive to animals that ordinarily would not eat it.

Cyanogenic plants cause hydrocyanic acid poisoning. Distributed throughout the world, such plants produce cyanogenetic glycosides, compounds that, in the presence of certain enzymes, hydrolyse giving off free hydrocyanic acid (HCN). Hydrocyanic acid poisoning depends upon the amount of the glycoside and hydrolysing enzyme present in the plant, the mixing of these in the rumen, and the total intake of the plant by the animal. Young tissues of sorghum, Sudan grass, arrowgrass, and chokecherry are often involved in hydrocyanic acid poisoning. Wilting, frost damage, disease, parasites, and mechanical damage may induce high glycoside content; regrowth after cutting may be hazardous.

Experiments have proved that rumen microflora may cause release of HCN. When the HCN content is high, the porphyrin enzyme, cytochrome oxidase, becomes inactivated causing acute anoxia. The minimum lethal dose is 2.0 to 2.3 mg per kg of body weight. Clinical signs of poisoning are seldom seen because most HCN-poisoned animals die rapidly; they are usually found near their source of drinking water.

PHOTOSENSITIZATION

Certain plants contain compounds which make animals abnormally sensitive to the direct rays of the sun. The white and pink areas not protected by photodynamic pigments in the skin, hair, or wool are affected. Photosensitization is classed as primary or secondary. The primary type results when certain plant pigments are not eliminated; they are carried by the blood to the skin which loses its protective mechanism; sunburning occurs in the white areas of the body. St. Johnswort, buckwheat, and spring parsley cause primary photosensitization.

In the secondary type, the photodynamic pigment is phylloerythrin, a derivative of chlorophyll. In animals having certain liver dysfunctions, the phylloerythrin is not removed from the circulatory system and interferes with the protective mechanism of nonpigmented skin; these areas suffer severe sunburn. Puncturevine and little horsebrush cause secondary photosensitization; in this type, severe liver necrosis may occur along with the skin lesions. Black sheep and Angus cattle usually do not suffer from photosensitization.

TERATOGENIC AGENTS

False hellebore, ingested by sheep around the 14th day of gestation, may cause malformation in lambs. Three distinct teratogenic agents have been identified in false hellebore; all are causal for cyclopian and related central-nervous deformities caused by this plant.

The congenital deformity called "crooked calf disease" has been induced by maternal feeding of two lupinus species, *L. caudatus* and *L. sericeus*. Fed from the 59th day to the 100th day of gestation, the cows produced calves with deformed front legs.

Tow weed and seeds of grass pea, Indian pea, and green vetch are known to cause deformities. Congenital deformities in the limbs of baby pigs have been induced by maternal feeding of poison hemlock and tobacco stalks.

CARCINOGENIC AGENTS

Bracken fern has been known to cause a disease of cattle called "red water." It is now known that grazing on this fern causes cancers in the bladder. The blood-colored urine results from hemangioma-type cancer in the lining of the bladder. Cattle are affected if on low-grade pasture, or if driven through bracken fern after a long, hard drive along trails devoid of adequate suitable forage.

REFERENCES

Aberg, E. 1958. Future problems in Swedish weed investigations seen against the use of chemical weed killers. Tiende International Symposium over Fytofarmacie en Fytiatrie, 6–7 Mei, 1958. In *Mededelingen van de Landbouwhogeschool en de Opzoekingsstation van de Staat te Gent.* 1958. Deel XXII No. 3–4, pp. 976–981.

Arend, J. L., and L. L. Coulter. 1955. Aerial applications of herbicides. A promising method for releasing conifers. *Down to Earth* 11(1):18–20.

Binns, W. 1972. Natural occurring toxic agents in plants and their relationship to poisoning of livestock and congenital malformations. *West. Weed Soc. Proc.* 25:7–11.

Bleasdale, J. K. A. 1959. The yield of onions and red beet as affected by weeds. *Jour. Hort. Sci.* 34:7–13.

————. 1960. Studies on plant competition. In *The Biology of Weeds. A Symposium of the British Ecological Society*, ed. John L. Harper. Oxford: Blackwell Scientific Publications, Ltd., July.

Bonner, J. 1950. The role of toxic substances in the interactions of higher plants. *Bot. Rev.* 16:51–65.

Börner, H., P. Martin, H. Clauss, and B. Rademacher. 1959. Experimentelle Untersuchungen zum Problem der Bodenmüdigkeit am Beispiel von Lein und Roggen. *Ztschr. f. Planzenkrank.* 66(11/12):691–703.

Brenchley, W. E. 1920. *Weeds of Farm Lands.* New York: Longmans, 239 pp.

Buchanan, G. A., and D. L. Thurlow. 1972. Competition of sicklepod in soybeans. *WSSA Abstr.* 46, 1972.

Buchholtz, K. P. 1955. Effectiveness of various herbicides in controlling quackgrass. *N. Cent. Weed Conf. Res. Rpt.* December, p. 39.

Burrows, V. D., and P. J. Olson. 1955a. Reaction of small grains to various densities of wild mustard and the results obtained after their removal with 2,4-D or by hand. I. Experiments with wheat. *Canad. Jour. Agr. Sci.* 35:68–75.

———— and ————. 1955b. Reaction of small grains to various densities of wild mustard and the results obtained after their removal with 2,4-D or by hand. II. Experiments with flax. *Canad. Jour. Agr. Sci.* 35:193–201.

Butler, G. W. 1955. Minerals and living cells. *Jour. New Zeal. Inst. Chem.* 19(3):66–75.

Cates, J. S., and H. R. Cox. 1912. The weed factor in the cultivation of corn. *U.S. Dept. Agr. Bur. Plant Indus. Bul.* 257:1–35.

Chappell, W. E., and L. I. Miller. 1956. Effects of certain herbicides on incidence of plant pathogens. Reported by Paul Miller in *Agr. Chem.* 11(6):67–70, 135, 137.

Cords, H. P. 1960. Factors affecting the competitive ability of foxtail barley (*Hordeum jubatum*). *Weeds* 8(4):636–644.

Day, B. E., and R. C. Russell. 1955. The effect of drying on the survival of nutgrass tubers. *Calif. Agr. Expt. Sta. Bul.* 751.

Eaton, B. J., K. C. Feltner and O. G. Russ. 1973. Venice mallow competition in soybeans. *Weed Sci.* 21:89–94.

Engle, M. 1957. Unpublished work.

Eplee, R. E. 1972. Induction of witchweed seed germination. *WSSA Abstr.* 43, 1972.

Evans, R. A., H. R. Holbo, R. E. Eckert, Jr., and J. A. Young. 1972. Functional environment of downy brome communities in relation to weed control and revegetation. *Weed Sci.* 20:154–162.

Feldman, I., M. K. McCarthy, and C. J. Scifres. 1968. Ecological and control studies on musk thistle. *Weed Sci.* 16:1–9.

Godel, G. L. 1935. Relation between rate of seeding and yield of cereal crops in competition with weeds. *Sci. Agr.* 16:165–168.

Grümmer, G. 1957. Die Beeinflussung des Lemertrages durch Unkrauter. *Internationaler Pflanzenschutz-Kongress. Abs.*, vol. IV, p. 61.

————— and H. Beyer. 1960. The influence exerted by species of *Camelina* on flax by means of toxic substances. In *The Biology of Weeds. A Symposium of the British Ecological Society*, ed. John L. Harper. Oxford: Blackwell Scientific Publications, Ltd., July.

Hartwell, B. L., and S. C. Damon. 1917. The persistence of lawn and other grasses as influenced by the effect of manures on the degree of soil acidity. *R. I. Agr. Expt. Sta. Bul.* 170.

Helgeson, E. A., and R. Konzak. 1950. Phytotoxic effects of aqueous extracts of field bindweed and of Canada thistle. A preliminary report. *N. Dak. Agr. Expt. Sta. Bimo. Bul.* 12:71–76.

Horowitz, M., and T. Friedman. 1971. Biological activity of subterranean residues of *Cynodon dactylon* L., *Sorghum halepanse* L. and *Cyperus rotundus* L. *Weed Res.* 11:88–93.

Hoveland, C. S., and G. A. Buchanan. 1973. Soil acidity and growth of warm season weed and crop species. *WSSA Abstr.* 119, 1973.

Hull, H. M. 1958. The effect of day and night temperature on growth, foliar wax content, and cuticle development of velvet mesquite. *Weeds* 6(2):133–142.

Kinsinger, F. E., and R. E. Eckert, Jr. 1961. Emergence and growth of annual and perennial grasses and forbs in soils altered by halogeton leachate. *Jour. Range Mangt.* 14(4):194–197.

Kommedahl, T., J. B. Kotheimer, and J. V. Bernardini. 1959. The effects of quackgrass on germination and seedling development of certain crop plants. *Weeds* 7(1):1–12.

Le Tourneau, D., G. D. Failes, and H. G. Heggeness. 1956. The effect of aqueous extracts of plant tissue on germination of seeds and growth of seedlings. *Weeds* 4(4):363–368.

————— and H. G. Heggeness. 1957. Germination and growth inhibitors in leafy spurge foliage and quackgrass rhizomes. *Weeds* 5(1):12–19.

Love, R. M. 1961. Forage. In *Range, Pastures and Their Improvement*, eds. Hughes, Metcalf, and Heath. Iowa City: Department of Publications, State University of Iowa.

Martin, P., and B. Rademacher. 1960a. Experimentelle Untersuchungen zur Frage der Nachwirkung von Rapswurzelrückständen. *Ztschr. f. Acker-u. Pflanzenbau.* 3(2):105–115.

_____ and _____. 1960b. Studies on the mutual influences of weeds and crops. In *The Biology of Weeds. A Symposium of the British Ecological Society*, ed. John L. Harper. Oxford: Blackwell Scientific Publications, Ltd., July.

McGrath, H., W. C. Shaw, L. L. Jansen, B. R. Lipscomb, P. R. Miller, and W. B. Ennis, Jr. 1957. Witchweed (*Striga asiatica*): A new parasitic weed in the United States. *U.S. Dept. Agr., Agr. Res. Serv. Spec. Pub.* 10.

Ohman, J. H., and Thor Kommedhahl. 1960. Relative toxicity of extracts from vegetative organs of quackgrass to alfalfa. *Weeds* 8(4):666–670.

Oliver, L. R., and M. M. Schreiber. 1973. Competition for carbon dioxide in a heteroculture. *WSSA Abstr.* 123. 1973.

Osvald, H. 1947. Växternas vapeni kampen om utrymmet. *Växtodling* 2:288–303.

Parker, R., and M. C. Williams. 1972. Effect of nitrogen on miserotoxin metabolism in three varieties of timber milk vetch. *West. Soc. Weed Sci. Proc.* 25:35.

Pavlychenko, T. K., and J. B. Harrington. 1935. Root development of weeds and crops in competition under dry farming. *Sci. Agr.* 16:151–160.

Pfeiffer, R. K., and H. M. Holmes. 1961. A study of the competition between barley and oats as influenced by barley seed rates, nitrogen level, and barban treatment. *Weed Res.* 1(1):5–18.

Rademacher, B. 1959. Gegenseitige Beeinflussung höherer Pflanzen. *Handbuch der Pflanzenphysiologie*, vol. II. Berlin: Springer.

Robinson, E. L. 1960. Growth of witchweed (*Striga asiatica*) as affected by soil types and soil and air temperatures. *Weeds* 8(4):576–581.

_____. 1961. Soil-incorporated pre-planting herbicides for witchweed control. *Weeds* 9(3):411–415.

_____ and I. E. Stokes. 1960. Witchweed: A potential pest of sugar cane in the United States. *Sugar Jour.* 23(5):25–27.

Scholl, J. M., and D. W. Staniforth. 1957. Establishment of birdsfoot trefoil as influenced by competition from weeds and companion crops. *Agron. Jour.* 49:432–435.

_____ and _____. 1958. Birdsfoot trefoil establishment. *Down to Earth* 13:8–9.

Schroeder, M. H. 1972. Relationships of range and forest management with herbicides on wildlife. *West. Soc. Weed Sci. Proc.* 25:11–15.

Selleck, G. W., and R. T. Coupland. 1961. Studies in the life history of *Artemisia absinthium. Weeds* 9(3):485–490.

Shadbolt, C. A., and L. G. Holm. 1956. Some quantitative aspects of weed competition in vegetable crops. *Weeds* 4(2):111–123.

Staniforth, D. W. 1957. Effects of annual grass weeds on the yield of corn. *Agron. Jour.* 49:551–555.

————. 1958. Soybean-foxtail competition under varying soil moisture conditions. *Agron. Jour.* 50:13–15.

————. 1961. Responses of corn hybrids to yellow foxtail competition. *Weeds* 9(1):132–136.

———— and C. R. Weber. 1956. Effects of annual weeds on the growth and yield of soybeans. *Agron. Jour.* 48:467–471.

Sunderland, N. 1960a. The production of the *Striga* and *Orobanche* germination stimulants by maize roots. *Jour. Expt. Bot.* 11(32):236–245.

————. 1960b. Germination of the seeds of angiospermous root parasites. In *The Biology of Weeds. A Symposium of the British Ecological Society,* ed. John L. Harper. Oxford: Blackwell Scientific Publications, Ltd., July.

Timmons, F. L. 1941. Results of bindweed control experiments at the Fort Hays Branch Station, Hays, Kansas, 1935 to 1940. *Kans. Agr. Expt. Sta. Bul.* 296:1–50.

Vengris, J. 1953. Weed populations as related to certain cultivated crops in the Connecticut River Valley, Mass. *Weeds* 2(2):125–134.

Weber, C. R., and D. W. Staniforth. 1957. Competitive relationships in variable weed and soybean stands. *Agron. Jour.* 49:440–444.

Welbank, P. J. 1960. Toxin production from *Agropyron repens.* In *The Biology of Weeds. A Symposium of the British Ecological Society,* ed. John L. Harper. Oxford: Blackwell Scientific Publications, Ltd., July.

Welton, F. A. 1931. Soil reaction not an efficient method of controlling some lawn weeds. *Ohio Agr. Expt. Sta. 50th Ann. Rpt.* 40–41.

Wicks, G. A., and D. E. Smika. 1973. Chemical fallow in a winter wheat-fallow rotation. *Weed Sci.* 21:97–102.

Williams, E. D. 1969. Effects of time of sowing of spring wheat and defoliation of *Agropyron repens* (L.) Beauv. on competition between them. *Weed Res.* 9:241–250.

————. 1970. Effects of decreasing the light intensity on the growth of *Agropyrons repens* (L.) Beauv. in the field. *Weed Res.* 10:360–366.

Worsham, A. D., D. E. Moreland, and K. C. Klingman. 1959. Stimulation of *Striga asiatica* (Witchweed) seed germination by 6-substituted purines. *Science* 130:1654–1656.

Young, J. A., and R. A. Evans. 1969. Control and ecological studies on Scotch thistle. *Weed Sci.* 17:60–63.

———— and ————. 1971. Germination of dyers woad. *Weed Sci.* 19:76–78.

6

Principles of Weed Control

As long as tillage, cropping, and management constituted the principal methods for combating weeds, it was necessary to relate these methods to the life histories of the weeds under consideration. Such methods were dictated by factors that determine the vigor, competitiveness, and survival of the weeds. Among these factors are the habitat, the cropping system, the size of infestation, the prevalence of the weed, the availability of equipment, the economic status of the farm, etc. As mentioned in Chapter 4, prevention is better than control, but unfortunately the vast majority of our farm lands were infested with noxious weeds before scientific agriculture made the farmers conscious of weed prevention.

With the introduction of herbicides the emphasis has shifted, and now information on the properties and functions of the various chemicals available may be more important than detailed knowledge of life histories, competitive abilities, and ecological relations of crops and weeds. Toxicity as related to dosage and degree of control, selectivity as related to crop and weed species, and residual action as related to the method of application are the important factors which must be considered once chemicals enter the picture. Culture, cropping, and management are still important in weed control, but now these must be integrated with chemicals into the over-all scheme of operation, for some of our present chemical procedures are cheaper and more effective than any of the older methods. Anyone proposing to control weeds by present-day methods must have knowledge of all of these factors if he hopes to do an effective and economical job.

101

CONTROL VERSUS ERADICATION

A distinction should be made between control and eradication of weeds. In some situations it may be possible and altogether desirable to eradicate a certain weed that is limited in extent; in other situations control may be the only feasible objective.

Eradication is desirable when the weed infestation is of limited area, when the weed species is not prevalent in the locality, when the weed is noxious in nature, and where a satisfactory method is available. The farmer may choose to grub out the weed and destroy all parts so that there is no chance for reinfestation, or he may use chemicals, preferably a soil-borne fumigant or sterilant that will kill every vestige of the root system. A decade ago only volatile fumigants such as carbon bisulfide, methyl bromide, or DD were available; now less volatile materials such as metham (SMDC, Vapam), dazomet (DMTT, Mylone), trifluralin, and EPTC (Eptam) may be employed. These compounds may be applied in solution to the top of the soil and washed in by rainfall or irrigation, or incorporated mechanically into the soil. They have the advantage over the more volatile materials of affecting shallow surface roots and germinating seeds. The volatile materials, when sealed in the soil, move in the vapor phase to deep soil layers and kill roots of perennial weeds. Both types may be combined to eradicate weeds that must be killed at all cost. Whatever method is used, the infested area should be carefully watched for several years for seedlings that might develop.

In contrast with the eradication procedure, control may be the only practical program where weeds are widespread and difficult to eliminate, for eradication might cost far more than the land is worth. By control is meant a procedure that enables the grower to produce a profitable crop in spite of the weeds. A case in point is spraying with 2,4-D to control Russian thistle, prostrate knotweed, or fiddleneck. These weeds are seldom killed but, when their growth is inhibited, the crop may make a normal yield. The repeated use of preplant and preemergence herbicides to suppress growth of annual weeds in row crops is another example; the immense store of seeds in the soil precludes the possibility of eradication. And the biological control of weeds with insect predators is an excellent illustration; to be successful year after year there must exist a balance such that neither weeds nor insects disappear, for weeds are necessary as food for the insects and the insects are the agent responsible for controlling the weed.

Control, then, is a case of learning to live with weeds and to keep them at a level that does not interfere with crop production.

METHODS OF CONTROL AS RELATED TO WEED CHARACTERISTICS

The successful culture of a crop plant presupposed a knowledge of its life history, its habits, and its growth requirements. Likewise, the devising and intelligent application of methods for controlling or eradicating any pest, be it fungus or insect or weed, require a knowledge of the life history and growth requirements of that pest. Specifically, as regards weeds, one must know how they reproduce and spread, how they react to environmental changes, how they are adapted to different habitats, and how they respond to herbicides.

Weeds are notorious for their success in invading new areas and in establishing themselves even under adverse conditions, where they may persist in spite of man's most intensive efforts to eradicate them or keep them within reasonable bounds. Plants we choose to call "weeds" are well equipped to survive in the struggle for existence in the various habitats controlled by man in his agricultural, pastoral, and other economic pursuits.

What are the principal characteristics that enable certain species to behave as weeds under a given set of conditions? We shall mention briefly the most important of these, mindful of the fact that any one species does not necessarily possess all of them.

PRODUCTION OF NUMEROUS SEEDS

Most individual weeds produce several thousand seeds, and large individuals of such species as tumbling pigweed may bear several million. Moreover, a large percentage of these seeds may be viable.

ADAPTATIONS THAT PROVIDE EFFECTIVE DISPERSAL OF SEEDS (Fig. 2–1)

The seeds of many species are especially designed for dispersal by wind, water, or animals.

DORMANCY OF SEEDS

The seeds of some weeds will not germinate immediately after maturing, even though they are placed under favorable conditions; thus, individual seeds may not germinate for several years after they are produced. Lengthening the period of germination of a crop of seeds assures continuation of the species in cases where those seeds which germinate in unfavorable seasons are unable to reproduce.

LONGEVITY OF BURIED SEED

Even nondormant seeds may not lose their viability for several years if they are buried in the soil. The buried seeds of wild mustards will survive for at least 30 years.

ABILITY TO SURVIVE ADVERSE CONDITIONS

Many weeds are able to survive and reproduce under climatic and soil conditions that are too severe for crop plants.

ADAPTATIONS THAT REPEL GRAZING ANIMALS

Some weeds have a disagreeable odor or flavor; others are equipped with thorns of spines.

ABILITY TO PROPAGATE VEGETATIVELY

Many weeds will propagate themselves from small pieces of roots or stems as well as from seed.

ABILITY TO SPREAD VEGETATIVELY

Creeping perennial types of weeds, such as perennial sowthistle, may invade new areas, by vegetative structures as well as by seeds.

RESISTANCE TO CHEMICALS

Some weeds are remarkably resistance to the toxic action of herbicides. These survive chemical methods and flourish in the absence of competition from susceptible species. Rotation of chemicals is useful in these cases if proper chemicals are available.

HISTORY OF WEEDS AS RELATED TO METHODS OF CONTROL

Successful control of weeds presupposes an understanding of their life history. It is apparent that a weed that lives but a year may be controlled by practices not applicable to weeds that live for a number of years. As to life span, weed species fall into the following groups: *annuals*, *biennials*, and *perennials*.

ANNUALS

Annuals live but a year; they produce a crop of seed and then die. They reproduce by seed only; a few, such as hairy crabgrass and common chickweed, produce adventitious roots on prostrate stems. If such rooted stems are cut and planted, each piece will survive that season as a new plant, but will not live over until another season. Annuals are classified into two groups, *summer annuals* and *winter annuals*, on the basis of seasons of germination and maturity. Summer annuals germinate in the spring; the plants grow to maturity during summer and die by winter. Examples are rough pigweed, lambs-quarters, and common sunflower. Winter annuals germinate in the fall or early winter; they overwinter in a vegetative condition, often in a rosette form. In the spring, they complete their vegetative growth, mature a crop of seed, and then die in the late spring. Examples are shepherdspurse, fanweed, downy chess, wild oats, mustards, and wild radish.

Although the ultimate objective of controlling annual weeds is prevention of seeding, relief of the current crop from competition is the most compelling need. This is done by the use of pre- or postemergence selective herbicides. If there is no satisfactory soil-borne herbicide, directed spraying of a nonselective material may be the answer; flaming is a common practice in cotton. In row crops, weeds may be controlled chemically in narrow bands that include the crop; usually it is more economical to kill the weeds in the middles by tillage. Any method of killing the weeds preemergence or in the crop, for example mustard in cereals with 2,4-D, will prevent seeding; such control, carried out for many years, will deplete the stored seed in the soil and eventually eradicate the weeds.

BIENNIALS

Biennials have a life span of two years. The first year's growth is purely vegetative, with top growth usually confined to a rosette of leaves. The taproot is often fleshy and serves as a food-storage organ. During the second year, a flower stalk arises from the crown. After producing seed, the plant dies. Examples of biennial weeds are wild carrot, purple starthistle, and great burdock. As weeds, biennials are usually restricted to noncultivated areas, such as pastures and roadsides.

Biennials are controlled like annuals, the treatment best being made during the first year. Late fall or early spring tillage will destroy the rosettes before they have an opportunity to send up seedstalks. Biennials sometimes send forth seedstalks early and rapidly, hence it is advisable to destroy them in the rosette stage.

PERENNIALS

Perennials live for three or more years. In many cases no seed is produced the first year, but seeding occurs each year thereafter for the life of the plant. Perennials are classified on the basis of vegetative reproduction into simple perennials, bulbous perennials, and creeping perennials.

SIMPLE PERENNIALS

Ordinarily, simple perennials reproduce almost solely by seed. Vegetative reproduction occurs only when roots or crowns are cut by tillage implements. Each cut piece may then send out feeding roots and stems and become a new plant. Examples of this class are dandelion, curly dock, and common plantain.

FIGURE 6-1. A. Quackgrass rhizomes from a plant grown in sand culture.

BULBOUS PERENNIALS

These propagate by bulbs and bulblets as well as by seeds, In wild garlic (Fig. 2–4), for example, aerial bulblets as well as seeds may be produced in the flower heads; below ground, secondary bulbs develop at the base of the old bulb.

CREEPING PERENNIALS

These spread by lateral extension of stems (stolons) along the soil surface, by stems (rhizomes) beneath the soil surface, by roots, or by seeds. Examples of perennials that spread by *creeping stems* along the

FIGURE 6-1. B. Rhizomes of a young Johnsongrass plant. (Photograph by courtesy of L. E. Anderson.)

soil surface are mouseear chickweed, knotgrass, and lawn pennywort. Those spreading by rhizomes include quackgrass (Fig. 6–1A), hedge bindweed, and Johnsongrass (Fig. 6–1B). Familiar examples of weeds that spread by *creeping roots* are perennial sowthistle, sheep sorrel, and western ragweed. In some creeping perennials, new shoots may develop from both roots and rhizomes. Among such are field bindweed and Canada thistle.

It is of value to recognize the differences between *shallow-rooted creeping perennials* and *deep-rooted creeping perennials*. Shallow-rooted creeping perennials, such as Bermudagrass, quack-grass, and sheep sorrel, usually have the reproductive structures (rhizomes in the first two examples cited and roots in the third) confined to the surface 6 to 10 in. of soil. They are therefore subject to removal by the plow and cultivator. Deep-rooted perennials, on the other hand, resprout from structures at soil levels below those that can be reached even by deep plowing. Field bindweed, for example, will send shoots to the surface from a depth of 3 to 6 ft or more.

The practical significance of this distinction between shallow-rooted and deep-rooted perennials lies in the differences in mode of attack where tillage or chemicals are used for controlling them. Roots or rhizomes of the shallow type may be loosened by plowing and then killed by sun drying when pulled to the surface by a spring-tooth harrow or other suitable implements. They are also subject to the toxic action of chemicals localized in the topsoil. Control of deep-rooted perennials by tillage is dependent on exhausting the food reserves through continued shoot cutting. Control by chemicals requires deep penetration of herbicides into the soil or into the root system.

In combating perennial weeds, two problems are involved. First, to check the spread or reinfestation by seedlings, the old plants must be prevented from ripening seed, and seedlings developing from seed already present in the soil must be killed. Second, the existing stand of old, established plants must be eradicated.

In handling the seedling situation, one may use methods similar to those already described for annuals, except that the greater hazard involved makes it much more important to prevent the spread of seed. Mowing in the blossoming stages (before seed formation), spraying with contact sprays, or burning will accomplish this purpose. Plowing or shallow cultivation, if done early enough, will kill seedlings of perennials.

All perennials need sunlight, oxygen, water, and certain mineral nutrients from the soil. If any one of these factors is limited by cultivation, smothering, immersion under water, or competition with other plants, the vigor of the plant is reduced. In addition, the perennial plant goes through a more or less normal annual cycle of vegetation, reproduction, storage, and dormancy; any disturbance of this cycle lowers its vigor. A plant may be induced, furthermore, under certain conditions, to take up a chemical through cut or injured tops; the poison is then translocated to the roots, killing all tissue with which it comes in contact; under other conditions, a plant may absorb toxic chemicals from the soil and die when these accumulate sufficiently. Finally, the sprayblade method of repressing growth of perennials offers relief from the constant tillage program aimed at the depletion of root reserves. There is evidence that this method for laying down a thin sheet of chemical at a depth of 4 to 8 inches beneath the soil surface acts through the vapor phase. Only chemicals having the correct volatility are effective; more volatile ones diffuse away and give only a short effect; less volatile ones do not provide a tight layer of sufficient toxicity. Dichlobenil, the first chemical that proved useful by this method, has a vapor pressure of 5.5×10^{-4} mm Hg; trifluralin has a vapor pressure of 1.99×10^{-4} mg Hg. Other chemicals that give results by the sprayblade method will undoubtedly be found. The two above chemicals stop the growth of shoots from rhizomes or roots in the soil; the growing shoots swell, become heavily callused, and finally decay. The root tissue below this injury is unharmed, except for lack of the restoration of reserves.

If these various modes of attack are kept in mind, the problem of controlling or eradicating perennial weeds becomes largely one of formulating a program to meet the requirements of each particular situation and carrying it out rigorously until the aims are accomplished.

VARIATION IN THE LIFE SPAN OF WEEDS

The life span of a given weed species is not fixed, but may vary to some extent according to the climate. Some species that are normally biennial may assume the annual habit when growing in regions with a mild winter climate; an example is wild carrot. In parts of California, during mild winters, some individuals of the yellow starthistle, which is normally annual, remain alive through the winter and may come to bloom in the second year. Likewise, short-podded mustard, although usually biennial, may be perennial in a region with mild winters. Even in those regions having severe winters, certain species may behave as either winter annuals or summer annuals; others may be annual but occasionally biennial; and biennials may now and then live into the third or later years.

CLASSIFICATION OF METHODS OF WEED CONTROL

Many methods of weed control and weed eradication have been devised. For convenience, these may be grouped as follows:

I. Mechanical methods
   A. Hand pulling
   B. Hoeing and spudding

    C. Tillage
    D. Mowing
    E. Flooding
    F. Burning
    G. Smothering (nonliving materials)
  II. Cropping and competition methods
 III. Biological methods, involving use of parasites
 IV. Chemical methods
    A. Selective herbicides
        1. Foliage applications
            a. Contact
            b. Translocated
        2. Root applications
    B. Nonselective herbicides
        1. Foliage applications
            a. Contact
            b. Translocated
        2. Root applications
    C. Miscellaneous
        1. Trunk injection (woody plants)
        2. Jar method (perennial weeds)
        3. Chemical treatment in irrigation canals (aquatic weeds)
        4. Sprayblade treatment

DESCRIPTION OF METHODS OF CONTROL

HAND PULLING

The hand pulling of individual plants is a practical and efficient method of eliminating weeds in home gardens and within the rows and hills of certain cultivated crops in which the weeds are difficult to reach with the hoe or cultivating implements. The method is best applied to annuals and biennials, for such weeds do not recover from the pieces of roots left in the ground. In the case of perennial weeds, on the other hand, pulling usually leaves portions of roots or rootstocks in the ground, and new sprouts may be sent up from these structures; to eradicate such weeds by pulling, the operation must be repeated time and time again.

In lawns, especially new ones, pulling is an effective method of eradicating certain weeds. This is best done when the lawn is soaked with water, for then the weeds are readily removed without breaking the root. Even weeds with a pronounced taproot, such as burclover, mallow, plantain, and even dandelion, may be removed without breaking the main root if pulled when the lawn is very wet.

It has long been a practice of farmers to pull objectionable weeds, such as mustards, in grainfields. The weeds may be so scattered that chemical spraying is impractical; but the weeds must not be allowed to produce seed. Pulling is done just as soon as flowers become evident.

Although hand pulling of weeds is justified in many of the special situations noted above, Holm (1971) emphasized that the widescale use of hand pulling, hoeing, scything, and cutting by means of the machete that prevails in many of the underdeveloped nations of the world should be substituted for by mechanical and chemical methods to free women to work in their homes and children to attend school.

HAND HOEING

The ordinary hand hoe is woefully underestimated as a weeding tool. "The man with the hoe" should still command respect, because frequently he is accomplishing results that cannot be attained so effectively and cheaply in any other manner. All too often, a substitute for the hoe is sought, even for small weed patches, when, as a matter of fact, hoeing most satisfactorily meets the needs. The hoe is still useful as a tool in all garden work and as a supplement to cultivators in weeding all kinds of row crops.

Sometimes in waste places supporting small weed infestations, the scythe is employed rather than the hoe. The difficulty with mowing is that many weeds send out seedstalks from the base of the plant, and repeated mowings are necessary if seed production is to be wholly prevented. One hoeing properly done, cutting below the crown of the plant, gives complete destruction of all top growth. Perennials may make regrowth before the season ends but annuals and biennials are completely destroyed.

Not only is the hoe a proper weeding tool in gardens and in cultivated row crops but it is often the most practical one to eliminate scattered weeds in pastures and grasslands. In such places, care should be exercised that the weeds are cut off well below the crown.

It has been demonstrated (Timmons, 1941) that even such a persistent perennial as field bindweed can be eradicated with the hoe. Hoeing regularly every 10 days is recommended, especially during the first 3 or 4 months; after the plants have become weakened, as indicated by less vigorous growth, the intervals of hoeing can be lengthened to 14 to 16 days. In hoeing a perennial like field bindweed, it is important that all plants be cut off. Hoeing to eliminate field bindweed is particularly adapted to infestation around trees, in parkings, and in other places that cannot be treated with chemicals or reached with mechanical equipment.

It might be well to point out that Timmons (1941) work was done in Kansas where bindweed may be relatively shallow rooted and where it is subject to severe conditions in the winter. In California with deep soils and a milder climate, eradication of bindweed by mechanical methods may take many years; treatment with translocated herbicides is a preferred method under these conditions.

TILLAGE

Tillage is a practical method of fighting weeds of all classes: annuals, biennials, and perennials. There is abundant evidence that the principal function of tillage is the destruction of weeds and reduction of weed seeds in the soil rather than its effect on the physical properties and the chemical and biological activities of the soil. This applies to both uncropped and cropped land. In the case of annuals, it is sufficient to destroy top growth only; of biennials, top and crown; but of perennials, both top and underground growth must be destroyed or starved.

As stated, one of the functions of tillage is to reduce the weed-seed population of the soil. If tillage is properly performed, weeds of arable lands are prevented from maturing seed and from scattering them on the soil; then surface tillage creates conditions that encourage the germination of weed seeds; and, if timely tillage follows, the seedlings are destroyed. In other words, an objective of weed control, involving tillage, is the reduction of potential weed growth by encouraging the germination of weed seeds in the soil. In this connection, deep plowing with the aim of burying weed seeds is a wrong practice, in that many weed seeds may retain their viability longer at deep soil levels than at shallow ones, and subsequent tillage operations may bring them to the surface. Generally speaking, in order to control annual weeds by tillage methods, this operation should be shallow rather than deep.

In both row crops and in cereals, blind tillage is a successful weed-control practice. Blind tillage is tillage of the soil after seeding a crop, either before the crop plants are up or while they are in the early stages of growth.

Most annual weeds may be controlled by one season's fallow. However, since the soil contains many viable weed seeds, a season of fallow must be followed the next year by row crops and clean cultivation to prevent seed formation.

In controlling perennial weeds, one season of fallow is insufficient. It is usually not economical to rely on fallowing alone, because land lies idle too long. Smother crops and a limited, judicious use of herbicides should be combined with clean cultivation.

For a number of years, perennial weeds have been controlled by tillage methods alone. The methods vary in effectiveness, depending chiefly upon the weed species, the age of the infestation, and, to a lesser degree, upon the physical characters of the soil, soil fertility, and depth of soil to the water table. Here we must distinguish between shallow-rooted and deep-rooted perennials. Shallow-rooted perennials, such as Bermudagrass, St. Johnswort, and western ragweed, may be greatly reduced by one plowing if this is done so as to turn the mass of rootstocks to the surface, where they will be dried out. A certain amount of surface tillage should follow plowing in order to prevent the formation of new roots and shoots from partly buried rootstocks. With deep-rooted perennials, such as field bindweed, hoary cress, Canada thistle, and others, one or more seasons of tillage at intervals are required to effect control. With such perennials, the object of tillage is to exhaust food reserves in roots and rootstocks by repeated destruction of top growth. It is apparent that an old infestation of a deep-rooted perennial, in which there are large stores of food in the underground organs, will require more cultivation to effect eradication than a relatively young infestation, in which there are smaller quantities of reserves. Field observations seem to show that control of deep-rooted perennials by tillage is somewhat slower in a sandy-loam soil than in a clay or clay-loam soil. When the water table is high and the roots and rootstocks are confined to a small volume of soil, control by tillage may be attained in shorter time than when the water table is low and roots and rootstocks are deeply penetrating. Likewise, in a shallow soil underlain with a clay pan, hard pan, or bedrock, tillage control may be accomplished in a shorter time than in the case of a deep alluvial soil.

Tillage methods are discussed in greater detail in Chapter 7.

MOWING

The only objects of mowing are to prevent seed production and to remove unsightly weed growth. It may be employed to prevent seeding of all classes of weeds. The method is used along roadsides, in waste places, and in meadows and pastures. It is true that repeated close mowing of perennial weeds may tend to weaken somewhat the food reserves in roots and rootstocks. However, with these weeds, as with certain annuals such as yellow starthistle and prostrate knotweed, seeds may be produced on low branches, hence the main purpose is thwarted.

FLOODING

In western states, flooding is popular for controlling perennial weeds. It is accomplished by surrounding the infestations with dikes and covering them with 6 to 10 in. of water for 3 to 8 weeks in the summer. The infested area should be plowed before immersing, and no growth must appear above the water.

Flooding first attracted attention when areas infested with field bindweed and other noxious perennials were planted with rice. Such weeds were usually eradicated. This method has been used rather extensively against camel-thorn and hoary cress and yields excellent results in sandy soils. In heavy soils, flooding has not been so satisfactory. White horsenettle, occurring in several of the camel-thorn areas, has been killed in nearly every instance by flooding. In California a 13-acre area of Russian knapweed, flooded for 60 days, was completely killed. In several other places, knapweed has given the same response. Occasionally, submergence for 3 to 5 weeks has given satisfactory control.

Flooding is effective only when the area is completely immersed for the whole time of treatment. Many failures have resulted from allowing the water level to decrease so that regrowth has occurred. Not all weeds react in the same way to flooding. Since flooding kills plants by excluding the air, it is effective only when the plant is covered and the roots are completely surrounded with water. Under certain soil conditions, some plants apparently become dormant and thus, through lowered oxygen consumption, are able to survive. The effect of submergence on weed seeds is discussed in Chapter 2.

HEAT

Heat kills living cells by coagulating the protoplasm and inactivating enzymes. The thermal death point for most plant cells lies between 45 and 55°C (113 to 131°F). These figures are for prolonged exposures. Higher temperatures kill in shorter times. Dry seeds, however, withstand considerably higher temperatures and longer exposures than do structures in which the cells are more active.

There are four purposes for which heat, in the form of flame or steam, is used in weed control in field practice: (1) Fire is used to destroy dry tops of weeds that have matured or that have been killed by mowing or spraying. (2) Flame throwers and steam boxes are used to kill green-shoot growth in situations where cultivation or other common methods are impracticable, as on gravel walks and railroad tracks. (3) Flame cultivation is used in cotton to destroy weed seedlings in the rows. Such treatment may be used repeatedly from the time the cotton stem attains a diameter of 3/16 in. until lay-by. (4) Heat is occasionally used in killing buried weed seeds and the subterranean organs of perennial weeds.

In general, the burning of naturally matured weeds is to be considered an expedient for destroying objectionable debris rather than a weed-control practice. Except with certain species in which the seeds are retained in the fruits for some time after maturity, it is usually found that plants dry enough to burn well have shed a considerable percentage of their seed and that only few of these already scattered seeds are consumed or devitalized. Many of them will have fallen into cracks or have been buried by wind-drifted or water-carried soil.

According to Durrell (1929), even seeds on the soil surface are not significantly injured in most cases. On the contrary, burning has stimulated germination of some shallowly buried seed. Lonsdale (1935) reports that gorse seedlings spring up in unusual abundance on infested areas immediately the ashes have cooled following a burn; and Sampson and Parker (1930) found greater than usual numbers of St. Johnswort seedlings on burns where thermometers buried ¼ in. below the soil surface registered 260°F. In laboratory tests, heating St. Johnswort seeds to that temperature for 5 min. resulted in a higher germination than that of unheated controls, and seeds heated to 212°F for periods up to and including 30 min. germinated better than the controls.

Weeds that have been mowed or sprayed with diesel oil during the blooming period should be burned to prevent maturation of seed on the cut or killed tops. Such mowed or oil-sprayed vegetation burns more readily and completely than when it is standing at maturity. Weeds mowed after a part of the seeds are mature are preferably burned in place without raking and bunching, since these operations scatter seed.

Although burning of mature weeds is not particularly effective as a control measure for the reasons mentioned, it is often desirable for other reasons, such as: (1) removal of fire hazard, (2) clearing waterways, (3) killing insect and fungus pests that the weeds may be harboring, (4) lessening the amount of trash in plowing or discing, and (5) removal of unsightly debris.

Various types of burners utilizing liquid and gaseous fuels have been devised for killing green shoots with a hot flame. Steam from locomotive boilers is also sometimes used by railroads. Hand-operated burners of the vaporizing type are widely used in killing weeds on small areas, such as walks, driveways, clay tennis courts, and on streets and gutters where weeds push up through cracks in the pavement. In this type of torch, the fuel, under 30 to 50 lb pressure, is vaporized by passing through coils surrounding the base of the flame. Such burners require refined fuels such as gasoline, kerosene, or distillate (Fig. 6–2). In killing green weeds, the rate at which the flame is passed over the plants should be adjusted to give an exposure that causes wilting but not charring. This results in death and drying out within a few days. The dead plants may then be consumed by a second treatment. Going over the area twice uses less time and fuel than attempting to consume the plants completely with one application.

Burning may be used to kill young weed seedlings in certain row crops, notably onions and cotton. Small units, arranged on a cultivator chassis or on a tractor drawbar, are aimed to burn the weed seedlings and to avoid the foliage of the crop plants (Fig. 6–3).

Flame cultivation is an economical and practical means of controlling mid-season and late-season *annual* broadleaf weeds and grasses in the cotton row. It can greatly reduce the amount of hand labor required for weed control when used in combination with mechanical cultivation. It requires the application of a carefully controlled flame to the drill row of cotton plants at a rate that does not injure the crop. Most plants, including cotton, will be killed if they are kept within the flame too long.

Since flaming is selective burning, the cotton plants must be larger than the weeds. A practical control depends upon the ages of desired

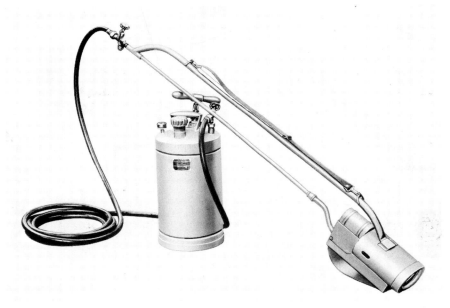

FIGURE 6-2.   Vaporizing type of weed burner. (Illustration courtesy of Hauck Mfg. Co.)

plant (cotton) and unwanted weed, the intensity and volume of flame, the length of exposure, and the location of the burner with respect to the plant. The cotton plant can resist the flame if the flaming is done as suggested: by the proper setting, adjustment, and timing of the treatment. Cotton plants are safe from flame when about 8 in. tall; until cotton reaches flaming heights, other suitable means of weed control must be used.

Weeds are not destroyed during flame cultivation by complete combustion or burning. High temperatures in the plant cause dehydration or cell rupture to the extent that the exposed parts of the weeds die. The effects are not always immediate, but death usually occurs within a few hours.

TIMING

Time of application is important to get effective control. Flaming before seedling weeds are more than 2 in. tall is most successful. Flame cultivation should be used to control *small* weeds and grasses instead of waiting until they are the size that requires hand hoeing. Where fields are extremely grassy, a series of successive flamings should be used. After cotton is once clean, flaming after each irrigation will usually keep it clean of annual weeds in the drill row.

FIGURE 6-3. The Sizz weeder developed for controlling small weeds in row crops. (Photograph courtesy of Fijelen Research and Development Co.)

Norris (1972) has found flaming to be very effective in killing weeds and alfalfa weevils. One or two flamings just before the alfalfa starts growing in the spring have given increased yields throughout the season.

The burning off of the surface few inches of peat soils is a special case of destroying weed seeds and such shallow-rooted perennials as nutsedge (*Cyperus* spp.). Burning was formerly common in the peat lands of the Sacramento-San Joaquin Delta in California. Its repeated practice has almost ruined formerly productive land, since by destruction of the fertile peat nothing is left but the infertile clay underlay.

Other uses of heat are the devitalizing of weed seeds, the killing of insects and pathogenic organisms in greenhouse soils, and the devitalizing of weed seeds in crop seeds from which they are not readily separated by mechanical means. It has been found that alfalfa seeds withstand exposure to dry heat that will kill seeds of dodder and other weeds.

Smothering with Nonliving Materials

Attempts are often made to control weeds by the use of an artificial mulch: straw, hay, manure, paper, plastic film, and rice hulls. The object is completely to exclude the light and thus prevent all top growth. In the case of perennials, if straw, hay, or manure is used, the layers may need to be very thick, since it is possible for new shoots of certain weeds to grow through 2 to 4 or more feet of the material, depending upon its looseness. Weeds with indeterminate vegetative growth, like field bindweed, are extremely difficult to keep under cover. Others, like Bermudagrass, Johnsongrass, and Russian knapweed, are more easily controlled by this method. In general, straw, hay, and manure mulches are unsatisfactory and impracticable as weed-control measures. In any event, they are applicable only to small infestations.

The use of paper mulch on a large scale in agriculture was originated in 1914 by G. F. Echart for sugar-cane culture in the Hawaiian Islands. The use was later extended to pineapple culture. Weed control in these two crops is a problem of major importance. Limited use of this mulch in vegetable gardens in the mainland United States has been made. The effectiveness of different types of paper, the best manner of laying the paper, and the influence of paper mulch on soil temperature, soil moisture, and crop production have been studied. Sheet-plastic materials are now available for soil mulching and weed control. They are available in various weights, and they are usually black, hence impervious to light.

In general, properly laid paper or plastic that is impervious to light and moisture is effective in weed control. On sugar cane and pineapple plantations in the Hawaiian Islands, mulching has proved not only effective but economical. On truck farms and in home gardens, it is doubtful if it is as economical as ordinary tillage methods.

Paper- or plastic-mulched soil, as compared with cultivated soil, usually has more moisture and a higher daily mean temperature, but there is no consistent difference in the nitrate nitrogen of the soil. Therefore, such treatment has special merit in the culture of early, quick-maturing crops, especially in periods of moisture deficiency.

In vegetable culture, three general methods of supplying mulch materials are employed: (1) small squares at regular distances—this method is applicable to watermelons, squashes, cucumbers, and similar annual crops; (2) extended strips with alternate uncovered soil areas; and (3) extended strips without any uncovered soil areas. Of course, the last-mentioned gives the greatest degree of weed control. When a continuous covering is made, the seed is planted or plants are set out through holes cut in the mulching material. Recently, mulch strips with vegetable or flower seeds impregnated in them have been placed on the market. These are particularly handy for the home gardener.

CROPPING AND COMPETITION METHODS

Reference is made here to types of crops, including smother or competitive crops, and crop rotation; to a system of farming that utilizes to the fullest extent varieties best adapted to soil and climatic conditions such that vigorous competitive stands of crops are secured; and to proper rates and dates of seeding—in short, to "good" farming practices.

Proper rotation and sequence of crops result in an increased vigor of the different crops. Moreover, any one type of crop has its own characteristic weeds, and these weeds tend to accumulate when this crop is repeated year after year. For example, continuous cropping to small cereals invariably results in an increase in the weed population, chiefly annuals. Again, repeated plantings of the same crop favor the development therein of plant diseases and insects, resulting in weak or patchy stands which are easily invaded by weeds. In planning a crop-rotation or weed-cropping sequence, one cannot ignore the weed factor; the nature of the weed growth may determine to a large extent the rotation. It is apparent that rotations planned to combat deep-rooted perennials will be different from those that have as their aim the control of annuals. Generally speaking, the crop rotation should be such that no group of weeds has a possibility of undisturbed development.

Competitive crops, also known as "smother crops" in certain cases, have value in any weed-control or weed-eradication program. They compete with weeds for water, light, and mineral nutrients. The principal competitive crops valued in weed control are: millet, Sudan grass, crested wheatgrass, sweet clover, sunflower, rape, barley, rye, sorghum, buckwheat, soybeans, alfalfa, cowpeas, clovers, hemp, Jerusalem artichoke, and ensilage corn.

It needs to be emphasized that an effective and economical method of control of extensive infestations of perennial weeds on arable land involves intensive tillage alternated with cropping (Timmons, 1941). The tillage must be thorough and regular; the crop must be one that grows quickly, produces an abundance of shade, and may be harvested early enough to permit fall cultivation. Environmental conditions will determine the type of competitive crop to use; also, the weed combatted will be a determining factor.

Pavlychenko (1942) has shown that in Saskatchewan three seasons of crested wheatgrass have completely smothered thick stands of perennial sowthistle and toadflax; four seasons eliminated a solid stand of Canada thistle, quackgrass, and other perennial weeds.

A combination of tillage and competitive crops has given encouraging results in the control of all classes of weeds, including deep-rooted perennials. It has the advantage that it permits the growing of a crop that, in a measure, will help to repay the costs of weed eradication.

BIOLOGICAL METHODS

In biological control (Chapter 8), use is made of insects or fungus organisms that live on specific weeds. The most notable example of biological control is that of prickly pears in Australia by the Argentine moth borer (*Cactoblastis cactorum*). This insect was introduced to Australia from Argentina in 1925. Mass distribution of eggs was started in 1928. In Queensland, which had about 50 million acres of cactus-infested lands, it has been estimated that 12 years after the introduction of the Argentine moth borer, cactus has been reduced by 95 percent. Introduction of two leaf-feeding beetles (*Chrysolina* spp.) on St. Johnswort in California has resulted in effective control of that weed. This control measure is now in effect in several western states. Care needs to be exercised in the introduction and utilization of these enemies of weeds, because they may flourish not only on the weeds but also on closely related crop plants.

PASTURING

The maintenance of ditch rights-of-way involves considerable expense. Several methods are employed, the usual ones being mowing, cultivation, or use of herbicides. Mowing is only partially effective because many weeds scatter their seeds before mowing, and a second crop of seedstalks is sometimes produced by certain species that have the habit of sending out shoots close to the ground after mowing. Cultivation has the disadvantage of disturbing and modifying the surface and grade of roads and ditchbanks.

On the Rio Grande Reclamation Project, the fencing of ditch rights-of-way for pasture has been tried on a large scale (Bainbridge, 1939). There are reports on the efficiency and costs of these demonstration fences. The first such fence was established near Clint, Texas; here, grazing bindweed with sheep for two years kept the weed well under control. In 1938, a total of 19 miles of laterals was fenced, enclosing sufficient pasture for about one thousand sheep. The fences were of wood posts, set 1 rod apart, with one intermediate stay.

Pasturing is useful in combination with other practices in controlling certain weeds. For example, in the control of perennial sowthistle, a fairly good practice is to plow the infestation and turn sheep on the summer fallow. Goats have been found fairly effective in the control of brush and certain herbaceous weeds. In New Zealand, goats have given good control of the blackberry. Tansymustard is successfully controlled in the northwest United States by pasturing sheep. Although regarded as a poisonous plant, it affects sheep less than cattle and horses.

CHEMICAL WEED CONTROL

Research during the past five decades has brought increased knowledge and new chemicals for use in the control of weeds. At present, there are few weed problems in which chemicals cannot aid, and the feasibility of their use depends largely upon the relative costs and benefits of the treatment. Herbicides are now used on a large scale, and they may be indispensable for controlling small initial infestations and for cleaning up the last few plants after tillage or cropping methods have been used. The costs of preventive weed control should be charged against the total acreage endangered and not against the infested areas alone.

A classification of herbicides is given in Chapter 9. There are two main groups of these chemicals: selective and nonselective.

SELECTIVE HERBICIDES

These are chemicals that, when applied to a mixed population of plants, will severely injure or kill certain species with little or no injury to others. Advantage is taken of this selectivity in the control of weeds in many crops. A notable example of a selective herbicide is 2,4-dichlorophenoxyacetic acid (2,4-D), a chemical, applied as a spray to the foliage, that destroys wild mustards and other broadleaf weeds in cereal crops without serious injury to the cereals. Another selective herbicide of very extensive use is atrazine. In contrast to 2,4-D this chemical is applied to the soil for absorption by the roots. It tends to remain confined to the shallow topsoil in which weed seeds germinate; it is used in maize, sorghum, sugar cane, and similar crops. Selective herbicides are now available which are useful on a great variety of crops, such as small cereals (including rice) (Fig. 6–4), cotton (Fig. 6–5), soybeans, corn, sugar cane, sorghum, flax, peas, alfalfa, turf, carrots and other members of the Umbelliferae, onions, garlic, and a number of other species. These may also be used on pasture and range lands (Fig. 4–2).

NONSELECTIVE HERBICIDES

These are chemicals, applied either to the foliage or to the soil, that kill all growth regardless of the species of plants. Common examples are arsenicals, chlorates, oils, carbon disulfide, and boron compounds.

Both selective and nonselective herbicides consist of two main groups: (1) those applied to the foliage, either as a spray, dust, or granules and (2) those applied in similar forms to the soil, thus coming

FIGURE 6-4.   Selective control of wild oats in wheat with barban. Wild oats are in the check strip in the center; the sprayed strips are on each side.

in contact with the roots. These last are commonly spoken of as "soil treatments." Herbicides applied to the foliage are of two types: (1) those that kill only the tissues with which they come in contact and (2) those that are absorbed by the foliage, enter the conducting tissues, and are *translocated* to other parts of the plant.

The contact herbicides include such materials as certain petroleum oils, dinitrophenols, solutions of strong acids or bases, and solutions of such salts as sodium arsenite, sodium chlorate, ammonium thiocyanate, ammonium sulfamate, dinitro compounds, diquat, and paraquat.

The principal translocated herbicides are 2,4-dichlorophenoxyacetic acid (2,4-D), 2,4,5-trichlorophenoxyacetic acid (2,4,5-T), and their analogues, amitrole, dalapon, maleic hydrazide, 2,3,6-TBA, dicamba, picloram, and glyphosate; these compounds are all applied as foliar sprays and they penetrate the leaves and translocate in the phloem.

Examples of selective herbicides, used in 1961, applied to the soil and absorbed by the roots were 2,4-D, isopropyl phenylcarbamate (IPC), isopropyl chlorophenylcarbamate (CIPC), salts of trichloroa-

FIGURE 6-5. Preemergence control of weeds in cotton with Premerge. Twelve-inch bands over the rows were sprayed.

cetic acid (TCA), sodium pentachlorophenate (NaPCP), dinitrosec-butylphenol (DNBP), α-chloroacetamides, dithiocarbamates, substituted urea compounds, symmetrical triazines, chlorinated benzoic acids, and amiben. A decade later there were almost a hundred selective herbicides used in this way. They are listed in Appendix Table 1.

Nonselective herbicides applied as soil treatments are usually spoken of as "soil sterilants." They include such chemicals as carbon disulfide, chloropicrin, methyl bromide, ammonium sulfamate, arsenicals, boron compounds, chlorates, substituted ureas, and symmetrical triazines at proper dosage rates; since 1961 this list has grown to include about thirty compounds.

REFERENCES

Bainbridge, A. W. 1939. Fencing ditch-rights-of-way for pasture to control noxious weeds. *Reclam. Era.* 29:78–79. U.S. Bureau of Reclamation.

Durrell, L. W. 1929. Weed control in Colorado. *Colo. Agr. Expt. Sta. Rpt.* 1928:22–24.

Holm, LeRoy. 1971. The role of weeds in human affairs. *Weed Sci.* 19:485–490.

Lonsdale, T. W. 1935. Eradication of gorse and the utilization of gorse-infested lands. *New Zeal. Jour. Agr.* 50:235–236.

Norris, R. F. 1973. Winter weed control in alfalfa—shattering the myth. *Calif. Weed Conf. 25th Annual.* Anaheim, Calif., p. 105.

Pavlychenko, T. 1942. The place of crested wheat grass in controlling perennial weeds. *Univ. Saskatchewan Agr. Ext. Bul.* 109, 4 pp.

Sampson, Arthur W., and Kenneth W. Parker. 1930. St. Johnswort on range lands of California. *Calif. Agr. Expt. Sta. Bul.* 503:148.

Timmons, F. L. 1941. Results of bindweed control experiments at the Fort Hays Branch Station, Hays, Kansas, 1935 to 1940. *Kans. Agr. Expt. Sta. Bul.* 296:1–50.

7

The Role of Tillage in Weed Control

On arable land, tillage alone or in combination with cropping, and under some conditions with chemical treatment, may be the most economical method of weed control. The grower who consistently follows good farming practices usually has little trouble with weeds. In addition to weed destruction, tillage plays an important role in good farming, in seedbed preparation, trash incorporation, land preparation for irrigation and bed planting.

In contrast with recommendations of a decade or two ago, two aspects of tillage practice need stressing today. As a result of current agricultural research, it is becoming evident that manipulation of soil may be deleterious to soil structure, particularly when the soil moisture is around field capacity or above. Repeated stirring of the soil, as in weed control, often results in the formation of an impervious cultivator pan. The frequent and continuous use of heavy machinery on soils may bring about a compacted condition that restricts movement of air and water. These effects are particularly serious in irrigated regions, in regions where soils are not frozen during winter, and in heavy soils. Frequent cultivation for weed control or any other purpose contributes to this condition.

Because the principal virtue of cultivation of row crops is weed control (Cates and Cox, 1912), any method for handling weeds that minimizes or eliminates tillage is advantageous from the standpoint of soil structure. On the other hand, a well-prepared seedbed seeded to a row crop is subject to crusting if heavy precipitation is followed by hot sunshine, and the resultant impervious surface layer may so restrict gaseous exchange as to reduce crop growth.

When Swanson and Jacobson (1952) studied the relative effects of controlling weeds by (1) preemergence 2,4-D treatment alone, (2) preemergence 2,4-D treatment plus one cultivation, (3) scraping to give a minimum disturbance of the soil surface, and (4) the normal three cultivations used in growing corn, they found a positive effect of tillage on corn yield. Under their experimental conditions involving heavy rainfall after planting and hot, drying sun later, the soil formed a heavy crust with clogged pore spaces and reducing conditions in the root zone. Nitrate analyses proved that the crusted soil condition resulted in less nitrification, and penetrometer measurements proved that 78 percent more force was required to break through the 2 surface inches of soil in the untilled plots. Swanson and Jacobson point out that this is not proof of the need for tillage under all conditions but that, when heavy crusting occurs, corn yield will respond to cultivation that breaks up the surface layer and allows free gaseous exchange.

Under conditions where herbicides will control weeds throughout the growing season by eliminating the need for frequent tillage, they are beneficial in maintaining favorable conditions of culture without injuring soil structure. However, the balance may not all be on the side of chemicals, for some of these may themselves alter soil structure, some may leave toxic residues, and all entail a certain expense. Obviously there are a number of things to consider, and sound management involves balancing out the various interacting factors. Often tillage methods of weed control are the least expensive; under some conditions, they may be the least harmful to the soil; and under all conditions of cropping, some manipulation of the soil is necessary. The actual amount involved in tillage weed control may be inconsequential in consideration of the total tillage required, and hence this method may prove to be by far the most economical. Furthermore some of the chemicals employed in weed control today have not been in use long enough to have been proved entirely harmless to the soil. Hence, in any cropping practice, the various factors of tillage as related to compaction, erosion, and soil depletion should be balanced against the convenience, cost, and possible residual properties of chemicals in arriving at a management program. Crop rotation, green manuring, deep tillage, dry plowing, trash incorporation, and other practices may be used to counteract the compacting effects of cultivation for weed control. And when soil incorporation of chemicals becomes more widely used, as present trends seem to indicate, these same processes may be useful to counteract the effects that chemical weed control may have on soil structure.

A current trend in tillage tools is the increased use of supplementary power for more complete manipulation of the soil. Power take-off attachments are being used on cultivators, soil-incorporation tools, and various soil-working machinery. Wherever these are used on moist soils, there is the ever-present hazard of structure deterioration. A true philosophy of soil conservation should consider these effects along with erosion and depletion, for they are going on in our most productive soils. In considering tillage methods of weed control, soil condition and the effects of tillage should always be kept in mind. Where deterioration of soil structure has already occurred, use of chemicals should be considered along with crop rotation and other management practices.

One method for minimizing soil manipulation in row-crop agriculture is strip processing. This involves working plowed land in narrow strips for making the seedbed, leaving the root bed between the rows for minimum tillage or chemical treatment. In strip processing a narrow band of soil 8 in. wide and 5 to 7 in. deep is prepared for seeding, using a rotary hoe. Since many row crops demand a good seedbed only during germination and early seedling growth, this narrow band suffices until the crop is established; then weeds are controlled by minimum shallow tillage or by chemicals.

Strip processing has a number of valuable features: it is effective in moisture conservation and minimizes erosion losses; it is economical, saving from $3 to $6 per acre in seedbed preparation; it uses less machinery during peak-load seasons as during planting; and it requires smaller and less elaborate machinery (Ryder, 1961).

Finally the effects of cultivator damage to plants deserves consideration. Zopf (1955) points out that deep tillage may cause sufficient root damage to reduce yields. He recommends a 1-in. depth of tillage in beans, for the plants recover from this slight amount of damage (Fig. 7-1). It must be kept in mind, however, that this practice is feasible only to control small, annual weeds. Against perennial weeds such shallow tillage soon forms a cultivator pan, and the tool may ride on top of the vegetation and fail to sever the tops from the roots.

TYPES OF TILLAGE MACHINERY

The principal kinds of tillage machinery are: (1) the *plow*: moldboard, disc, one-way disc, lister, and buster; (2) the *harrow*: disc, spiketooth, spring-tooth, clod crusher, and packer; and (3) the *cultivator*: shovel, duckfoot (Fig. 7-2), blade, rotary hoe, finger weeder (Fig. 7-3A), thinner-weeder (Fig. 7-3B), rod weeder, bull tongue, spike, etc. Each of these three types of machinery has definite uses in weed control. The species of weed, the nature of its root system or underground stem system, its age, the crop, the soil in which it occurs, and the degree of infestation are all factors that must be considered in choosing the tillage implements that will be most effective in weed control.

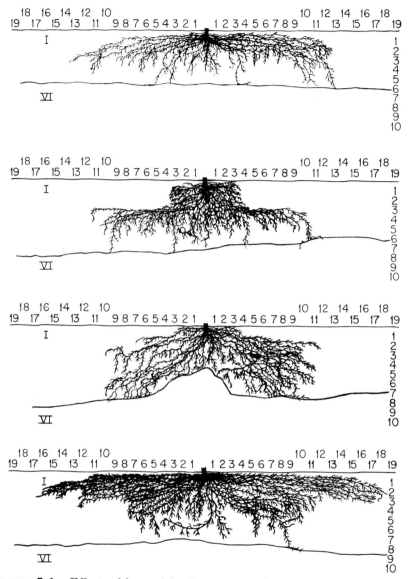

FIGURE 7-1. Effects of deep cultivation on roots of bean plants. A. Bean roots before tillage: B. Roots after tillage to 3-inch depth to an 8-inch bed row; C. Slow recovery of the root system; D. Fine root distribution. Had the practice used in B been continued the roots would have been permanently damaged.

The duckfoot cultivator is the one most commonly used in the control of perennial weeds. Its sweeps are usually from 10 to 15 in. in width; however, sweeps of 24 to 39 in. are in use. With the wider sweep, there seems to be less tendency to choke. However, an objection to wide sweeps is that they leave the ground alternately furrowed and ridged. Regrowth of weeds makes its appearance in the furrows several days ahead of growth on the ridges. The straight-blade type of weeder is also popular as a weed-control implement. Repeated use of the blade weeder often results in successively shallower cultivations and forma-

FIGURE 7-2. Modern, tractor-drawn cultivators equipped with duckfeet of a type used in Kansas to combat field bindweed. (Photograph courtesy of American Society of Agricultural Engineers.)

tion of a sole. The rotary rod weeder, although used to some extent, often proves unsatisfactory because of excessive packing of the soil, especially if it is heavy. As a result, each successive working with the rotary rod weeder, as with the blade type, is necessarily shallower, and after two or three cultivations, summer plowing is necessary. As a result, the ground is left cloddy, and weeds are induced into a state of dormancy. The V-blade weeder is especially adapted to heavy soils. It has two blades, set at an angle, and the total cut is usually from 6 to 10 ft. All tillage implements should be in good order, i.e., sharp and properly adjusted.

Special types of weeders adapted to unique crop-weed situations can be found wherever row crops are raised. One such machine, a special finger weeder, is used by celery growers in the lake states and along the eastern seaboard. This machine consists of sets of flexible

FIGURE 7-3. Top: Finger weeder, a machine for taking small weeds out of sugar beets and similar crops. (Photograph courtesy Raymond Olney, American Society of Agricultural Engineers.) Bottom: A four-row thinner and weeder used in modern, mechanized, sugar-beet production. (Photograph from the Great Western Sugar Co.)

coil-spring fingers attached to cones, pitched so that the fingers in contacting the soil cause the cones to rotate. The coils are specially tempered to be stiff enough to work the soil yet flexible enough to avoid injuring crop plants. The cones are mounted in pairs, one on each side of the crop row with the fingers crossing slightly in the row. Thus the fingers reach into the row, stirring the surface soil and uprooting the young weeds.

These rotating units can be mounted on the cultivator bar of a tractor. Tandem units are used where soil conditions are difficult. In these the front cone has stiff fingers angled to break crust, and the rear or weeder cone has two types of fingers—a few are steeply angled to cause rotation by friction with the soil, the rest are limber and bent so that they sweep the soil surface and uproot the weeds. Many different arrangements can be designed to take care of different crop-weed-soil situations.

The development of precision seeding and tillage instruments allows tillage within 1 inch of standing crop plants. When the crop plants attain heights above 6 inches, soil can be thrown into the drill row covering small weed seedlings.

Special methods for controlling certain weeds will be described in later chapters. Here it will serve our purpose to discuss tillage in weed control sufficiently to emphasize its effectiveness, usefulness, and practicability.

INFLUENCE OF TILLAGE UPON THE WEED-SEED POPULATION OF THE SOIL

Brenchley and Warington (1930, 1933, 1936) studied the influence of cultivation methods on the weed-seed population of soil cropped for many successive years to fall-sown wheat. These studies showed that tillage, designed to reduce weed-seed populations in soils, must be carried out more frequently than usual and that reduction of many weeds can be brought about more economically by intensified cultivation while the land is in crop than by tillage between crops. Their studies showed that weeds differ greatly in their ability to reseed the soil, that the type of crop grown largely determines the weed-seed population of the soil, and that reduction of weed seeds in a soil requires growing of a crop in which weed seedlings may be destroyed by frequent tillage operations to prevent reseeding. Finally, dormancy of weed seeds must be taken into account in determining depth and timing of tillage.

In regions lacking summer rainfall, intercrop tillage is even less effective. When one considers the longevity of buried weed seeds, weed-seed dormancy, the possible presence of weeds that produce wind-borne seeds, and the common neglect of weed control along fences, roadsides, and other uncropped areas, it seems that tillage control of weed-seed populations in soil is quite futile under most cropping systems.

CONTROL OF ANNUAL WEEDS BY TILLAGE

In many cases, some form of tillage is the most practical method of combating annual (and biennial) weeds. Generally speaking, tillage to control such weeds should be shallow rather than deep; the aim is not only to destroy all top growth with a minimum of labor but to keep weed seeds near the soil surface, where conditions are suitable for germination. However, it must be kept in mind that many seeds have a period of natural dormancy during which they will not germinate, even though put under suitable conditions. Deep plowing, with the resultant effect of burying seeds, merely delays seed germination. It has been determined that aeration of the soil by tillage encourages germination of dormant seeds. Tillage to control annuals should begin as early in spring as possible and continue until a crop is planted. By each stirring of the soil, weed seeds are induced to sprout, and those already sprouted are destroyed. Moreover, after the crop is removed in the fall, surface tillage should follow promptly. It is good practice to disc or harrow grain stubble in order to encourage fall germination of weed seeds. Under dry-farming conditions, this is particularly desirable. In Manitoba, a most successful method of combating Russian thistle consists of double-disking the grain stubble immediately behind the binder.

As regards time and frequency of tillage, consideration must be given to germination habits of various weed species. For example, certain species show maximum seed germination in the autumn, others in the spring and early summer, whereas others show no marked regular periodicity of seed germination; i.e., they germinate freely throughout the year.

In regions where the climate is mild, there are many weed species that produce seed late in the fall and very early in the spring and often at a time when the soil is too wet to till. Among these weeds are shepherdspurse, groundsel, sandwort, Byzantine speedwell, and annual bluegrass. Consequently, such species may maintain a high seed population in the soil, unless they are destroyed by chemicals before maturing seed. Application may be by air when soils are too wet for ground treatment.

BLIND TILLAGE

The tillage of the soil after seeding a crop, either before the crop plants are up or while they are in the early stages of growth, is known as "blind tillage." It is a method extensively employed to combat weeds both in row crops and in cereals.

Many types of flexible harrows have been built to carry out blind tillage of crops, especially small grains and corn. Tillage, using various types of harrows, is done as soon as weeds appear, even though seedlings of crop plants are not above the ground, and is repeated as may be necessary until the plants are well advanced. Drottij (1929) showed that one harrowing to control weeds in cereals resulted in an average increase of about 8 percent in grain yield as compared with no treatment. A second harrowing gave an additional increase of about 3 percent. If the original stand of cereals is sparse or the crop is too far advanced, harrowing may result in a noticeable decrease in yield.

In the Columbia River Basin, wild mustard in fall-sown wheat is successfully combated by repeated harrowing in the spring.

The rotary hoe and the spike-tooth harrow have been employed with success in the control of weeds in young corn, cotton, and other row crops. The first cultivation is usually about two weeks after seeding, whether the crop is up or not. This cultivation, in most cases, is a harrowing across the rows.

Peters, Klingman, and Larson (1959) used combinations of rotary hoeing with herbicides and other types of cultivation in attempts to mechanize weed control in soybeans. Rotary hoeing generally increased yields of soybeans over checks. Hoeing while weeds were small was superior to later treatment. Pigweeds and crabgrass were the weeds in these plots, and both were reduced in number and vigor by rotary hoeing. Hoeing while the soil was still moist was not harmful to the soybeans and allowed the operation to be done while weeds were small. The workers concluded that rotary hoeing was only moderately effective.

Amiben, dinoseb, 2,4-DB, tolban, diphenamid, tenoran, treflan, planavin, vernam, and many mixed formulations are now used and tillage is minimized in soybean culture.

CONTROL OF PERENNIAL WEEDS BY TILLAGE

The effectiveness of cultivation as a practical method of perennial weed control may be judged by the fact that in Idaho, in 1941, the perennial weeds on about 40,000 acres of land either were eradicated or were under a cultivation program, and that after two years of cultivation, 90 percent of the land was turned back to crops. In Kansas and other states, large acreages of land infested with field bindweed have been successfully cleared by tillage alone. Most farmers have been able to free their land of the pest by tillage through two growing seasons; some have required a third season.

Methods vary, depending upon the weed species, the age of the infestation, physical characters of the soil, soil fertility, and depth of soil to the water table. For example, field bindweed and lens-podded hoary cress are more resistant to cultivation than Canada thistle and Russian knapweed. Old infestations are more resistant than young ones. In lighter soil types, it usually requires a longer time to eradicate perennials by cultivation than in heavier and tighter soils, possibly because the roots penetrate deeper. As a rule, in a fertile soil in which there is vigorous regrowth after cultivation with resultant exhaustion of root reserves, eradication requires a shorter time than in a nonfertile soil. In shallow soils or in those with a high water table, the time required to effect eradication is less than in a deep soil or in one with a low water table. Details of these methods will be given in the sections dealing with specific weeds and crops.

In the irrigated sections of Wyoming and other Rocky Mountain states, field bindweed, Russian knapweed, hoary cress, and Canada thistle are controlled by continuous alternate deep plowing and cultivation. Plowing at a depth of 8 to 10 in. is started in the spring, followed by cultivation at a depth of 4 to 6 in. at intervals of 10 to 15 days for the balance of the summer. The last operation in the fall is a deep plowing. If the ground is dry, it appears that irrigation is advisable to encourage resprouting and to facilitate the deterioration of roots during the winter season. The second season, the first operation is cultivation, followed by deep plowing in midsummer. This may complete the eradication in the case of Canada thistle, but with more stubborn weeds, such as field bindweed, hoary cress, and Russian knapweed, it may be necessary to continue the cultivations for several more seasons. It is important to follow the cultivations with a row crop in order to destroy seedlings and straggling plants that may grow from roots or rootstocks that have survived.

In Saskatchewan, perennial sowthistle has been completely eradicated by tillage methods. The operations are as follows: (1) plowing to a depth not greater than 3 or 4 in. during the middle of June, followed immediately by the harrow or disc, and (2) shallow cultivation during the next 12 weeks to keep the soil free from top growth. These methods are described as bringing about the death of sowthistle roots in one season, regardless of their depth of penetration. The foregoing procedure gives equally good results with quackgrass.

In western Canada and in the western United States, Canada thistle is eradicated by one season (or at most, two seasons) of tillage, provided the work starts not earlier than the blooming stage and continues until the soil is frozen. However, in western Canada, such weeds as hoary cress, leafy spurge, Russian knapweed, field bindweed, and povertyweed cannot be eradicated by one season of cultivation.

Derscheid, Nash, and Wicks (1961) investigated the relations between cultivation, cropping, and chemicals in the control of Canada thistle and perennial sowthistle in South Dakota. They found that intensive cultivation with a duckfoot or a one-way disc to a 4-in. depth at 4-week intervals or double coverage with a tandem disc harrow at 2-week intervals eliminates over 99 percent of both thistle species in 1 year. A season of intensive cultivation followed by a late summer seeding of alfalfa or bromegrass eliminates 95 to 100 percent of the thistles in 2 years. When good grass stands are maintained, application of 2,4-D or MCPA may help. Canada thistle and perennial sowthistle proved much less difficult to eliminate than leafy spurge or Russian knapweed and somewhat less difficult than field bindweed.

TILLAGE IN ITS RELATION TO ROOT RESERVES OF PERENNIAL WEEDS

Tillage as a method of controlling field bindweed has been the subject of investigations at the following stations: Hays, Kansas; Lamberton, Minnesota; Genesee, Idaho; Cherokee and Hawarden, Iowa; and York, Nebraska. These were uniform, cooperative experiments [U.S. Bureau of Plant Industry (1939) and various state agricultural experiment stations] involving a number of variables, including time of beginning and frequency of cultivation.

The usual practice in combating deep-rooted perennials by tillage was to cut the plant below the soil surface with a weed knife just as soon as any growth appeared above ground. The theory was that the new green growth, unless destroyed, would immediately manufacture food which would then move into the roots and rootstocks underground, increasing the store of reserve. Upon this principle, the farmer was usually advised to cultivate the infested area at least once a week for 2 or more years.

According to studies with field bindweed at the several stations given above, such frequent cultivations are not only unnecessary but undesirable. During the first 8 to 14 days after emergence of the new shoots, these shoots use more food reserves than they manufacture; in other words, there is a movement of foods upward from the roots. Consequently, if cultivation is postponed and if the new growth is allowed to develop for several days, the plant tends to exhaust itself of reserves instead of adding to them during this period. The practical application of this principle in a tillage program is that it materially reduces the number of cultivations necessary to effect eradication. For example, Timmons (1941) reports that at Hays, Kansas, "cultivation 12 days after each emergence eliminated bindweed with 16½ operations as an average of seven experiments, compared with 33 cultivations when cultivated immediately after they emerged, which until recently has been the commonly accepted practice."

SEASONAL TREND OF ROOT RESERVES IN FIELD BINDWEED

The general plan of the experiments cited involved the use of bindweed plots in pairs, one of which was tilled at first emergence of shoots in the spring and at intervals after each subsequent emergence, the other of which was left undisturbed during the entire season. Root samples were taken periodically from each plot at various depths and analyzed to determine total sugars, starch equivalent, "readily available" carbohydrates (total sugars plus starch equivalent), dry weight in grams per cubic foot of soil, and percentage of dry matter.

At Hays, Kansas, in 1936, where samples were taken every 2 weeks throughout the growing season at a depth of 6 to 18 in. in the undisturbed plots, the percentage of readily available carbohydrates on Apr. 15, the date of first sampling, was 15.01; during the next 2 weeks, this dropped to 8.23 percent, after which there was a rise to 29.48 percent on June 15, when the first seed matured; the trend was gradually downward, reaching 20.36 percent Sept. 15; fall showers started growth, and by Nov. 2, the readily available carbohydrates had reached 28.64 percent. In the plots cultivated every 2 weeks, the reserves decreased steadily from 19.44 percent on Apr. 15 to 4.66 percent on July 15, after which no more analyses were made because of insufficient material. As an average for the years 1935 to 1940, in the plots cultivated every 2 weeks, the reserves decreased steadily from about 22 percent on Apr. 15 to about 6 percent on July 1, after which they remained the same until the end of the growing season.

At Lamberton, Minnesota, in 1937, on undisturbed plots, readily available carbohydrates on May 10 were 19.59 percent; there was a sharp drop to 11.03 percent by May 26; then followed a rise to 30.85 percent on July 23, after which there was only slight decrease. On plots cultivated every 2 weeks, there was a decrease from 14.57 percent on May 10 to 9.29 percent on Aug. 18, after which there was a marked increase. Apparently this rise at the end of the season was due to movement of food reserves from roots at greater depths, since there were no tops on the plants to provide carbohydrates.

At other stations where the seasonal trend of root reserves in field bindweed was determined, the general trends were similar to those cited above. It is obvious that a single season of frequent cultivations reduces the reserves in the roots, even to the extent of causing starvation. For example, at Hays, Kansas, by the end of one season, 95 percent, on the average, of the roots in the 18 surface inches of soil had died.

Trend of Root Reserves in Field Bindweed after Cultivation

If we know how soon, after the top growth is removed, the field bindweed ceases to use root reserves and begins to store them, we can tell if it is better to allow no top growth to appear above ground or to permit the plant to make some regrowth before cultivation. In the various cooperative experiments, there were three series of plots: (1) those that were cultivated or plowed early at first emergence of shoots, (2) those so treated from July 1 to 15, and (3) those so treated about Aug. 15. There was no cultivation of the plots after the initial treatment, but root samples were taken at six intervals, 4 days apart. At each station, the trend of readily available carbohydrates in the roots was downward and continued downward a number of days after regrowth. In other words, food reserves in the root did not start to increase immediately following the development of green growth, indicating that there is a period, variable in length after emergence, when root reserves move upward. In the plots plowed early, the interval between cultivation and the time when root reserves reached the lowest point varied from 18 to 25 days; in the summer series, from 20 to 29 days; and in the fall series, from 9 to 32 days. The average results for the years 1935 to 1940 at Hays, Kansas, show that from "about 16 days after first emergence (24 days after cultivation) bindweed is able to produce not only the carbohydrates needed for growth but also a considerable surplus which is stored in the roots for future use" (Timmons, 1941).

TIME OF BEGINNING CULTIVATION OF FIELD BINDWEED

In the field bindweed experiments described above, plots were established in which the variable was the stage of growth when cultivation began, as follows: at first emergence in spring; on the first (approximately) of May, June, July, August, and September; and at blooming time, which is usually between June 1 and July 1. On each series of plots, cultivations were made at frequent intervals throughout the remainder of the season and during subsequent seasons until the plants were killed. At certain stations, namely, Hays, Lamberton, York, and Genesee, tillage which began soon after emergence (within 2 or 3 weeks) in the spring gave a higher percentage of kill than tillage started later in the season. It will be recalled from the studies of root-reserve trends that these reserves are at a low point about 2 weeks after emergence; thus the best results follow when the first cultivation coincides with this condition of the plant. It was found that at Hays, Kansas, 1 year of fallow, begun in May or June, usually gave an almost complete kill at the end of the first season; but at Lamberton, Minnesota, it was necessary to extend the cultivations well into the second season; and, at York, Nebraska, 3 years of tillage were required to effect eradication. At Davis, California, in a deep alluvial soil and with dry summers, a cultivation program carried on for 5 years failed to eradicate old field bindweed plants.

Frequency of Cultivation of Field Bindweed

In the uniform cooperative experiments, two series of plots were established: (1) plowing at first emergence in the spring, and (2) plowing immediately after grain harvest. In each series, the intervals between cultivations were 4, 8, 12, and 16 days after emergence of new shoots. Cultivations were continued into subsequent years if necessary to complete a kill. At Hays and Lamberton, cultivation 16 days after emergence gave as good results as at any shorter intervals; at York, cultivations 8 days after emergence were slightly the best; and at Genesee, the 12-day interval after emergence was superior to others. The number of cultivations required to give eradication will vary, inasmuch as under different soil and climatic conditions the time of emergence differs.

Other Studies of Root Reserves in Perennial Weeds

The studies of organic reserves in the roots of field bindweed by Barr (1940) point to the same general conclusions as those given above. He says, "The data showed that cultivating at emergence had essentially no greater effect than the less frequent cultivations in reducing the carbohydrate content of bindweed roots in the top foot of soil."

Arny (1932) determined the organic reserves of five perennial weeds: quackgrass, leafy spurge, Austrian fieldcress, perennial sowthistle, and Canada thistle. Variation in the percentages of total readily available carbohydrates based on dry weight in the underground parts of these weeds was observed. In Austrian fieldcress and leafy spurge, readily available carbohydrates reached a low point during the latter part of April and first part of May; those of perennial sowthistle and Canada thistle reached a low point somewhat later, about the latter part of June or the first part of July. It is significant that the low point in these reserves coincides with the beginning bloom stage of these four weeds. In quackgrass, carbohydrate reserves reached a low point the latter part of June. Arny suggests that "starting eradication operations against these weeds as they reach the beginning bloom stage appears to be an opportune time so far as readily available carbohydrates are concerned."

Welton, Morris, and Hartzler (1929), in their study of food reserves of Canada thistle, found that organic reserves stored underground reached a minimum about June 1, after which they gradually increased until the end of the season.

REFERENCES

Arny, A. C. 1932. Variations in the organic reserves in underground parts of five perennial weeds from late April to November. *Minn. Agr. Expt. Sta. Tech. Bul.* 84:1–28.

Barr, C. G. 1940. Organic reserves in the roots of bindweed. *Jour. Agr. Res.* 60:391–413.

Brenchley, Winifred E., and Katherine Warington. 1930. The weed seed population of arable soil. I. Numerical estimate of viable seeds and observations on their natural dormancy. *Jour. Ecol.* 18:235–272.

———— and ————. 1933. The weed seed population of arable soil. II. Influence of crop, soil, and methods of cultivation upon the relative abundance of viable seeds. *Jour. Ecol.* 21:103–127.

———— and ————. 1936. The weed seed population of arable soil. III. The re-establishment of weed species after reduction by fallowing. *Jour. Ecol.* 24:479–501.

Cates, J. S., and H. R. Cox. 1912. The weed factor in the cultivation of corn. *U. S. Dept. Agr. Bur. Plant Indus. Bul.* 257:1–35.

Derscheid, L. A., R. L. Nash, and G. A. Wicks. 1961. Thistle control with cultivation, cropping, and chemicals. *Weeds* 9(1):90–102.

Drottij, S. 1929. Harrowing to control weeds in cereals. *Centralanst. för Försöksv. Jordbruksomradet Meddel.* 348:1–23.

Peters, E. J., D. L. Klingman, and R. E. Larson. 1959. Rotary hoeing in combination with herbicides and other cultivations for weed control in soybeans. *Weeds* 7(4):449–458.

Ryder, G. J. 1961. A new tillage short cut. *Agr. Leaders' Digest* 42(4):14–15.

Swanson, C. L. W., and H. G. M. Jacobson. 1952. Herbicides: a new tool for use in studying soil physical properties affecting crop growth. *Weeds* 1(2):174–184.

Timmons, F. L. 1941. Results of bindweed control experiments at the Fort Hays Branch Station, Hays, Kansas, 1935 to 1940. *Kans. Agr. Expt. Sat. Bul.* 296:1–50.

Welton, F. A., V. H. Morris, and A. J. Hartzler. 1929. Organic food reserves in relation to the eradication of Canada thistles. *Ohio Agr. Expt. Sta. Bul.* 441:1–25.

Zopf, P. E., Jr. 1955. Shallow cultivation found best for beans: Florida tests indicate deep cultivation cuts yields in half. *Market Growers Jour.*, November.

8

Biological Weed Control

With the increasing interest in conserving our environment and the apprehension concerning pollution by pesticides, biological control of pests is getting increased support and research efforts are being expanded.

Though the biological control of plants by insects and plant diseases is a natural process that has been going on since the origin of land plants, the conscious use of the method by man to control weed pests is of fairly recent origin. The natural processes of biological control are part of the process of evolution, and the results are reflected in the balance between plant and animal species characteristic of any endemic population. The successful use of biological control for suppression of weeds, on the other hand, depends upon at least two acts of man that in a sense might be termed artificial or unnatural: (1) The weed species, to submit successfully to biological control, must have been introduced and in the process of introduction to have been freed of its natural predators. (2) Natural predators on the weeds must be introduced, but the predators, in turn, must have been freed of parasites so that they can carry out their destruction unhampered by their natural enemies (Tillyard, 1928).

These two requirements presuppose that there is, in the native habitat of the weeds, an insect that successfully controls the weed; that this insect will thrive in the new habitat of the weed; that it can be introduced into the new habitat free of native predators; and that it will not be subject to control by new predators native to the new habitat. Furthermore, this insect must be highly specialized so that it is unable to thrive and multiply on agricultural plants of the new

140

habitat. It is known that root borers, stem borers, and internal seed or fruit feeders are more highly specialized than leaf or foliage feeders. For this reason these types of insects have been preferred for biological weed control. However, experience has proved that leaf and stem feeders can be highly selective and that they may be much more effective in destroying weed pests than are the more specialized insects. This is certainly true in the case of *Chrysolina gemellata*, the insect that has been so successful in controlling *Hypericum perforatum*.

In order to prove the limited feeding habits of an insect, careful feeding tests ("starvation tests") must be carried on before it is released in a new locality. Only after all important crop plants of the new habitat have been refused by the insect is it deemed safe to release it for weed-control purposes. Both weed and insect populations may fluctuate for some time after the introduction of an insect, and several years may be required before equilibrium is attained. Complete eradication is impossible by the biological method; the best result is an equilibrium in which the weed, though present, is no longer an economic pest.

Biological control of weeds was used initially only because other methods had failed. The reason for this limited use was the supposed danger that, following introduction, a plant-feeding insect might change its feeding habits and attack crop plants. The fact that no insect, among hundreds that have been introduced after testing, has changed its basic feeding habits and become a pest has largely dispelled this fear.

When effective, biological control by introduced natural predators is cheap, permanent, without need for successive expense, and does not add toxic pollutants to the environment.

Biological control of diverse types of weeds is being explored and a number of successes are on record. Perennial weeds of rangelands have yielded best to biological methods, but other possibilities include annuals in both range and croplands, weeds of forests, orchards, recreational and urban areas, rights-of-way, and waterways.

Biological control of weeds has, to date, been accomplished mainly by use of insects, but mites, snails, fish, ducks, geese, manatees, parasitic higher plants, and pathogenic microorganisms are under investigation. The use of geese to control weeds in cotton is popular in some areas in the South and West. This method requires fencing of the fields, control of "varmints," dogs, and, at times, thieves, and it is successful only where well managed. Management consists of acquiring the young geese soon after cotton-planting time, fencing in units that distribute the birds so that weeds are effectively controlled, arranging some supplemental feed, and disposing of the geese at the end of the season, usually after a period of pen feeding.

To be a good agent of biological control, an insect should have the ability to kill the target plant, or prevent its reproduction; it should have a high dispersability, a propensity for locating its host plant, adaptibility to the host plant and to its environment, and the capacity to reproduce at a rate sufficient to maintain control of its host. The question of climatic adaptation and the synchrony of living relations between insect and weed host are important. In equitable climates, problems of synchrony may not occur; in more temperate situations the insect must be adapted first to the climatic extremes, and secondly to the host plant itself so that synchrony exists. (Huffaker and Andres, 1970).

BIOLOGICAL CONTROL POLICY

Policy in biological control has been to introduce only species that, through prolonged and detailed testing, have proved safe. Since specialization in feeding is a deeply ingrained habit of an insect, there is little chance that this habit will change in a new location which, because it is promotive for the weed, does not represent a major change in environment. While starvation tests have played an important role in past introduction, current research is directed toward a more fundamental approach to establishing host-plant relationships.

Because the starvation tests used have the limitations that they do not establish a true degree of restriction in diet, that they cover only a small portion of the possible economic hosts, and that they tend to exaggerate the host range of an insect, the new approach is designed to establish insight into the basic host-plant relationship. Testing covers all aspects of the life cycle of the insect and it involves plants closely related to the specific hosts upon which the insect breeds. Thus it is possible to ascertain whether an insect is restricted to a single species in a genus, to a genus, to closely related genera, or to a plant family. The more closely confined is this feeding, the lesser the risk that the insect will attack some plant outside this range. However, the dietary range of some plant-eating insects may be associated with a particular chemical that may occur in several unrelated plant groups. For example a hawkmoth is known that feeds both on sweet potato (*Ipomoea batatas*) and yam (*Dioscorea* sp.), two plants widely separated taxonomically. Both of these plants contain tropane alkaloids. The cinnabar moth (*Tyria jacobaeae*) larvae parasitize *Senecio jacobaea*, tansy ragwort. Senecio alkaloids are found in one tribe of compositae (*Senecioneae*), one genus of Leguminosae (*Crotolaria*) and in *Boraginaceae*. Feeding of an insect attacking ragwort is not necessarily determined by these chemicals, but if there were a dependency, then all plants lacking these chemicals would be immune from attack. In this case *T. jacobaeae* would not attack *Crotolaria* species nor genera of

Boraginaceae. Although similar, the alkaloids in these plants are not identical with those in *Senecioneae* so the chemical might still be the determining factor. In such a case it would not be wise, on the basis of starvation tests on beans or peas, to assume an immunity in all legumes including *Crotalaria* (Huffaker and Andres, 1970).

From the above discussion it is evident that, although control of *Opuntia* species in Australia and of *Hypericum perforatum* in California, Australia, and Chile has been eminently successful, there is a calculated risk in introducing a predator into a new country; such policy decisions are always difficult. For example, a number of insects that are strictly confined to their weed hosts under field conditions feed on certain economic plants in laboratory tests. Their subsequent release, however, against their respective weed hosts in various countries has never resulted in their becoming pests. Examples include *Tyria jacobaeae, Microlarinus lareynii, M. lypriformis, Antholcus varinervis, Schematiza cordiae, Cactoblastis cactorum,* and *Mecas saturnina* (Huffaker and Andres, 1970).

EARLY ATTEMPTS AT BIOLOGICAL CONTROL OF WEEDS

The first attempt at biological control of a pest plant was carried out in the Hawaiian Islands (Perkins and Swezey, 1924). The prickly shrub *Lantana camara* had been introduced into the islands as an ornamental. Escaping from gardens, it spread to neighboring hill and pasturelands, but its increase might not have been so rapid had it not been for the introduction of two birds, the Chinese turtledove (*Turtur chinensis*) and the Indian myna (*Acridotheres tristis*), which fed on the fruits and rapidly carried the plant to new lands.

Introduced about 1860, by 1900 *Lantana* had spread throughout the Hawaiian Islands and occupied thousands of acres of land that had formerly afforded fine pasturage. Perkins and Swezey mention five insects observed on *Lantana* in 1902. Those were the caterpillars of *Plusia verticillata*, those of two tortricid moths, and the caterpillars of one or two species of the native *Scotorythra*. The scale insect *Orthezia insignis*, though adapted to many plants, was found to injure *Lantana* severely and in spite of warnings from entomologists was spread by ranchers in attempts to control the plant.

In 1902, Koebele, an entomologist from the Islands, visited Mexico, the native habitat of *Lantana,* and sent back some twenty-three species of insects which he found limited in their habits to this plant. Eight of these became established and by various means have so injured the plant and restricted its reproduction that large areas formerly infested have been recovered for pasturage or cropping use. The most effective of the introduced insects are the following: larvae of the tortricid moth *Crocidosema lantana*, which bore into flower stems, feed on receptacles of flower clusters, and eat flowers and fruits; larvae of the seed fly *Agromyza lantanae*, which eat many berries and cause others to dry so that birds do not eat and carry them; and larvae of lycaenid butterflies *Thecla echion* and *T. bazochi*, which destroy many flowers.

So effective are the introduced insects in controlling *Lantana* that, where the weed is cleared from the land for grazing or cropping purposes, it does not again take possession even if the land is abandoned. Instead of *Lantana*, several other species of shrubs and trees tend to come in, and unfortunately some of these are more difficult to control than *Lantana*.

Huffaker (1959), reviewing biological control of weeds with insects, mentions some nine additional insects that have been introduced and a tenth that is still to be introduced. With this additional help the control of *Lantana* should be assured.

Huffaker (1959) reports that *Lantana* has also been subject to control by insects in Fiji, India, and Australia. Several insects were introduced into Australia via Hawaii and Fiji in 1914 and 1917 and later in 1935; the lace bug *Teleonemia scrupulosa* was the most effective. Three additional Lepidoptera were cleared for release in 1957. This work is continuing.

CONTROL OF PRICKLY PEAR

The outstanding example of biological control of plants is that of prickly pear (*Opuntia* spp.) in Australia. Sweetman (1936) lists seven species that are considered pests in Australia: *O. inermis*, *O. stricta*, *O. aurantiaca*, *O. monacantha*, *O. streptacantha*, *O. imbricata*, and *O. tomentosa*. Introduced in the late eighteenth century and during the nineteenth century, these cactus species were gradually spread throughout the colonized portions of Australia, where they were used as potted plants and for hedges around the homesteads.

O. inermis spread over the greatest area and was considered the most serious pest. Introduced prior to 1839, it was planted from 1850 to 1875 for hedges or as a potential fodder plant in many places in Queensland and New South Wales. *O. stricta* was introduced about 1860, and it also was widely planted and later spread rapidly.

By 1870, the natural spread of cactus began to assume alarming proportions, and control measures were initiated. Reports from New South Wales indicate an active attempt at control by 1893, with considerable expenditures of money, and in 1895, it was listed among the noxious weeds of Queensland.

From 1900 on, the spread of prickly pear gained rapidly, and by 1925 the total acreage was estimated at 60 million, with an annual increase of about 1 million acres (Dodd, 1940). This represents an area of land approximately the size of the state of Oregon that was rendered uninhabitable with a yearly increment about four-fifths the size of Delaware. Since most of this land has an annual rainfall of from 20 to 30 in., it was practically all potentially arable, and its occupation by the pest plants represented an immense loss.

Mechanical methods of control, useful on small, scattered infestations in occupied land, could not be employed on this vast area, because it was largely overgrown with trees. Experiments on chemical control, established by the Queensland government at Dulacca in 1912, proved the usefulness of arsenic pentoxide or arsenic acid solutions. These poisons,, sprayed on the plants or injected into the cladodes, did kill the plants.

The chemical method at its best cost around £ 10 per acre, whereas the land in the unimproved state was worth only from 5 to 30 shillings. Obviously some less laborious and less expensive method was needed if this vast area of land was to be reclaimed for agricultural use.

Active work on biological control started in 1912 with the appointment by the Queensland government of a Prickly-pear Travelling Commission. This group, after visiting many countries in America where prickly pears were indigenous, recommended the introduction of insect pests to control them. In 1920, the Commonwealth government and the governments of New South Wales and Queensland formed the Commonwealth Prickly-pear Board, and active work was immediately initiated. Entomologists were sent to America in 1920, where work was continuously pursued until 1927. At the same time, a laboratory was set up at Sherwood, a suburb of Brisbane, to handle the receiving, testing, acclimatization, and dissemination of the insects.

Great care was exercised by the board to ensure that: (1) only insects restricted to cactus plants were imported into Australia, (2) these were freed of their parasites, and (3) under Australian conditions the introduced insects, even under starvation conditions, remained restricted in their feeding to prickly pear.

Of many insects introduced, some eight species were successfully acclimatized in the field to prey on the major pests, *O. inermis* and *O. stricta*. They are as follows: the moth borer *Cactoblastis cactorum* from Argentina; the moth borer *Olycella junctolineela* from the United States; the coreid bug *Chelinidea tabulata* from the United States; the coreid bug *C. vittiger* from the United States; the cochineal *Dactylopius opuntiae* from the United States; the cerambycid beetle *Moneilema ulkei* from the United States; the cerambycid beetle *M. variolare* from Mexico; and the red spider *Tetranychus opuntiae* from the United States. Some six other insects, pests of the less important prickly pear species, have also been successfully introduced and most of the species listed above also attack the other species with some success.

By 1924, five of the insects listed above had been established, and by the end of 1927 the coreid bug *Chelinidea tabulata*, the cochineal *Dactylopius opuntiae*, and the red spider *Tetranychus opuntiae* were distributed throughout the prickly pear territory and had increased to great numbers. Many of the denser infestations were being thinned out, and fruits were being destroyed in great numbers. Had only these above named insects been introduced, the prickly pear areas would have been greatly reduced and the work of the board justified.

CONTROL OF PRICKLY PEAR BY *Cactoblastis*

However, in 1925, the moth borer *Cactoblastis cactorum* was introduced from Argentina. This moth belongs to the phyticids, the most dominant group among the cactus insects, and upon its successful acclimatization, the campaign against prickly pear entered a new phase.

One shipment of 2,750 eggs of *C. cactorum* left Argentina in May, 1925, and arrived in Australia in the larval stage.

The first introductions into the field were made in 1926; rearing in cages was also continued until the end of 1927, by which time 9 million eggs had been distributed in the field. Mass distribution was started in 1928 and completed in 1930. By the middle of 1929, the insects in certain field centers had increased to the point where eggs could be collected directly in the field, and further distribution involving over 2 billion eggs was carried out from this source. A total of about 3 billion eggs was used in the whole operation.

It is evident that *C. cactorum* was eminently successful as a control agent on the major cactus pests. Two generations, on an average, are produced annually. The moths are free-flying and have been known to fly 10 miles. Winter is spent in the larval stage. The larvae, living almost entirely inside the cladodes in colonies of 20 to 100 individuals, tunnel through the plants, eventually destroy all portions aboveground, and even penetrate into the underground bulbs and roots (Fig. 8–1). They eat out the whole inside of young cladodes but leave the fibrous vascular tissues in older structures. However, their ravages allow entry of bacteria and fungi that complete destruction, and the combined attacks are highly successful, causing complete collapse of the plants under most conditions.

At times the larvae may leave one plant and wander for a few hours, entering at a new point and, during exceedingly hot weather, they may cluster on the lower sides of the cladodes. They emerge to pupate in debris, on fallen cladodes, or on the bark of trees and logs. The pupal stage lasts from 3 to 6 weeks.

FIGURE 8-1.   A. Left, initial entry of *Cactoblastis cactorum* into the cladode of *Opuntia* (prickly pear). Right, wilt and breakdown associated with feeding by *C. cactorum*. (Photographs by courtesy of J. K. Holloway.)
B. Left, cladode of *Opuntia* showing cocoons of *Cactoblastis cactorum*. Right, skeletonization of *Opuntia* by *C. cactorum*. The plants rapidly decay. (Photographs by courtesy of J. K. Holloway.)

DESTRUCTION OF THE DENSE PRICKLY PEAR AREAS

Following the first liberations of *C. cactorum* in 1926, the insects increased rapidly and spread from the points of liberation; in 15 months, the numbers had increased to several millions. By June, 1928, areas from a few up to 1,500 acres had collapsed, large numbers of insects were working, and a natural spread of 10 to 15 miles had taken place.

Mass distribution of eggs from 1928 to 1930 brought about a greatly accelerated rate of destruction, and during the years 1930 to 1932, vast areas throughout Queensland and northwest New South Wales were virtually freed of the pest. The last big area of dense infestation in Queensland was destroyed in 1933. The rapidity of the onslaught, the completeness of destruction, and the vast areas cleared stand out as the finest example of biological plant-pest control on record. Of the immense infestations that existed in 1925, 95 percent of those in Queensland and 75 percent of those of New South Wales had been destroyed 10 years later.

This immense destruction of the primary cactus infestations in Queensland and New South Wales resulted in an enormous drop in the population of *Cactoblastis* through starvation and was followed from 1931 to 1933 by a big wave of cactus regrowth. This second growth occurred in nearly all the originally infested areas and approached in mass the original size and density. By 1933, however, the insects increased again, and within a year the regrowth was largely under control. Successive waves of regrowth have been much smaller and in many areas have ceased entirely. Much of the land has been opened up and colonized. That near the railroads is being developed as dairy and farming land; that more remote makes excellent range for sheep and other livestock.

Certain types of cactus that were somewhat resistant to attack by *C. cactorum* are slowly giving in. A rather stunted chlorotic type, found in hilly, timbered country, proved to be deficient in nitrogen and was not adequately nutritious to support the insects. Removal of the trees, however, is proving a satisfactory method of coping with this problem, since the plants then grow normally and are consequently subject to insect attack. A second resistant type of robust, thick-jointed plants is slowly succumbing to repeated attacks by the insects.

Other insects, particularly the cochineals *Dactylopius ceylonicus, D. opuntiae, Moneilema ulkei,* and *Lagochirus funestus,* are proving valuable in the control of other *Opuntia* species that are serious pests in Australia. With the greater portion of the major infestations well under control, more efforts are being made to eliminate these lesser pests, and eventually all cactus areas will be reduced to a point where they will no longer constitute a serious problem.

Recent introduction of *Cactoblastis* and *Dactylopius* against *Opuntia* species in Hawaii is meeting with success, and control of this pest on the drier portion of these islands marks another advance in biological effort.

Prickly pears are serious weeds in India and Ceylon (Huffaker,

1959). Some control of *O. vulgaris* had occurred by the cochineal *D. indicus* which apparently arrived along with the cactus. The cochineal *D. tomentosus*, introduced from 1924 to 1926, was effective, and over 100,000 acres were freed of cactus by 1954. Cactus has also been controlled in Celebes, South Africa and Mauritius. Complications have been met because, in South Africa, secondary depradation of imported cochineals interfered with progress of the control campaign, and a coccid, *Dictylopius tomentosus*, which proved very effective in controlling *Opuntia* attacked spineless cactus and had to be handled with DDT sprays. However, with the numbers of known predators on cactus and with the insecticides that can be used to control these where necessary, it seems that tools are available to control cactus species under almost all conditions where they are economic pests.

CONTROL OF ST. JOHNSWORT

Hypericum perforatum is a common roadside plant of Europe. Under favorable conditions this plant becomes dominant, and it is also a serious weed in the United States and Australia. In 1930, it was estimated to have covered 70,000 acres in Humboldt County, California, and from 250,000 to 400,000 acres in Victoria, Australia. Since then it has spread steadily. In the United States, it is a common range weed in Washington, Oregon, and northern Idaho, and in the north coast and northern Sierra Nevada ranges in California.

Three beetles, *Chrysolina varians*, *C. hyperici*, and *C. brunsvicensis*, were introduced from England into Australia in 1934. Within a year they had all apparently disappeared. However, in 1939 large numbers of the adult *C. hyperici* were found feeding on *H. perforatum* and causing serious damage to the plants. Adults were collected and liberated in other Australian districts: in 1939, about 6,500; in 1940, 52,000; and in 1941, 90,000. Eighteen liberations out of twenty-four have continued to develop, and this insect seems to be well established. Meanwhile two other insects, *Chrysolina gemellata* and *Agrilus hyperici*, were introduced to Australia from France, and these are also well established. *C. gemellata* is a leaf and stem feeder, *A. hyperici* a root borer; the latter, because it is less subject to depredations by predators, seems to offer great promise for the eventual control of *H. perforatum* in Australia.

In 1944, importations of *Agrilus hyperici*, *Chrysolina hyperici*, and *C. gemellata* were made into California. Tests on *C. hyperici* were completed in May, 1945, and four colonies were released late that year. Additional releases were made in 1946 and 1947, 370,000 adults having been put out by that time (Holloway, 1948). Colonies were established in 17 counties in California and 2 in Oregon. Feeding tests were completed with *C. gemellata* in January, 1946, and adults were released in

January and February of that year. All colonies of this species became established, and by the spring of 1947 adults could be found ¼ mile from the point of release.

By February, 1949, 122 colonies of beetles had been released of which 97 percent became established (Huffaker and Holloway, 1949).

FIGURE 8-2.   Beetles on St. Johnswort stems. (Photograph courtesy of James K. Holloway.)

In Humboldt County one colony had spread until it had destroyed the weed on about 20 acres of land (Fig. 8–2 and 8–3). Distribution went on rapidly during 1949 and 1950 with colonies going to Oregon, Washington, and Idaho. Destruction of St. Johnswort has continued and thousands of acres of excellent range land have been virtually freed of this weed.

Agrilus hyperici is a root borer. Its introduction and acclimatiza-

FIGURE 8-3. A. Site of the original release of *Chrysolina gemellata* in Humbolt County, California; foreground shows the growing St. Johnswort. B. The same field 1 year later, showing complete destruction of the weed and return of grasses. (Photographs by courtesy of J. K. Holloway.)

tion have presented difficulties; however, releases were made in the spring of 1950 in Shasta and Placer counties in California. Though not as spectacular as the leaf feeders, the root borer has become established. This insect feeds on plants growing in the shade and hence supplements the work of the leaf feeders. The root borer is not dependent on fall rains and the winter growth of St. Johnswort, hence it is less important that its life history be synchronized with the growth phase of the weed.

The root-borer beetles are active in June and July, feeding on the leaves and flowers of the host (Holloway and Huffaker, 1953). They oviposit on the stem just above the soil surface. When the larvae hatch, they bore into the plant and burrow downward into the roots. In early autumn they complete their feeding; they move upward as full-grown larvae, pupate, and by spring emerge as adult beetles. The feeding activities of the larvae destroy the roots and kill the plants.

The beetles of the root borer are more active than the leaf feeders; they are collected with difficulty. The natural spread of these insects may be accelerated by transplanting infested roots in the spring.

A gall fly, *Zeuxidiplosis giardi*, has been introduced into California and has spread rapidly. This insect requires green foliage for most of the year, and it finds its niche in localities where the plant is green during summer and fall. Under moist growing conditions the plant will support several generations of gall flies in a year. This insect migrates rapidly, and flies released in one location have been found many miles away in succeeding years. Its spread may be hastened by placing potted St. Johnswort plants in infested areas and then moving them as soon as galls are formed. The gall fly is most active during the summer months when the leaf-feeding beetles are inactive. It has a great ability to reproduce, and it affects the weed by converting its leaf buds into galls; a heavy production of galls reduces the foliage and the roots of the plants; their vigor is impaired and their competitive ability reduced. This insect may prove most useful in regions where irrigated pastures are infested with St. Johnswort.

FURTHER EXAMPLES OF BIOLOGICAL CONTROL

The problem of prickly pear control represents an ideal problem for use of the biological method. The plant pest, a highly specialized type, having no near relatives of agricultural importance, was introduced into an isolated region in which no similar plants were growing. Consequently, it was possible to go to the original source of the pest, collect predators that were limited to the species concerned, and introduce them free of their natural parasites. These predators, having no natural enemies and supplied with almost unlimited food, increased with great rapidity, reducing the host plant to a low level of survival before they themselves were reduced in numbers.

The success of other biological-control projects can be measured largely by the way in which they fit these fundamental requirements. The case of *Lantana camara* has been described. The plant is less highly specialized, infestations are more scattered and, where scattered, a great number of other plants intervene in the total plant population. For this reason, in these outlying infestations, the actual finding of the host plants by the predatory insects becomes a problem, and the balance of many factors tends to maintain the noxious plants at a higher level than in the case of the prickly pear. In the sense of the term defined by Sweetman (1936), the plant resistance is higher in the case of *Lantana*.

ACAENA SANGUISORBAE

The native piripiri of New Zealand and Australia, produces burs that get into the wool of sheep and cause serious losses. In Australia, the plant is held in check by a chrysomelid beetle, *Haltica pagana*. However, since this insect also attacks strawberries, it has not been introduced into New Zealand. A sawfly, *Antholcus varinervis*, introduced from Chile, has failed to become established, possibly because of depradations by birds. Piripiri is a serious weed. Huffaker and Andres (1970) list it among weeds that have not been successfully controlled.

CLIDEMIA HIRTA

A native plant of the West Indies and central and northern South America, *C. hirta* has proved to be a serious pest in Fiji. It is a shrubby plant with hard, tough stems and produces quantities of berries filled with small seeds. The berries are relished by many birds, particularly the Indian myna that proved so active in spreading *Lantana*. Leaves of the plant are pubescent and are not eaten by cattle. In Trinidad, a thrips, *Liothrips urichi*, was found that proved specific on *C. hirta*, and this insect has been liberated, free of parasites, in Fiji. The first importation was in 1930. Since then the thrips have spread all over the islands they have infested, and are affecting a satisfactory control of the weed. Though they do not kill it outright, these insects so inhibit its growth that other plants can successfully compete with it. Under the influence of the introduced thrips, *C. hirta* has been reduced to a minor rank in the flora and is no longer considered a noxious weed pest. Under severe grazing, competition is reduced and *Clidemia* becomes dominant again. In Hawaii *C. hirta* has been parasitized with *L. urichi*, and the weed is reduced in seriousness, particularly in sunny, exposed sites.

CYPERUS ROTUNDUS

Common nutsedge or nutgrass, is an important pest in the Hawaiian Islands. A weevil and a tortricid from the Philippines were introduced in 1925 but, after making a promising start, they became parasitized and failed to give effective control. Chemicals are being used in controlling nutsedge at present, and when the close relationship of this species to important crop plants is considered, it seems somewhat doubtful if biological control will meet the needs of this problem. The same two insects were introduced in Australia but were not released because they fed on *Cyperus* species that are useful forage plants. *Cyperus rotundus* and *C. esculentus* are serious weed pests in the tropics around the world, and specific insect pests would aid greatly in their control.

ULEX EUROPAEUS

Common gorse or furze of western Europe and North America has become a pest in New Zealand, Australia, and Tasmania. Though a useful hedge plant relished while young by sheep, it tends to spread in pastures and form large, brushy areas that livestock seldom penetrate. The weevil *Apion ulicis* prevents seeding of this pest in Europe, and large numbers have been released in New Zealand. It has become established in some areas, but it will take some time to determine the effectiveness of control, since only reproduction by seed is affected. Several other insects may be useful in controlling this plant, but none has proved outstanding at the present time.

Gorse is also a pest in Hawaii on range lands. *A. ulicis* has been introduced but without outstanding results. Other insects are being sought to help handle the pest. Gorse is also present along the Pacific coast in California, Oregon, and Washington. The infested area in California was estimated at 15,000 acres in 1951 and is steadily increasing. *A. ulicis* was released in 1952 and is well established in California and Oregon, but results are not definite as it only reduces production of seed (Holloway and Huffaker, 1957). Some plant mortality associated with adult feeding was found in 1959.

RUBUS FRUTICOSUS

The common blackberry, is now considered to be the worst weed pest in New Zealand. It is also serious in the humid portions of Australia and is found in orchards and pastures in Oregon and California. In New Zealand, the introduced blackbird has proved an important factor in the spread of blackberry. This weedy species, spreading rapidly by seeds and also vegetatively, produces immense masses of vegetation. Its roots sprout vigorously; cutting and burning usually only stimulate it to greater vegetative reproduction. Chemical control is expensive and is not particularly effective because of the moist habitat favored by the plant.

From the standpoint of biological control, the plant is botanically allied with the raspberry, boysenberry, loganberry, and other commercial sports and hybrids; it is not far from the common fruit trees; and somewhat more distantly, it is related to a host of rosaceous ornamentals. Also, in almost any locality, insect predators of blackberry would probably find native species of the Rosaceae that would prove satisfactory hosts. In view of the principles of biological control, it seems evident that any insect, to be satisfactory, would have to be a stem or root borer or a fruit feeder. One of the most promising insects so far studied is the buprestid beetle *Coraebus rubi*, which is known to attack only the roots and crown of strawberry and also attacks *Rosa indica*, a stock for ornamental roses. The insect has not been liberated so far because of the danger to other plants. Efforts are being made to find other insects to solve this serious plant-pest problem.

CORDIA MACROSTACHYA

This plant called black sage was accidentally introduced into Mauritius in the last century and is a major pest on grazing lands and sugar-cane plantations. In 1947 the beetle *Schematiza cordiae* was introduced and released a year later. By 1950 much of the weed had succumbed. A second insect, a seed-infesting *Eurytoma* sp., was introduced in 1949, and so successful have these parasites been that the weed is now considered to be under satisfactory control. Huffaker and Andres (1970) list control of black sage as being substantially successful.

EUPATORIUM ADENOPHORUM

This shrub, termed pamakani or Crofton weed, has become widespread in Hawaii and Australia. In Hawaii a gall fly, *Procecidochares utilis*, was introduced from Mexico in 1945 which effected control and reclaimed some 25,000 acres of grazing land. The same insect was introduced into Australia in 1952 and shows promise of bringing about a satisfactory suppression of the weed.

LEPTOSPERMUM SCOPARIUM

Known in New Zealand as manuka, this is a native plant that has proved to be a pest on low-grade grazing land. In the 1940s a mealy bug, *Eriococcus orariensis*, accidentally introduced from Australia, was found to be preying on the manuka, and it has apparently spread to such an extent as to effect a practical control. Huffaker and Andres (1970) list control of this pest as completely successful.

SENECIO JACOBAEA

Tansy ragwort has been a serious poisonous plant in New Zealand for many years. The cinnabar moth *Tyria jacobaeae* was introduced from England in 1927 with indications of promise, but this insect was soon rendered ineffective by birds and by insect parasites of a closely related insect predator of *S. jacobaea*. A seed fly, *Pegohylemyia jacobaeae*, was also introduced, and it has had some success in parasitizing the weed. These same two insects have been introduced into Australia, and the cinnabar moth has been released in northern California where tansy ragwort is spreading. Only time will tell how effective these efforts toward biological control will be. Huffaker and Andres (1970) consider tansy ragwort control in California, though slow, to be promising.

EMEX SPINOSA AND E. AUSTRALIS

These are serious weeds of range lands in Hawaii. *Apion antiquum* from Africa was introduced as a predator in 1956 and shows promising results. *A. neofallax*, a stem-boring weevil from Morocco, has been introduced but as yet has not been released. Huffaker and Andres (1970) list this weed among those whose control is a substantial success.

XANTHIUM STRUMARIUM

The Noogura burr of Australia, closely related to the cocklebur in the United States, is a serious weed of grazing lands as it sticks in the wool of sheep and lowers its value. The germinating seeds of cocklebur are known to be poisonous to pigs. Several efforts have been made to introduce insect predators on this weed to Australia but so far without eminent success. This weed is listed in Anon (1968) as among those that are still being studied.

Many other weeds have been considered as possibly susceptible to biological control. *Halogeton glomeratus*, a poisonous weed that has spread over several million acres of desert range in the western United States, has been studied. Search for means of control in the Mediterranean and Near East has so far not been successful (Major, 1960).

A large number of weeds are still the subjects of control projects in different countries. In the United States the following weeds are in this group: alligator weed, Banks melastoma, blackberry, Canada thistle, christmas berry, elephantsfoot, gorse, halogeton, Italian thistle, Mediterranean sage, nutsedge, pamakani, puncturevine, Russian knapweed, salt cedar, Scotch broom, starthistle, tansy ragwort, and water hyacinth (Anon, 1968). In Australia, Noogura burr and pamakani are being studied; in Canada, St. Johnswort, toadflax, tansy ragwort, and Canada thistle; in Fiji, lantana and tobacco weed; in New Caledonia, prickly pear and lantana; in the West Indies, prickly pear and water hyacinth; in Africa, prickly pear, lantana, and St. Johnswort (Anon, 1968).

Weeds which have not been successfully controlled by biological methods include firebush and downy rosemyrtle in Hawaii, Noogura burr in Fiji and Australia, tansy ragwort and piripiri in New Zealand, and tansy ragwort in Australia.

Work against puncturevine in California using two weevils is having a measure of success but the wide range and longitudinal distribution of this weed are such as to make control by one or even by a few insects almost out of the question.

Baloch and Mohyuddin (1969) suggest that the mistletoe *Loranthus longiflorus*, common in Pakistan, Sumatra, and New Guinea, which parasitizes a number of important plants, may be a target species for biological control. Larvae of *Delias eucharis* have been seen to feed on this weed. The authors list 13 insects that feed on *L. longiflorus*; larval parasites have been reared from some of these insects and there may be many more since records of the phytophagous fauna are not complete.

CONTROL OF AQUATIC WEEDS

A somewhat different example of biological control is the destruction of aquatic vegetation in ditches by herbivorous fish. The Hawaiian Sugar Planters Association reports that *Tilapia mossambica* of the sunfish family was introduced to Hawaii in 1955 by the Territorial Board of Agriculture and Forestry. By eating the vegetation and burrowing in the bottom of ditches to form spawning nests, these fish destroy the roots of aquatic weeds and control their growth. A second introduced species of fish, *Tilapia zilli*, feeds on grasses and promises to be effective in grass-infested ditches.

Experimental work on aquatic weed control has been expanded in recent years. Yeo and Fisher (1970) list some 35 species of bryophytes, chlorophytes, pteridophytes, and spermatophytes that have been tested using 9 species of fish; the spermatophytes include all of the economically important aquatic weeds. Pathogens, snails, and other competitive aquatic weeds have been used in addition to fish.

Of current interest is the Chinese grass carp (*Ctenopharyngodon idella*), commonly named the white amur. A native from rivers in China and the Amur region in Siberia and imported in 1964, this fish has proved to be a voracious consumer of aquatic weeds. It is being very carefully studied by the Bureau of Sport Fisheries and Wildlife of the U.S. Dept. of Interior.

Adult amur feed on some 35 or more species of aquatic plants; the daily consumption of weeds can exceed the body weight of the fish. Spawning takes place in streams but can be induced in ponds by treatment with hormones to stimulate ovulation. Studies in Arkansas indicate that the amur is completely herbivorous and suffers no competition from other fish; it has potential as a sport and food fish in the United States.

THE FUTURE OF BIOLOGICAL CONTROL OF WEEDS

During the early years of biological control certain generalizations were made concerning the preferable types of insects to use in controlling plant pests. These were arrived at by deductive reasoning from knowledge of the nature of the insects. One example is the rule that root borers, stem borers, and internal seed or fruit feeders, being more selective, are preferred to leaf feeders. Another is that biological control should be used only as a last resort, after all other methods have failed, because of the hazard of introducing pests that might not remain limited to the specific weed under consideration.

Experience has proved that these generalizations, though logical, may not be true. For instance, the leaf feeders, *Chrysolina hyperici* and *C. gemellata*, so far have proved to be highly specific for *Hypericum perforatum* and have proved to be much more effective than the root borer *Agrilus hyperici* and the gall fly *Zeuxidiplosis giardi*.

Another fact that was not apparent before the experience with *Chrysolina hyperici* and *C. gemellata* is that parasites, like weeds, may thrive and be more aggressive in a new habitat than in their homeland. And a third observation is that, in the new environmental complex, unanticipated factors that come into play following introduction of a parasite may work to the advantage of the control procedure. For example, it is doubtful if the introduced beetles would control *Hypericum perforatum* so effectively as they have if the parasite and the weed life cycles were not synchronized. The spring and early summer feeding of the beetles weakens the deeper roots of the weed so that it is unable to survive the long, dry summer period; heavily parasitized weeds simply die for lack of soil moisture. In the case of cactus control by *Cactoblastis cactorum*, secondary invasion of the parasitized cladodes by fungi and bacteria proved to be an important factor in the rate and extent of destruction. Huffaker (1957) has discussed these relationships in detail, stressing the role of insects in plant ecology. Holloway and Huffaker (1951) have pointed out how this same factor of dry summer soil conditions has favored reproduction of *C. gemellata* over *C. hyperici*.

As for the future of biological control of weeds, it is obvious that there are many weed situations where this method offers the only hope of control. In such situations, exemplified by the wide occurrence of *Halogeton* on millions of acres of low-value land, all possible efforts should be made to find satisfactory insect predators. From the above examples, it seems that workers in this field should not be limited in their outlook by the old generalizations but should view each problem on its own merits, testing all candidate predators under all relevant conditions, and that any predators which seem promising should not be abandoned until thoroughly tried in the habitat of the weed. Because of the seriousness of some of these weed problems and because of the great unanticipated success of the efforts on cactus and St. Johnswort, it seems obvious that every possible effort should be made to seek out and put into action insect predators to control many weeds that now are completely out of hand.

REFERENCES

Anon. 1968. Weed control. Principles of plant and animal pest control. Vol. 2. *Natl. Acad. Sci. Publ.* 1597. Wash., D.C., 1968.

Baloch, G. M., and A. I. Mohyuddin. 1969. The phytophagous fauna of a mistletoe (*Loranthus longiflorus* Desr. Loranthaceae) in West Pakistan. *Weed Res.* 9:62–64.

Dodd, Alan P. 1940. The biological control of prickly-pear in Australia. *Imp. Bur. Pastures and Forage Crops Herbage Pub. Serv. Bul.* 27:131–143.

Holloway, J. K. 1948. Biological control of Klamath weed. *Prog. Rpt. 10th Ann. West. Weed Control Conf. Proc.*, p. 19.

_____ and C. B. Huffaker. 1951. The role of *Chrysolina gemellata* in the biological control of Klamath weed. *Jour. Econ. Ent.* 44:244–247.

_____ and _____. 1953. Establishment of a root borer and a gall fly for control of Klamath weed. *Jour. Econ. Ent.* 46(1):65–67.

_____ and _____. 1957. Establishment of the seed weevil, *Apion ulicis* Forst., for suppression of gorse in California. *Jour. Econ. Ent.* 50:498–499.

Huffaker, C. B. 1957. Fundamentals of biological control of weeds. *Hilgardia* 27:101–157.

_____. 1959. Biological control of weeds with insects. *Ann. Rev. of Ent.* 4:251–276.

_____ and L. A. Andres. 1970. Biological weed control using insects. *F.A.O. Internatl. Conf. on Weed Control.* Davis, Calif., pp. 436–449.

_____ and J. K. Holloway. 1949. Changes in range plant population structure associated with feeding of imported enemies of Klamath weed (*Hypericum perforatum* L.). *Ecology* 30(2):167–175.

Major, Jack. 1960. Private communication.

Perkins, R. C. L., and O. H. Swezey. 1924. The introduction into Hawaii of insects that attack *Lantana*. *Hawaii. Sugar Planters' Assoc. Expt. Sta. Bul. Ent. Ser.* 16.

Sweetman, Harvey L. 1936. *The Biological Control of Insects.* Ithaca: Comstock.

Tillyard, R. J. 1928. The biological control of noxious weeds. *4th Internatl. Cong. Ent. Trans.* 2:4–9.
Yeo, R. R., and T. W. Fisher. 1970. Progress and potential for biological weed control with fish, pathogens, competitive plants, and snails. *F.A.O. Internatl. Conf. on Weed Control.* Davis, Calif., p. 450–463.

9

Use of Chemicals in Weed Control

Chemicals have been used for centuries to control weeds. Salt, ashes, smelter wastes, and other industrial by-products have been applied to roadsides, fence rows, and pathways to rid them of vegetation; old manuals on agriculture recommended these materials for eliminating weed infestations from agricultural lands. Most of these materials, however, have found only limited use because their bulk and weight prohibit their transportation. To be widely useful in weed control, a chemical should be highly toxic and relatively inexpensive.

DISCOVERY OF SELECTIVE HERBICIDAL ACTION

Little progress was made in the scientific investigation or the practical use of weed killers until the latter part of the nineteenth century. Then with amazing rapidity, the newly expanding science of chemistry found many applications in industry and agriculture. The development of the chemical theory of plant nutrition by Liebig and the increasing use of chemical fertilizers pointed the way to entirely new practices in agriculture. The introduction of bordeaux spray for plant-disease control heightened the interest in the use of chemicals. Apparently the discovery of the selective action of copper salts on broadleaf weeds in cereal crops resulted accidentally from trials on the control of fungus diseases. Almost simultaneously and quite independently, Bonnet (cited by Rademacher, 1940) in France, Schultz (1909) in Germany, and Bolley (1908) in America found that solutions of copper salts applied to mixed stands of broad-leaved weeds in cereals would kill the former and not harm the latter; this discovery occurred

161

in 1896 and 1897. Martin (1897) in France used iron sulfate for the same purpose, and Duclos (1897) had success with both sulfuric acid and copper nitrate.

By 1900, it was shown that solutions of sodium nitrate, ammonium sulfate, and potassium salts were also successful as selective herbicides, and the practice of spraying for the control of mustards and other common grainfield weeds soon spread throughout Europe and the British Isles. Somewhat later, dry powdered kainite and calcium cyanamide were added to the list of selective herbicides. On small farms where hoeing and hand pulling were commonly used, spraying and dusting methods saved much time and labor. On these small, intensively cultivated farms, careful application, generally high humidities, and the pressing need for high yields all favored the successful use of these methods.

Meanwhile Bolley (1908), reporting twelve years of successful experimentation with common salt, iron sulfate, copper sulfate, and sodium arsenite in North Dakota, stated: When the farming public has accepted this method of attacking weeds as a regular farm operation . . . the gain to the country at large will be much greater in monetary consideration than that which has been afforded by any other single piece of investigation applied to field work in agriculture.

These were the words of an agricultural prophet forty years ahead of his time. Today this prophesy has been fulfilled and growers and vegetation managers are making use of herbicides in a thousand ways.

Following this initial period (1896–1910) of development, interest in the control of annual weeds lapsed in America. The lag in the production of adequate spray machinery, the frequent lack of success because of low humidity, and, above all, the immense scale upon which grain farms were operated, precluding the possibility of completing a successful spray program within the short time during which both weeds and cereals were in the proper stages for treatment, all contributed to this declining interest. With the introduction of cleaner seeds, the change to a fallow system, and the adoption of new crops, the weed problem was somewhat alleviated, and interest in chemical weed control gradually shifted to other types of weeds, particularly to the perennials.

DEVELOPMENT OF SELECTIVE WEED CONTROL IN EUROPE

Although interest lagged in America, a new period of development had started in Europe (Aslander, 1927). Rabate (1911), reporting experiments with copper sulfate, iron sulfate, and sulfuric acid on winter wheat, concluded that the acid in 6 to 10 percent solutions (the strength depending on local conditions) was a thoroughly satisfactory spray for grainfield weeds. It killed most of the annual weeds, left the cereals practically uninjured, and had a fertilizing effect on the soil. Morettini (1915) in Italy, Rabate (1926) in France, and Korsmo (1932) in Norway found that selective sprays not only killed most of the broadleaf weeds in cereals but in many cases resulted in a definite

FIGURE 9-1. Comparative yields of barley and mustard seed from plots sprayed with a dinitro selective material (bottom) and unsprayed plots (top). The proportion of weed seeds to barley in the sprayed plots is insignificant. (Photograph by courtesy of the California Agricultural Experiment Station.)

increase in yield. An average of 211 of Korsmo's (1932) experiments carried out from 1914 to 1922 in spring-sown grains in Norway showed an increase in yield on sprayed plots of 25.3 percent above unsprayed plots (Fig. 9-1). His yield increases were comparable on wheat, barley, and oats, and in all cases, weed growth was reduced to a mere fraction of that on untreated plots. Sulfuric acid generally gave better results than harrowing, hand pulling, spraying with iron sulfate or nitric acid, or dusting with calcium cyanamide or other dry herbicides. Its bulk and corrosiveness were the principal drawbacks to its use.

Meanwhile, there was developing in the humid sections of central and northern Europe, a combined weed-control and fertilization practice by means of dry powdered chemicals. Kainite, a double salt of magnesium sulfate and potassium chloride with certain impurities, was prepared in a finely powdered form for weed control. Where the soil was deficient in potash, this material was applied while the weeds were in the seedling stage. Calcium cyanamide is used on nitrogen-deficient soils, and more recent work has shown that a mixture of calcium cyanamide and kainite at a ratio of 1:6 is superior to either alone. The profitable use of either of these depends upon both its herbicidal properties and its benefit as a fertilizer; therefore mineral deficiencies of the soil must be considered when these chemicals are used.

EARLY TRIALS OF SOIL STERILIZATION

While these various developments with respect to controlling annual weeds in cereals were in progress, chemicals were also tried for killing perennial weeds and for sterilizing soils. Jones and Orton (1899) of Vermont and Stone (1909) of Massachusetts tested a number of chemicals for permanently sterilizing soils. They found salt was slow and ineffective except in extremely large amounts. Copper sulfate was also ineffective when applied to the soil. Arsenicals proved the most satisfactory.

SODIUM ARSENITE AS A WEED KILLER

Following these early trials, arsenicals were more and more widely used, and sodium arsenite solution became the standard commercial "weed killer." Wilcox (1914), reporting from Hawaii, found no ill effects upon the soil after two years of arsenical spraying in the sugar-cane plantations, and this herbicide was widely used with no deleterious effects. This lack of toxicity to the soil results from: (1) the low rate of application, (2) the high rainfall, and (3) the highly ferruginous nature of the soil that tends to fix enormous quantities of arsenic in a form unavailable to plants.

The largest use of sodium arsenite in the United States and central Europe has been by railroads. Handled largely by commercial contractors in this country, this herbicide has been sprayed along the rights-of-way throughout the land, resulting in only an incomplete control of weeds and in considerable losses of livestock. Though this spray practice has so benefited the railroads that they are reluctant to give it up, recent advances in our knowledge of the use of herbicides certainly indicate that use of sodium arsenite solution is no longer desirable or necessary. In too many instances, chemical weed control has become identified with sodium arsenite spraying, and consequently it has fallen into disrepute. For example, a news item records that the government of Malaya has placed a ban on sodium arsenite as a weed killer because of a cattle loss to the extent of $65,000. The item states that sodium arsenite is widely used on rubber and coconut estates.

LATER DEVELOPMENTS

During the decade 1915–1925, acid arsenical spray, carbon bisulfide, sodium chlorate, and other chemicals were introduced into weed-control practice. Physiological studies on the responses of weeds to herbicides were made. Later, boron compounds, thiocyanates, dinitrophenols, ammonium sulfamate, selective and nonselective contact foliage-applied oils, and other chemicals were brought into use. Finally, with the introduction of 2,4-D and the realization of the potentialities of chemical weed control by the chemical industry, herbicides in increasing numbers have been discovered and placed on the market. In contrast with some of the traditional herbicides, all of the more recently developed ones are organic compounds. Listed alphabetically the chemical groups represented include:

Inorganic Herbicides

    Acids, Salts,

    Oils

Organic Herbicidal Compounds

    Aliphatics, Amides, Arsenicals, Benzoics, Dipyridiliums, Carbamates, Nitrils, Nitroanilines, Phenols and Phenyl ethers, Phenoxyacid compounds, Pyridazones, Thiocarbamates, Triazines, Triazoles, Uracils, Ureas

Unclassified Herbicides

These include some 200 compounds many of which are too new to have become established in the field. There will probably be additional chemicals to add to this list by the time this book comes from the press.

During the past fifty years, weed control has developed many techniques as sound and scientific in their basis as those used in the fields of pathology, entomology, and mineral nutrition.

Present-day agriculture, with its specialized crops and methods, its rapid mechanization, and its efficient handling of fungus and insect pests, demands adequate weed control. Though hand pulling, hand hoeing, and small-scale spraying have sufficed in the past, the decreasing numbers of hand laborers and the narrowing margins of profit require more effective methods. Agriculture, following the lead of industry, is resorting to chemical aids; with the difficulties sometimes experienced in using cultural and cropping methods of weed control, chemical methods have received increasing attention and have become an important factor in the mechanization of agriculture, particularly in the newer districts where large-scale crop production by machine methods is found (Fig. 9-2).

FIGURE 9-2. Application of a herbicide to young sugar cane by aircraft. It would take hundreds of men to cover the area by hand methods that this airplane covers in one day.

Recommendations regarding herbicides have in the past been largely empirical and have often involved dosages and spraying methods of limited applicability. To be widely useful, methods should be based upon broad chemical and physiological principles, should entail a complete understanding of the relations between the environmental factors involved, and should be adjustable to meet the demands of a wide variety of situations. Only by understanding the underlying principles can farmers or others interested in weed control hope to attain the degree of success indicated by the thousands of experiments which have been performed.

SCOPE OF CHEMICAL WEED CONTROL

Because modern transportation has speeded up the dissemination of many weeds and machine methods of farming have aggravated at least certain weed problems, it is hoped that chemical weed control may compensate in part by providing efficient methods that will assist in holding these pests in check. A survey of the extent of present-day pest control indicates the progress that has been made concerning weeds.

The use of petroleum oils, boron compounds, sodium chlorate, borate-chlorate mixtures, 2,4-D, substituted ureas, uracils, triazines, and mixtures of the latter with chlorates and borates is constantly increasing on railroads, highways, and industrial sites each year (Klingman and Wilcox, 1960).

Use of selective herbicides has increased steadily since the introduction of the phenoxy compounds. Use of selective materials through the soil as preemergence herbicides is moving ahead rapidly at the present time, and this use promises the greatest advances in the immediate future. As compounds such as the α-chloroacetamides, the bipyridilium compounds, the carbamates and thiocarbamates, the dinitroanilines, the phenols and phenoxy compounds, the triazines, ureas, and uracils become widely used, pre- and postemergence selective weed control will ultimately eliminate practically all mechanical weed control. The preemergence use of these materials has none of the disadvantages of machine weeding, such as root injury to crop plants, increasing the incidence of water and wind erosion, and soil compaction. And it kills most weeds in their seedling stages before they can cause competition with the crop plants. Recent introduction of the sprayblade further advances chemical weed control.

Rice, flax, safflower, coffee, pineapples, sugar cane, and vegetable and horticultural crops are rapidly being changed from hoe culture to chemical pest control (Fig. 9–2). Herbicides used only in the United States and Europe two decades ago are now being introduced and adopted around the world. Japan, Indonesia, the Near East, and Africa are rapidly taking over these improved methods. In the foreign trade issue of *NAC News and Pesticide Review* of August, 1958, reports are given on the use of modern pesticides in Japan, Peru, Australia, Pakistan, Indonesia, and the U.S.S.R. Holm and Herberger (1970) have compiled a list of useful publications for a study of weeds and their control from most of the countries of the world. Naming 158 publications, this list includes the weed floras of many countries, books on the biology of weeds, weed control, manuals and text books, and specialized treatises on many aspects of weed science. Figure 9–3 shows the use of a knapsack sprayer in Venezuela to apply a soil sterilant in a field being prepared for planting sugar cane. Such illustrations might be found in hundreds of agricultural journals from countries around the world.

Tables 3–9 and 3–10 give data on production and consumption of herbicides. It is evident from these data that use of chlorophenoxy compounds is leveling off. However, the host of newer compounds that are currently coming into use indicate that chemical weed control is continuing to expand. In a survey carried on in Iowa (Beal et al., 1960), use of chemicals by farmers was studied for the years 1955, 1956,

FIGURE 9-3. Applying a selective soil-borne herbicide preplanting in sugar cane in Venezuela. (Photograph by courtesy of Compania Shell de Venezuela.)

1957, and part of 1958. The following list shows the percentage of the group who used six types of pesticides:

Weed killers..............	87%
Soil insecticides..........	30%
Brush killers	19%
Crop insecticides.........	14%
Grass killers..............	4%
Grain fumigants	4%

Forty-six percent of those using weed killers used them on less than 25 acres; average acreage treated was 33. Eleven percent of the group had used weed killers for the first time in 1957.

According to *The Pesticide Review* for 1972 (Anon, 1972), "Use of herbicides has grown more rapidly during the last decade than any other class of pesticides. Chemicals have replaced, to a large extent, more expensive labor and mechanical means for controlling weeds and are now used in almost every major crop. Synthetic organic herbicide production grew at an average rate of 10 percent a year during the 5 years previous to 1971, compared with 3.8 percent for all synthetic organic pesticides." Production growth in 1971 was 6.1 percent.

During the past few years there has been apprehension about the possible effects of pesticides in foodstuffs as a result of their increasing use in agriculture. This apprehension was heightened when the inspectors of the Food and Drug Administration found residues of amino triazole on cranberries and condemned large quantities during the holiday season of 1959. Since that time there has been a thorough reexamination of application practices, a review of labels and labeling procedures, and a study of tolerances and residues on foodstuffs, fodder, grain, and other agricultural products that are consumed as human food. Most herbicides are now used on a no-residue basis, and those that show residues are being systematically examined for mammalian toxicity. Although many herbicides were temporarily withdrawn from the market, most of them are back. The phenoxy compounds constituted one of the most serious problems because no one company was willing to spend the money necessary to have them registered.

As mentioned in Chapter 1, the Environmental Protection Agency (EPA), established in 1970, now regulates all use of pesticides in the United States.

Dreessen (1961) has emphasized the important uses being made of the chlorophenoxy herbicides and the great potential for expansion of their use on grazing lands. In discussing the residue problem, he states that there is no evidence for residues of 2,4-D in meat or milk; that because of the nature of its use, there is little probability that it could occur in meat as a residue; and that, where properly used, 2,4-D should not appear in milk. Dreessen lists the uses that may be made of 2,4-D on pastures and range land, and he describes the precautions to be observed in such use.

Dreessen cites a study made by the Agriculture Research Service in Beltsville, Maryland, of the residue data that were available in 1960, and he stresses the fact that all available evidence shows that, when 2,4-D was applied preharvest to wheat at 1 lb or less per acre, the residue found ranged from 0.4 ppm to 0.0 ppm. Such residues are of no significance in human nutrition; 5 ppm are allowed in citrus fruit where 2,4-D is used to prevent preharvest drop.

Dreessen states that during the period 1945–1960 more than 240 million acres of small grains received 2,4-D. There has not been a single reported instance in which this chemical has caused deleterious effects on the grain or on by-products made from it, on applicators applying the herbicide, on animals or humans consuming the grains, or on animal by-products. It seems from this record that, when 2,4-D is used at the recommended rates and times of application, significant residues do not occur. Any residues found by improved methods of analysis will be below any possible harmful level. Dreessen sees no reason why

FIGURE 9-4. Initial evaluation of new herbicidal chemicals. Several crops are seeded in each container, and at the proper stage sprays are applied. Toxicity and selectivity are noted. (Photograph by courtesy of the Dow Chemical Co.)

wheat should not be sprayed with 2,4-D in the future. This discussion was presented to quiet a lot of confusion that existed in 1960 concerning possible residues of 2,4-D, confusion that concerned grain growers throughout the Midwest and which even received congressional attention. Selleck (1973) has discussed the benefits of up-to-date pesticide uses.

Much of the apprehension concerning herbicides visualizes build-up of residues in soils to levels that affect yield of crops, that result in deterioration of the quality of underground waters, or that bring about compaction or laterization of soils. In order to obtain evidence on possible long-term effects of intensive herbicide use on farms, Fryer and Kirkland (1970) used four herbicides, each representing an important chemical group: MCPA (phenoxyalkanoic acids) simazine (substituted s-triazines) linuron (substituted ureas), and tri-allate (carbamates). They applied these herbicides to plots, either planted with the same crop each year or uncropped. MCPA was applied to barley at the 5-leaf stage, tri-allate preemergence to barley, simazine preemergence to maize, and linuron to carrots. Reporting on

FIGURE 9-5.   After the sprays are applied, repeated observations are made to detect the various stages of the injury that develops. Thousands of readings on hundreds of plant cultures may go into the selection of a single chemical for further development. (Photograph by courtesy of the Dow Chemical Co.)

six years of repeated tests they state their work provides evidence that these four common herbicides, when used at recommended rates, are unlikely to have any injurious effect on the capacity of the soil to produce healthy crops. Their conclusions are based on yields from paired plots, cropped and uncropped, from bioassays on residues in the soils, from chemical determinations, and from analyses on nutrient levels in the soils. These results substantiate many others reported in the herbicide literature, all agreeing that long-time use of herbicides at recommended dosages will not result in build-up, but that breakdown in the soil eliminates the chemicals soon after they are applied so that residue levels never reach dangerous proportions.

Table 9-1.   Categories of Herbicides
Physiological Basis

Selective Herbicides

| Condition of Crop | Foliar sprays | |
	Contact	Translocated
Preplant	dinoseb-acetate, dinoterb-acetate, diquat, dinoprop, dinosam, dinoseb, DNOC, paraquat, PCP, weed oil	amitrole, amitrole-T, AMA, AMS, atrazine + oil, barban,dalapon,DBA,dicamba, dichlorprop, glyphosate, MAA, MAMA, mecoprop, MH, PBA, picloram, silvex, tricamba, 2,3,6–TBA, 2,4–D, 2,4–DB, 2,4–DEB, 2,4–DEP, 2,4,5–T
Postplant, deep-rooted crops, trees, vines	chlorflurazol,dinosam,dinoseb, dinoseb-acetate, dinoterb-acetate, diquat, paraquat, PCP, weed oil	amitrole, amitrole-T, dalapon, DBA, DSMA, erbon, flurenol, MAMA,MSMA, 2,4–D, 2,4–DB
Preemergence	dinoseb-acetate, dinoterb-acetate, dinosam, dinoseb, DNOC, PCP, Stoddard solvent	amitrole, amitrole-T,DBA, dichloroprop,flurenol,mecoprop, MH, phenmedipham, sesone, 2,4–D, 2,4–DB, 2,4–DEB, 2,4–DEP, 2,4,5–T

It is apparent that chemical weed control has become a large and important practice, that it represents a large volume of business, and that it is rapidly expanding to meet the demands for more completely mechanized pest control for agriculture and for society in general (Figs. 9–4 and 9–5). The ability of chemicals to prevent plagues, to alleviate suffering from many ills, to provide more and better foods and clothing, and to reduce the burden of back-breaking toil is being recognized. Throughout the world and especially in the more backward countries where agriculture is still carried on by primitive methods, the use of agricultural chemicals is offering relief from the deadening toil of hoe culture. The data in Tables 3–9 and 3–10 indicate the rapid rate at which the change-over is taking place.

CLASSIFICATION OF HERBICIDES

Table 9–1 presents a physiological classification of herbicides that has been employed for several years in teaching a course in weed control. It is based on the common methods of application, and each category is related to a mechanism of action.

Selective Herbicides

Soil-applied Absorbed from Soil

azide, benefin, benoxazol, bentazon, butachlor, butralin, butylate, calcium cyanamide, CDAA, CDEA, CDEC, cycloate, dinitramine, diallate, isopropalin, napropamide, nitralin, pebulate, pyrazon, triallate, trifluralin, vernolate, vorlex

bromacil, chlorthiamid, dibulalin, dichlobenil, diphenamid, diuron, monuron, napropamide, nitralin, simazine, terbacil, trifluralin

alachlor, ametryne, anisuron, arsenate-tricalcium, asulam, atratone, atrazine, aziprotryn, bandane, benefin, benoxazol, bensulide, bentazon, bentranil, benzomarc, benzthiazuron, bifenox, bromacil, brompyrazon, butachlor, buturon, carbasulam, carbetamide, chloramben, chlorazon, chlorbromuron, chlorbufam, chlornidine, chloroxuron, chlorpropham, chlortoluron, cyanizine, cycloate, cycluron, cyprazol, DCPA, delachlor, desmetryne, destun, diallate, dichlormate, difenoxuron, dimethazone, dinoseb, diphenamid, diphenatrile, dipropalin, dipropetryn, diuron, EPTC, ethiolate, fenuron, fluchloralin, flumezin, fluometuron, fluorodifen, fluromedine, haloxydine, ipazine, isonoruron, isopropanil, karbutilate, lenacil, linuron, MCAA, medinoterb-acetate, methabenzthiazuron, methazole, methiuron, methometon, methoprotryn, metobromuron, metoxuron, metribuzin, molinate, monalide, monolinuron, nonuron, naptalam, neburon, nitrofen, No-Crab, norazine, norflurazon, nortran, nortron, oxadiazon, oxapyrazon, Pencal, profluralin, prometone, prometryne, pronamide, propachlor, propazine, propham, proxipham, pyrizon, sebuthylazine, sesone, siduron, simazine, simetone, simetryne, sumitol, Swep, TCA, TCBC, tebuthiuron, terbacil, terbuthylazine, terbutol, triallate, tridex, trietazine, trifluralin, trimeturon, Tri-PE, 2,4-D, 2,4-DEB, 2,4-DEP, 2,4-DES, 2,4,5-TES, vernolate

Table 9-1. (continued)

	Selective Herbicides		
	Foliar sprays		Soil applied, Absorbed from Soil
Condition of Crop	Contact	Translocated	
Postemergence	AMA, banair, bromofenoxim, bromoxynil, calar, chlorflurazol, CMA, cypromid, dichlormate, dicryl, dimexan, dinophenate, dinoprop, dinosam, dinoseb, dinoseb-acetate, dinoterb-acetate, DMPA, DNOC, etinophen, EXD, flurenol, glytac, HCA, hexaflurate, ioxynil, karsil, KOCN, lenacil, monalide, M0338, NOA, orga 3045, oryzalin, PMA, propanil, solan, TH-1568A, tribonate	AMA, amitrole, amitrole-T, atrazine + oil, barban, bidisin, CMA, dalapon, DBA, dicamba, dichlorprop, DSMA, fluorenol, MCPA, MCPB, mecoprop, MH, PBA, phenmedipham, picloram, silvex, tricamba, tritac, 2,4-D, 2,4-DB, 2,4,5-T, 2,3,6-TBA	asulam, aziprotryn, benazolin, bentazon, benzadox, benzazin, benzomarc, bifenox, bromofenoxim, chloropon, chloroxuron, chlorthiamid, cyprazine, DBA, decazolin, desmedipham, difenoxuron, dinoprop, diphenamid, diuron, EXD, fluometuron, fluorodifen, hexaflurate, isonoruron, karbutilate, lenacil, linuron, MCPES, methabenzthiazuron, methoprotryn, metobromuron, metoxuron, metribuzin, M0338, monalide, monlinuron, neburon, NIA-2995 (Swep) nitrofen, nortran, oryzalin, oxapyrazon, phenmedipham, prometryne, pronamide, propazine, prynachlor, pyrazon, terbacil, terbutryn, tritac
Turfweed control, spray or pellets	cacodylic acid, MAA, PMA	MCPA, mecoprop, silvex, 2,4-D, 2,4,5-T	benefin, bensulide, DCPA, siduron, terbutol

Mixed weeds no crop	Foliar sprays		Soil applied, Absorbed by Roots
	Contact	Translocated	
Roadsides, canal banks, rights-of-way, airfields, tank farms	arsenite-sodium, benzadox, cacodylic acid, chlorate, dinosam, dinoseb, diquat, DNOC, endothall, glytac, HCA + oil, morphamquat, paraquat, PCP	amitrole, amitrole-T, AMA, AMS, chlorate, CMA, dalapon, dicamba, dichlorprop, DSMA, MSMA, PBA, phenmedipham, picloram, silvex, tricamba, 2,4-D, 2,4,5-T, 2,3,6-TBA	arsenite-tricalcium, arsenite-sodium, atrazine, boron salts, bromacil, chlorates, diuron, erbon, fenac, fenuron, fenuron-TCA, karbutilate, metham, monuron, monuron-TCA, neburon, picloram, simazine, TCA, terbacil
Chemical fallow	dinosam, dinoseb, diquat, fortified oil, morphamquat, paraquat, PCP	amitrole, amitrole-T, dalapon, dicamba, erbon, tricamba, 2,4-D, 2,4,5-T	atrazine, bromacil, diuron, erbon, fenac, fenuron, karbutilate, monuron, monuron-TCA, neburon, simazine
Plant desiccant	Monoxone		
Woody plant	chlorate, cacodylic acid, diquat, weed oil	amitrole, amitrole-T, AMS, MH, picloram, silvex, 2,4-D, 2,4,5-T, cacodylic acid, DSMA, MSMA, 2,4-D, or 2,4,5-T, amine conc.	fenuron pellets, picloram (spray or pellets), fenuron-TCA
Seed bed fumigant			allyl alcohol, chloropicrin, metham, methylbromide
Aquatic weed control, irrigation, and drainage ditches, ponds, lakes, cooling systems	acrolein, aromatic solvents, coppersulfate, dichlone, diquat, endothall, fenac	amitrole, fenac, silvex, 2,4-D	atrazine, borates, bromacil, chlorate, diuron, erbon, fenac, monuron, monuron-TCA, simazine

REFERENCES

Anon. 1972. *The Pesticide Review.* U.S.D.A. Agric. Stabilization and Conservation Service, Washington, D.C.

Aslander, Alfred. 1927. Sulfuric acid as a weed spray. *Jour. Agr. Res.* 34:1065–1091.

Beal, G. M., J. M. Bohlen, and D. J. Hobbs. 1960. Agricultural chemicals: Farmer attitudes and use patterns. *Agr. Chem.* 15(9):38–39, 91, 92.

Bolley, H. L. 1908. Weed control by means of chemical sprays. *N. Dak. Agr. Expt. Sta. Bul.* 80:541–574.

Dreessen, J. 1961. Use of 2,4-D on wheat and pastures. *NAC News and Pesticide Review* 19(4):6–7.

Duclos. 1897. (Cited by Bissey and Butler.)

Fryer, J. D., and K. Kirkland. 1970. Field experiments to investigate long-term effects of repeated applications of MCPA, Tri-allate, simazine and linuron: report after 6 years. *Weed Res.* 10:133–158.

Holm, Leroy, and J. Herberger. 1970. World list of useful publications for the study of weeds and their control. *F.A.O. Internatl. Conf. on Weed Control.* Davis, Calif., p. 642–659.

Jones, L. R., and W. A. Orton. 1899. Killing weeds with chemicals. *Vt. Agr. Expt. Sta. 12th Ann. Rpt.,* pp. 182–188.

Klingman, G. C., and M. Wilcox. 1960. Chemical control of vegetation. *Amer. Ry. Engin. Assoc. Bul.* 556.

Korsmo, Emil. 1932. *Undersökelser* 1916–1923. Over ugressets skadevirkninger og dets bekjempelse I. Akerbruket. Oslo: Johnsen and Nielsens Boktrykkeri, 411 pp.

Martin. 1897. (Cited by Rademacher.)

Morettini, A. 1915. L'impiego dell'acido solforico per combattere le erbe infeste nel frumento. *Staz. Sper. Agr. Ital.* 48:693–716.

Rabate, E. 1911. Destruction des ravenelles par l'acide sulfurique. Jour. d'Agr. prat. (n.s. 21) 75:497–509.

————. 1926. The use of sulfuric acid against weeds and certain crop parasites. *Internatl. Rev. Sci. and Pract. Agr.* [Rome] (n.s.) 4:535–545.

Rademacher, B. 1940. The control of weeds in Germany. *Imp. Bur. Pastures and Forage Crops Bul.* 27:68–112.

Schultz, G. 1909. Ackersenf und Hederich. Deut. Lansw. Gesell Arb. 158. (Cited by Rademacher.)

Selleck, G. W. 1973. Pesticide benefits overshadow hazards. *Weeds Today* 4(4):14, 15, 22.

Stone, G. E. 1909. Effects of chemicals on vegetation. *Mass. Agr. Expt. Sta. 21st Ann. Rpt.,* pp. 62–72.

Wilcox, E. V. 1914. Killing weeds with arsenite of soda. *Hawaii Agr. Expt. Sta. Press. Bul.* 30:1–15.

10

Properties and Functions of Herbicides

Of the millions of possible chemical compounds only a few are useful herbicides. What sorts of compounds are these?

High phytotoxicity is the first prerequisite. Only compounds that are capable of destroying weeds at dosages ranging from a few ounces to a few pounds per acre are used in our current arsenal of weed killers. For example, 2,4-D will kill the cruciferous weeds in an acre of grain at ½ lb or less; paraquat at ½ lb per acre will knock down common annual weeds in preparation of a seed bed for maize; trifluralin applied preplant incorporated will control weeds in cotton at ¾ lb per acre; bromacil at 1.6 to 3.2 lb per acre will control many annual and some perennial weeds in a citrus grove; picloram alone or mixed with 2,4-D kills many perennial weeds and brush species at 2 to 3 lb per acre; glyphosate at similar rates kills Johnsongrass, Dallisgrass, Bermudagrass, and similar pests.

Second in importance is selectivity, the ability to kill weeds with little or no injury to the crop. This may result from differential killing of growing weeds as in mustard control in cereals, or by selective destruction of weed seeds or seedlings in the soil as with preemergence weed killers. Generally speaking, selectivity is relative; the mechanism may involve differential wetting, differential breakdown of the toxicant in the crop, or a selective effect on cell metabolism involving membrane integrity, protein synthesis, enzyme inhibition, or some other biochemical response.

Additional requirements for usefulness are low cost, convenience

177

of formulation and application, and low mammalian toxicity. The newer materials introduced during the past three decades must include these properties with no residue buildup to become registered under EPA jurisdiction. Public acceptance soon reflects how nearly these requirements have been met. For a summary of the chemicals, physical, and toxicological properties of herbicides in current use, the reader is referred to the *Herbicide Handbook of the Weed Science Society of America* (Anon, 1974).

CHEMICAL AND PHYSICAL PROPERTIES

Chemical compounds in general, including herbicides, can be divided into two groups: polar and nonpolar. Polar compounds have electrical charges; the valence charges of ions, H^+, OH^-, etc.; covalence forces of shared electrons as in benzene; and coordinate cova-

Table 10-1. *Physical Properties of Some Common Compounds Including Water*

Name	Formula	Molecular weight	Melting point, °C	Boiling point, °C
Methane	CH_4	16	–84	–1.53
Ammonia	NH_3	17	–77.3	–38.5
Water	H_2O	18	0	100
Hydrogen cyanide	HCN	27	–15	26.1
Hydrogen sulfide	H_2S	34	–83.8	–60.2
Hydrogen chloride	HCL	36	–112	–84
Carbon dioxide	CO_2	44	–57	–80*
Nitrous oxide	N_2O	44	–102.3	–89.4
Sulfur dioxide	SO_2	64	–76.1	–10
Sulfur trioxide	SO_3	80	16.8	44.9
Octane	C_8H_{18}	114	–56.6	125.5
Carbon tetrachloride	CCl_4	152	–19.5	76

*Sublimes.

lence forces characteristic of such compounds of hydrogen with oxygen (H_2O), fluorine (HF), nitrogen (NH_3), chlorine (HCl), or sulfur (H_2S). These molecules tend to associate, and in the liquid state they attain a quasi-lattice structure.

Water is a polar compound of very unusual properties; its molecular weight is only 18, yet it is a liquid at ordinary temperatures. Table 10-1 gives the physical properties of a number of compounds of similar or greater molecular weight.

Because of their residual valence forces, water molecules attract each other strongly, resulting in a high internal pressure or cohesion and a high surface tension. Furthermore, the fixed position of the regions of plus and minus charges (Fig. 10–1) result in the molecules tending to coordinate into a crystal lattice structure. Such a structure is attained in ice; in the liquid, it is not completely attained, but there is an ever-present tendency to coordinate. This results in a high viscosity and contributes to the high cohesive force and hence the high surface tension of water.

Likewise, when a salt is placed in water, the water molecules saturate the force fields between the ions and reduce their mutual attraction; the ions can wander from their fixed places in the crystal; the salt dissolves in the water. This, coupled with the fact that the ions (polar) of a salt attract water molecules and so become hydrated, explains why water is such an excellent solvent for polar compounds.

FIGURE 10–1.   Tetrahedral arrangement of secondary valence forces around the water molecule.

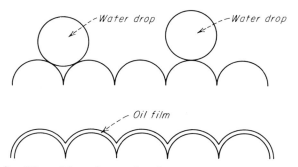

FIGURE 10–2.   Disposition of water droplets and oil film upon the waxy cuticle of a plant leaf.

Modern physical theory visualizes liquid water as being composed of two states: coordinated groups or clusters; and single, uncoordinated molecules forming a medium or matrix in which the clusters are embedded. Because the relaxation time for the formation and breakdown of the clusters is extremely short, these groups are termed flickering clusters. The phenomena of Brownian movement and membrane permeability to water support the flickering cluster concept (Crafts, 1968).

From the above discussion, several conclusions may be drawn with respect to the role of water in herbicidal solutions. Related to its high internal pressure or cohesion, water is more dense than many common liquids, particularly the oils. This gives a water spray driving force and aids penetration of dense vegetation.

Having high surface tension, water tends to form large, spherical droplets that do not readily wet the waxy cuticle of many leaves (Fig. 10–2). This is the basis for the differential wetting characteristic of many selective spray solutions.

Being a highly polar liquid, water serves as an excellent solvent and carrier for herbicidal chemicals of polar nature, such as the salts of common acids and bases.

Other polar compounds that are common herbicides are sulfuric acid, ammate, sodium chlorate, and the salts of phenols, cresols, trichloroacetic acid, chlorophenoxyacetic acid, propionic acid, butyric acid, picolinic acid, di- and trichloropropionic acids, maleic hydrazide, amino triazole, and many others.

Leopold et al. (1960) have studied the adsorption of a number of chlorinated derivatives of phenoxyacetic acid and have found a strong inverse correlation between adsorption and water solubility; phenoxyacetic acid is the most soluble and least adsorbed, and successive chlorinations decrease in solubility and increase in adsorption onto charcoal. From this it is apparent that solubility in water and polarity of the molecule go hand in hand. Among the chlorinated phenoxyacetic acids in both the disubstituted and trisubstituted series, the weakest auxins have the lowest adsorption values. Leopold et al. point out the possible relationships between adsorption, toxicity, selectivity, and mobility in soils.

Nonpolar compounds are relatively uncharged molecules held together by van der Waals forces and they usually exhibit low water solubility and high oil solubility. Prominent among these are the petroleum derivatives.

OILS

Hydrocarbons (compounds of hydrogen and carbon) derived from petroleum, coal, or shale are essential components in a number of herbicides: (1) Crude oil and distillates from petroleum or coal tar may be used directly as foliage-contact killers. (2) A number of higher-grade distillates are used as selective oils. (3) Aromatic fractions recovered by different refining processes are used as foliage-contact herbicides and as solvent and filming agents in emulsions. (4) Petroleum and coal-tar derivatives form the starting point for many organic syntheses that result in herbicidal compounds of complex organic nature (Crafts and Reiber, 1948).

Hydrocarbons are of four main types: saturated chain compounds (aliphatic), such as propane, butane, pentane, octane, etc.; saturated ring compounds (naphthenes), such as cyclopentane and cyclohexane; unsaturated chain compounds (olefins), such as ethylene and butadiene; unsaturated ring compounds (aromatics), such as benzene and naphthalene.

Of these four types the first two, the saturated hydrocarbons, are of low toxicity; the unsaturated ones are of high toxicity. The aromatic compounds are most useful as herbicides.

PROPERTIES OF WEED-KILLING OILS

To use oil sprays in weed control, the operator must know something about their composition and their effects on plants. In this way he will be able to choose the best oil for his own needs (Table 10–2).

Table 10-2. Physical Properties of Two Hydrocarbons and Water

Properties	Hexane	Benzene	Water
Molecular weight	86	78	18
Boiling point	68.7	80.4	100
Melting point	-95.5	5.4	0
Dielectric constant	1.8	2.28	81
Surface tension	20.5	31.6	75.6

In the oil trade, all oils are described by sets of specifications. These are either required by law or used by the manufacturer as a standard of quality for his own products. Every product must meet the specifications which its manufacturer has set up for it. These standards are intended to show a product's ability to do the job for which it was made. Certain oils now being tested as weed-killing sprays were not originally intended for this use. Thus specifications listed for these oils do not necessarily show how well they will act as weed killers; there are no absolute specifications for weed-killing oils. The only sure way to find out if an oil is useful as a weed killer is by tests in the field. Hence, in buying oils for weed killing, the user will have to rely on the ability of the oil dealer to supply a satisfactory product.

OIL TOXICITY

Little is known of the mechanics of oil toxicity to plant cells. According to some theories, fat solvents are toxic because they can penetrate the cuticle, enter the living cells, and disturb the delicate balance of the lipoid phase of the protoplasm of plant cells (solubilization; van Overbeek and Blondeau, 1954; Fig. 10–3). Thus an oil having a strong tendency to accumulate in the protoplasm would be more toxic than one that remains outside the cell. However, the fact that pure hexane is somewhat toxic and that toxicity increases through the series hexane, hexene, cyclohexane, cyclohexene, and benzene would seem to imply that toxicity depends upon configuration. Another factor is the increase in polarity of the molecules through this series.

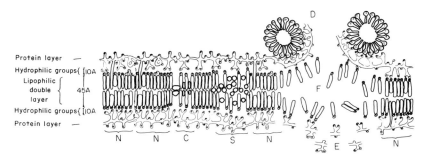

FIGURE 10–3. Mechanism of oil toxicity according to van Overbeek and Blondeau. The protein layers (N) bound a hydrophilic double layer; retain the sap within the cell. At S, xylene molecules are solubilized into the fatty layer. At C, polycyclic hydrocarbons are pushing apart the units. Detergent micelles at D have disrupted the protein layer, rendering the fatty layer unstable at F. At E agents that liquify the protein cause a similar disruption.

Two distinct processes are involved in the toxic action of an oil herbicide: (1) penetration of the cuticle and (2) reaction with the protoplasm. Because the plant cuticle is itself oillike in nature, an oily substance (nonpolar) will go through it more readily than a polar compound. Considering the analogues of benzene, we find that toxicity increases through the series benzene, methyl benzene (toluene), dimethyl benzene (xylene), trimethyl benzene, as follows:

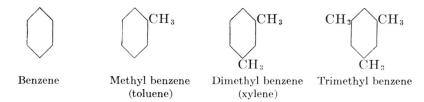

In di- and trimethyl benzenes other possible positions of substitution make for many isomeric compounds not shown here. Toxicity of the separate isomers is not well known.

Since the above series becomes more oillike and hence less polar with additional methyl substitutions, the conclusion must be that the methyl substitutions do not affect inherent reactivity or toxicity of the benzene molecule but that they promote penetration into the cells. There is considerable evidence that this is the case.

Since, in the use of herbicides, increase in toxicity provides convenience and efficiency in handling of the product as well as conservation of the basic chemicals, much research has been conducted to find highly toxic chemicals. From the consideration of the toxicity of the hydrocarbons given above, it is apparent that increase in polarity enhances the inherent reactivity of a molecule, whereas decrease in polarity promotes penetration. Since these two processes are opposed, there must be an optimum point in the balance between them, and this, in reality, represents a compromise between toxicity resulting from polarity of the molecule and compatibility with the cuticle resulting from oillike properties.

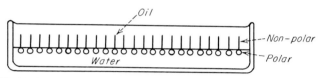

FIGURE 10-4.   Molecules of an emulsion stabilizer at an oil-water interface. The polar ends reside in the water surface whereas the nonpolar ends penetrate the oil surface.

In addition to the penetrating properties and reactivity of oils, volatility is important, as it determines the length of time that the oil may affect the plant cells. Light oils may evaporate in a few minutes; heavy oils may remain on the plant for weeks or months.

EMULSION STABILIZERS

In addition to the polar solvent (water) and the nonpolar carrier (oil), a third type of compound is commonly used in herbicides: the *surfactant, spreader,* or *emulsion stabilizer.* This type of compound has molecules that combine polar and nonpolar groups. The polar portion may be a salt, such as sodium sulfate, and the nonpolar portion may be composed on an oil chain, a higher alcohol, or some other organic radical. Such a molecule then will have a polar end and a nonpolar end (Fig. 10-4). Emulsion stabilizers tend to reduce the interfacial tension between two immiscible liquids (e.g., oil and water); hence they stabilize the surface.

When an oil-water mixture with such a stabilizer included is violently agitated, one phase is broken up into very small droplets; the other phase remains continuous.

In a normal oil-in-water emulsion, the oil breaks up and the water remains continuous. In an invert emulsion, this situation is reversed; i.e., it is a water-in-oil emulsion.

The oil droplets in a normal emulsion have the stabilizer molecules oriented around the outside with the polar portions on the surface (Fig. 10-5). Having definite and like charges, such droplets tend to repel each other and do not coalesce as would pure oil droplets. Hence if they are reduced to such small size that they are effectively stirred by thermal agitation, they remain at a uniform concentration throughout the mass of the emulsion. Such an emulsion is stable.

The emulsion stabilizer in a foliage-contact spray also serves as a wetting agent. The same coupling power that enables it to stabilize a water-oil interface makes it a good surface-tension reducer and hence allows the emulsion to assume a low angle of attack on the waxy cuticle. Wetting is necessary in such a herbicide because only the tissues that are wet are killed.

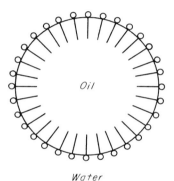

Water

FIGURE 10-5.   Emulsion stabilizer molecules on the surface of an oil droplet immersed in water. Stability is maintained by: (a) thermal agitation which tends to keep the droplets in constant motion and (b) like charges that make the droplets tend to repel each other.

Invert emulsions containing 2,4-D esters are currently being used where there is danger of crop injury from spray drift. Akesson et al. (1960) explain two advantages of invert emulsions: (1) being viscous, these formulations may be put out as coarse sprays through special nozzles to reduce drift that results in crop damage or toxic residues to a minimum, and (2) losses of the spray material from drift are virtually eliminated. Another advantage is that, in the invert emulsion droplet, oil constitutes the external phase; hence, on most plant surfaces, retention of spray droplets will be higher. Thus use of invert emulsions may permit phytotoxic chemicals to be employed in situations where normal emulsions are prohibited, and efficiency of application may be materially increased.

Emulsion stabilizers may perform a third important function: as a *penetrating agent*. From the dye industry it is known that mahogany soaps (petroleum sodium sulfonates) aid in the penetration of dyes, presumably by softening or loosening the microfibrils of the textile fibers. Such an action might open slightly the intermolecular spaces in the cuticle and allow a more ready penetration of the toxic chemicals. Some experimental evidence indicates this to be true.

The Agricultural Research Service of the U.S. Department of Agriculture is conducting extensive studies on the relation of surfactants to effectiveness of herbicides (Anon, 1961). These people find that a single surfactant may increase, decrease, or not affect the action of a herbicide. One such reagent increased the activity of dalapon sevenfold and trebled amitrole activity on corn; activity of 2,4-D and DNBP were unchanged. On soybeans the same surfactant doubled the action of dalapon and amitrole and trebled the action of 2,4-D and DNBP. One surfactant increased the activity of 2,4-D on mustard without increasing its toxicity to corn and other grass species. This work is described in more detail by Jansen et al. (1961). They provide activity indices, obtained by averaging a contact injury rating, a general injury rating, and height and weight reduction percentages for 63 surfactants, including nonionic, anionic, cationic, ampholytic, and blended materials. The herbicides, dalapon, 2,4-D, DNBP, and amitrole, were tested on corn and soybean in the greenhouse studies.

The most common response to this large group of surfactants was a progressive enhancement of herbicidal activity through the concentration range of 0.01, 0.1, and 1.0 percent. Some surfactants brought about progressive suppression of herbicidal activity, whereas a few had little or no effect. Many showed marked phytotoxicity at the highest concentrations; some produced stimulations at the low concentration levels. Phytotoxic effects were not necessarily the same on both plant species with all herbicides. No correlation was discernible between any one of the effects of a surfactant and the ionogenic class to which it belonged. Since the evaluation of these surfactants was made largely upon contact injury effect, results of the tests may not apply in the use of systemic herbicides.

METHODS OF USING HERBICIDES

Selective and Nonselective Herbicides

Both selective and nonselective herbicides are useful in vegetation management. Selective herbicides are used in field crops, forage crops, on pastures and ranges, in forests, and for controlling aquatic weeds in lakes, streams, irrigation ditches, and drainage canals.

Nonselective herbicides find use as preemergence treatments on crop lands, as directed sprays in corn, milo, sugar cane, and cotton after the plants have gained some height, for total weed control in nontillage agriculture and pasture renovation, and for total weed control on nonagricultural lands in innumerable situations.

FOLIAGE APPLICATIONS

Once weeds have emerged and become established, foliage applications are the only practical means for killing them. Success of foliar sprays depends upon a number of factors, principal of which are the nature of the solution and the type of leaf surfaces involved.

NATURE OF PLANT SURFACES

Plants originated in water; some still live continuously in water and some may live part of their lives in water, part on land. Those that live emerged from water or on the land possess a moistureproof waxy coating, the cuticle, which reduces or eliminates excessive loss of water from foliage.

The cuticle is a lipoid layer, nonpolar in properties, and relatively impervious to water either in liquid or in vapor form. It is electronegative in charge; water, polar solvents, and particularly anions (negatively charged ions) do not readily penetrate the leaf surface; nonpolar compounds enter leaves much more readily.

In addition to their chemical and electrical properties, leaf surfaces of many plants are uneven, being minutely ridged or made up of the outer walls of spherical cells. They often have hairs or wax protrusions of various shapes, sizes, and composition; these are the waxy bloom found on fruits, leaves, and stems.

Water droplets, as of a spray, assume spherical forms with minimum contact surfaces on such a leaf (Fig. 10-2). If the leaf is in a vertical position or if the spray droplet has considerable momentum as it strikes the leaf, an aqueous spray may bounce or run off to a large extent (Fig. 10-6). Oil, on the other hand, forms a thin film that readily spreads over the leaf (Fig. 10-2); if excess is applied, the oil film may creep downward along the leaf surface; on grasses it may run into and destroy the apical growing point. Adhesion of the oil depends upon the facts (1) that it is nonpolar like the leaf surface and (2) that it has low surface tension and spreads readily. Oils of low viscosity may, under the influence of gravity, spread so thinly that they have little killing power; such oils must be fortified to be used as weed killers.

SPRAY RETENTION

Both the over-all effectiveness and the degree of selectivity may be determined by the volume of spray that is retained on the leaves of the crop and weed species. Pubescence, leaf angle, contour of the leaf surface, bloom, and surfactants all enter into the retention of sprays by leaves.

Ennis et al. (1952) found that different formulations varied

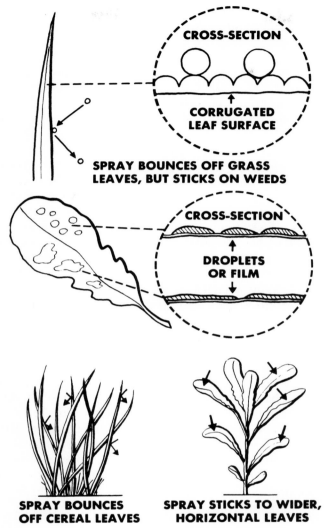

FIGURE 10-6. Diagrams showing the way in which water and aqueous sprays wet cereals and broadleaf weeds. (From Calif. Agr. Ext. Serv. Cir. 157.)

greatly in their retention on leaves. Some leaves (e.g., nutsedge) are readily wetted by pure water. Ennis and his coworkers found that peanut, cabbage, and oat leaves, among the species studied, repelled pure aqueous sprays, whereas 1 percent Tergitol solution was retained by all species in the test. A 1 percent solution of Vatsol K also proved to wet the leaves of some 22 species, including 6 grasses.

Dorschner and Buchholtz (1957) studied the injurious effects of varying spray volumes, different vegetation heights, and three 2,4-D concentrations on alfalfa undersown in oats. High spray volume (40 gpa) resulted in greater penetration of the foliage than low volume (5 gpa). However, toxicity to alfalfa was less from the high volumes because of poorer retention by the crop. Interception of sprays by oat-leaf canopies increased from 6-in. through 12- and 18-in. stages. The 12-in. height of oats was optimum for alfalfa survival. The canopy at this height retained sufficient spray to afford the alfalfa appreciable protection, and the legume had not been shaded sufficiently to make it weak and thus susceptible to 2,4-D injury.

Day and Jordan (1961) have investigated the retention of liquid in Bermudagrass by dipping shoots and measuring the increases in weight. Retention was greatest for distilled water and low concentrations of surfactant. It decreased by 25 percent as surfactant concentration was increased from 0.01 to 0.16 percent. Distribution was more uniform when surfactant was present. In four different populations of Bermudagrass, retention of 0.01 percent surfactant solution ranged from 247 gpa to 536 gpa. There were wide variations in the proportion of the liquid held by green leaves, green stems, and dead tissues. Dead tissues held ten times more water per unit weight than live stems and two to four times as much as green leaves.

FOLIAR PENETRATION.

Not only must a herbicide be retained by plant leaves to be effective, it must penetrate and enter or come in intimate contact with the living cells. To be translocated it must enter the symplast, migrate to the phloem, and move in the assimilate stream. Currier and Dybing (1959) have reviewed the topic of foliar penetration in detail, and Dybing and Currier (1959, 1961) have described methods for studying foliar penetration. Both formulation of the herbicide and physiological condition of the plants must be considered in arriving at the most effective method to use a herbicide (Fig. 10–7).

FUNCTIONS OF CONSTITUENTS OF SPRAY SOLUTIONS

In the spray method the spray solution may perform several functions, depending upon its constituents.

CARRIER

In many sprays the bulk of the volume is made up of a carrier or diluent. This extends the active ingredients so that they cover the plant surfaces evenly. Water is the most common carrier, and it lends driving force to the spray solution because of its high density and surface tension. Oil is a better carrier than water because it has a low surface tension and high wetting ability. This means that, instead of

FIGURE 10-7. Penetration of a fluorescent dye into leaves having open stomata as contrasted with leaves having closed stomata. Upper pair, leaves with open stomata dipped halfway into the dye; lower pair, leaves with close stomata similarly treated. (Photograph by courtesy of C. D. Dybing and H. B. Currier.)

running off the plants as water does, the oil creeps over them. Oil may be used where creeping of the spray solution into the crowns of grasses and rosettes of weeds is required.

FILMING AGENT

In oil-emulsion sprays, oil may be used to form a thin film over the plant surface that holds the toxicant in intimate contact with the cells. Oil may be included in foliage-contact sprays largely for this purpose.

WETTING AGENT

Where aqueous sprays are used to kill mixed weeds including grasses, a wetting agent or surfactant may be used to aid in spreading the water over the waxy surface of the plant leaves.

EMULSION STABILIZER

Where oil emulsions are used, a stabilizer may be employed to lower the interfacial tension between the oil and the water. This prevents aggregation of the disperse phase and inhibits breaking of the emulsion, prolonging the stability of the emulsion.

SOLVENT OR COUPLING AGENT

Where the solubility of the toxic ingredient is not suited to the diluent or to the filming agent, a cosolvent or coupling agent is often included. Polyethylene glycol was employed in early 2,4-D formulations; alcohol and aromatic oils are used in pentachlorophenol formulations; tributyl phosphate, methyl cellosolve, diacetone alcohol, and a host of other materials are being used in modern herbicides.

TOXICANT

The new organic herbicides are extremely toxic. In many formulations they may make up only a fraction of 1 percent of the total mix. Toxicants originally present in many oils are so low in effectiveness that they are not economical to use; fortification with the highly toxic organic compounds is now common practice. In the above discussion the characteristics of ingredients of herbicidal solutions are treated separately. Often one material will serve two purposes. For example, a surface-tension or interfacial-tension reducer may act as both a wetting agent and an emulsion stabilizer. Likewise, such a reagent may act as a cosolvent where the toxicant is not soluble in the carrier. Another case of dual use is that of oil as a filming agent, where the same oil may serve as a solvent for the toxicant.

To illustrate these points, in the fortified-oil emulsion spray consisting of water, an aromatic oil, an emulsion stabilizer, and a substituted phenol, water is the carrier; the aromatic oil is the filming agent and acts as the phenol solvent; the emulsion stabilizer acts as a wetting agent, an interfacial-tension reducer to stabilize the emulsion, and in some cases it aids in dissolving the toxicant; the substituted phenol is the toxicant upon which the killing action wholly depends. The other ingredients have very little toxicity in the amounts applied in the spray.

TYPES OF HERBICIDES

Some herbicidal materials are applied as sprays to be absorbed through the leaves; others are applied through the soil for absorption by roots; some may be partially absorbed by leaves and later washed into the soil where they are picked up by the roots.

SELECTIVE FOLIAGE CONTACT SPRAYS

Because of differences in the types of leaves, spray liquids, and toxicants used in weed control, a number of selective methods are possible.

Owing to *selective wetting*, an aqueous solution of iron sulfate, copper sulfate, sulfuric acid, potassium cyanate, a dinitrophenol compound, or 2,4-D may be applied to a mixed plant population, resulting in death of many broadleaf species and survival, with little or no damage, of grasses and several other tolerant plants. If 2,4-D is omitted from the above list, onions, garlic, peas, and a number of other crops may be protected.

Selectivity of oils on crops of the carrot family and of 2,4-D, when used in an oil or emulsion spray on cereals, depends not upon selective wetting but upon biochemical selectivity. Here the protoplasm of the cells of different plants responds differently to these toxic materials, possibly because of differences in the enzyme systems of the plants. Table 9–1 lists many selective herbicides.

NONSELECTIVE FOLIAGE CONTACT SPRAYS

Where it is desired to kill all weed growth, as on irrigation ditches, driveways, firebreaks, etc., all plants must be wet. Here oils are indicated; many toxic weed oils are available. Where they are not sufficiently toxic to kill all the plant tissues they can cover, they may be *fortified* by adding substituted phenol compounds. Where such fortified oils are made so toxic that they will kill more tissues than they will cover, they may be extended by adding water to increase the volume. Sodium arsenite, sodium chlorate, diquat, and salts of the dinitro compounds, when formulated with wetting agents, may be used as general-contact herbicides. Certain aromatic oils, chlorinated benzenes, and the compound acrolein are used to kill aquatic weeds by contact action. Table 9–1 lists a number of general-contact materials. Many of these are proving very useful in nontillage programs; paraquat is used in place of weed oil in orchards, vineyards, and on roadsides.

TRANSLOCATED HERBICIDES

Translocated herbicides are those that move from the locus of application to some other part of the plant where they exert their toxic action. They move through the vascular tissues of the plant at speeds that exceed diffusion or protoplasmic streaming. They are used principally to kill perennial weeds, although some kill young annual weeds.

Plant physiologists have two useful terms for discussing mechanisms responsible for translocation of solutes in plants; these are *symplast* and *apoplast*. The symplast is the total living portion of the plant; the term implies that all living cells are interconnected with protoplasmic connections, forming a continuum. The symplast is bounded by the plasmolemma membrane on its external surface and by the tonoplasts that limit the vacuoles of living cells. Crafts (1961) has proposed that the sieve tubes of the phloem are included within the symplast since they are living cells.

The apoplast is the sum total of nonliving cellwall material that surrounds and contains the symplast. Crafts (1961) considers the xylem system to be apoplastic since its conduits are nonliving and its cellwalls are not separated from the lumina by membranes.

According to these concepts, movement of water and salts from roots to leaves in the transpiration stream would be apoplastic. Movement of plant foods in the sieve-tube system of the phloem from sources to sinks is symplastic; this is the assimilate stream. Herbicides may move in either or both of these streams depending on the point of application and the chemical nature of the molecules.

Many herbicidal molecules, including the symmetrical triazines, the substituted ureas, and the uracils, are readily absorbed from the soil by roots and translocated to the foliar parts of the plant via the xylem in the transpiration stream. Under special conditions of severe water deficit, an acid solution of arsenic, applied to the foliage during the night when evaporation is slow, rapidly kills the foliage, rendering the cells permeable; the arsenic solution and the cell sap may be sucked back into the xylem and translocated apoplastically into the roots which will die. This acid-arsenical method is no longer used, but at one time it was the principal method for controlling field bindweed.

Transport through the phloem, on the other hand, depends upon the functioning of living cells and requires that the spray chemical be low in contact toxicity, be of the proper molecular structure to penetrate both cuticle and mesophyll, and be toxic when accumulated in actively growing or storing tissues. For effective herbicidal action on the woody or deep-rooted perennial plants upon which such sprays are used, the plant must be actively moving food materials, particularly into the roots. The 2,4-D type of herbicide meets these rigid requirements. In controlled greenhouse experiments, 2,4-D appears to be the form most actively absorbed and translocated. An acid pH, causing association of the 2,4-D molecule, has proved effective in enhancing 2,4-D absorption. Different esters of 2,4-D have very different properties with respect to phytotoxicity; 2,4-D salts are usually inferior. Some of the heavy (low-volatile) esters apparently are superior to the lighter ones, particularly under semiarid or arid conditions. There is evidence that 2,4-D esters are hydrolyzed during penetration of leaves and that the 2,4-D ion is translocated in the phloem tissue (Crafts, 1960). Morre and Rogers (1960b) and Szabo (1963) also found evidence for hydrolysis of 2,4-D esters.

Other readily translocated herbicides, in addition to the chlorinated phenoxy compounds, include the ring compounds amitrole and 2,3,6-trichlorobenzoic acid, the chlorinated aliphatic acid dalapon, picloram, glyphosate, and the dormancy inducer and grass killer, maleic hydrazide. Evidently, certain molecular configurations make for ready translocation, but little is known concerning the particular requirements.

Comparative studies have shown that, among translocated herbicides, 2,4-D and its analogues are often bound or fixed in plant cells and hence are not so readily mobile as amitrole, maleic hydrazide, dalapon, picloram, glyphosate, and the chlorinated benzoic acid derivatives (Crafts, 1959).

Studies with ^{14}C-labeled herbicidal molecules have proved that there are various degrees of mobility in both symplast and apoplast. Table 10–3 presents information on the mobility of a number of herbicides, growth regulators, and surfactants in plants as determined by autoradiography.

APPLICATIONS THROUGH THE SOIL

Foliage sprays have advantages in the control of growing weeds, particularly perennials, annuals treated selectively, and for general contact action on weeds in noncropped areas. Soil applications are useful for preplant, preemergence, and early postemergence selective treatments. Soil applications are useful in controlling all weeds in nonagricultural areas. And soil applications of dichlobenil and trifluralin by the sprayblade method are proving effective in controlling deeprooted perennials, particularly in orchards, vineyards, and on valuable crop lands where soil sterilization is too costly.

Recent work by Gentner (1973) indicates that progress is finally being made against yellow nutsedge with three soil-borne herbicides, acetochlor, destun, and alachlor; crop species used in the tests, from most to least susceptibility, were okra, cabbage, cucumber, and flax. Thus selective herbicides are being discovered to control what is considered to be one of the world's worst weeds.

SELECTIVE ROOT TREATMENTS

In recent years, a great number of selective preplant and preemergence chemicals have been found (Table 9–1). These are all applied through the soil to prevent germination of weed seeds or to kill the weeds in the young seedling stages. Postemergence, soil-borne herbicides are used selectively in crops by directed application, avoiding the

Table 10-3. Mobility of Tracers in Plants

(Mobility varies between compounds; it may also vary between plants and between various treatments.)

	Free mobility			Limited mobility			Little or no mobility
	In apoplast	In symplast	In both	In apoplast	In symplast	In both	
	Atrazine		Amino acids (some)	Barban	2,4-D	Naptalam	DCPA
	Bioxone	Amiben	Amitrole	Dichlobenil	2,4-DP	Amino acids (some)	2,4-DB
		Fenac				Ammonium thiocyanate	
	Bromacil	Maleic hydrazide	Benazolin	Diquat	MCPA	$77AsO_4\equiv$	DNBP
	Chlorpropham	Sucrose	Dalapon–^{14}C, dalapon–^{36}Cl	Paraquat	2,4,5-T		DNOC
	Diuron		Dicamba		TPA	Diallate	Endothall
	Fluorodiphen		Glyphosate			Duraset	Nitrofen
	Fluometuron		Picloram			EPTC	PCP
	Metobromuron		Pyriclor			Gibberellin	Trifluralin
	Monuron		TBA			IAA	
	Propham					Ioxynil	
	Pyrazon					Propanil	
	Simazine						
	Sodium lauryl sulfate						
	T-1947						
	TCA						
	Tween 20						
	Tween 80						

Note: Compounds having no alternative designations were ^{14}C-labeled. Maleic hydrazide, picloram, TBA, sodium, rubidium, and cesium move from roots into the ambient culture medium. 2,4-D and many other compounds have been found to do this under special circumstances.

growing crop plants. They may be used soon after emergence by applying a narrow band on each side of the crop row; they may be applied at lay-by time by the same method to kill late-emerging weeds that might interfere with harvest of the crop. These chemicals represent several types of selectivity and they may be used on a wide variety of crops, as noted in subsequent chapters.

NONSELECTIVE ROOT TREATMENTS

The use of nonselective, chemical soil sterilants is an important phase of weed control. Annual weeds are successfully controlled by using a chemical that is localized in topsoil. The application of nonfixed chemicals should be made in the spring to avert leaching by rains; or, a well-timed treatment may be made at other seasons when adequate time for contact between the roots and the toxicant is provided. Sprinklers may be used to wash the chemical into the soil.

Many chemicals are available now for nonselective root treatment. Some are true soil sterilants, having a broad spectrum of susceptible plants. Others may be used selectively at low dosage with a great broadening of the species spectrum as dosage is increased. Broadening of the control spectrum may also be accomplished by mixing chemicals of various selectivity.

Perennial-weed control by carbon disulfide and chlorates has been a common practice for many years. The manifest advantage of treating perennials through the soil is that all roots may be contacted and that the physiological condition of the plant is not usually critical in the success of the method. Disadvantages are the strict requirements for distribution of the various chemicals, the effects of the soil mass in inactivating the chemical, and the general lack of uniformity of soils with respect to structure and contour. Addition of alachlor, dazomet, EPTC, acetochlor, destun, pebulate, and vernolate has greatly amplified the uses that can be made of nonselective root treatments against perennial weeds.

INCORPORATION OF SOIL-BORNE HERBICIDES

When preemergence herbicides were introduced in many parts of the United States, they revolutionized weed control in row crops. In the more arid western states, however, they failed because of insufficient rainfall to leach them into the soil profile where weed seeds germinate. Soil incorporation into moist soil corrected this deficiency. Various methods, from cross harrowing to mechanical incorporation with power-driven incorporators, have been used. Incorporation has become standard practice where top soil is dry at the time of application; the practice makes for uniform distribution of the herbicide through the surface layer of soil, and it insures against failure of rainfall. Under some conditions sprinkler irrigation may be used.

INGREDIENTS OF HERBICIDAL FORMULATIONS—TOXICANTS

In the early years of weed control, inorganic compounds were used. The first organic compound to assume any importance was sodium dinitro-o-cresylate, developed in France in 1933 and introduced into the United States in 1937, under the name Sinox. This compound is an orange dye, readily soluble in water at the concentrations used in weed control. The commercial preparation is a dense suspension or slurry of fine crystals. It consists of 30 percent active ingredients and 70 percent water. The dry salt is flammable and is one of a number of compounds used in explosives. For this reason the proprietary material is marketed as a mixture with water. Ammonium dinitro-o-sec-butylphenylate is usually marketed as a solution in some one of the lower alcohols, at a concentration of 1 lb per gal.

Dust masks, such as those used to exclude injurious dusts from the respiratory passages, should be worn by spray operators who are exposed to the spray mist. Used as sprays, they are not flammable and not hazardous on dried vegetation or on clothing. Since sodium dinitro-o-cresylate is flammable when dry, it should not be allowed to dry out in open cans and should be washed from all equipment after use.

USE OF ACTIVATOR

The addition of an acid salt, such as ammonium sulfate or sodium bisulfate, to the sodium dinitro-o-cresylate solution greatly enhances its effectiveness. These salts, commonly called "activators," increase the hydrogen-ion concentration of the solution; this, in turn, brings about an increase in the concentration of dinitro-o-cresylic acid in the solution. Though less soluble in water than the sodium salt, this toxicant is more soluble in the fatty cuticle layers of the weeds and consequently is able to penetrate into the cells more rapidly. Though the "activated" solution becomes more toxic to all plants and consequently tends to burn the cereal somewhat more, this loss in selectivity of the solution is more than compensated for by its increased toxicity and has the practical advantage of allowing an appreciable reduction in dosage rate for spraying mustards and other common, broadleaf weeds. In addition, it increases the effectiveness of a more concentrated solution to the point where it can be used to control species, such as wild, purple, and hairy vetches (*Vicia* spp.), corn cockle, hungerweed, sunflower, and black nightshade, that are not ordinarily controlled successfully by selective herbicides.

Toxicity of Substituted Phenols

Studies on the toxicity of the analogues of benzene show increasing toxicity through the series benzene, phenol, nitrobenzene.

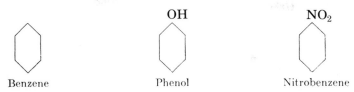

Benzene   Phenol   Nitrobenzene

The dielectric constants of these compounds are 2.3, 9.7, and 35.7, respectively. Dinitrophenol is highly toxic, but its symmetry and hence its polarity vary with the location of the second nitro group on the molecule.

Picric acid, a trinitrophenol, has been used in histology for many years as a rapid killing agent for fixing tissues.

Phenol has the formula

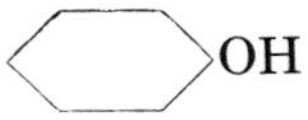

$$\langle\ \rangle\text{—OH}$$

and trinitrophenol, the formula

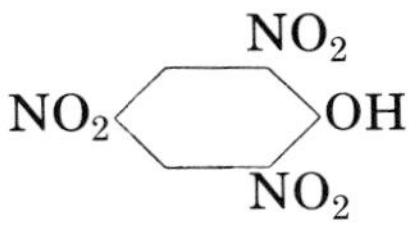

$$\text{NO}_2\text{—}\langle\ \rangle\text{—OH}$$

with NO_2 and NO_2

Orthocresol has the formula

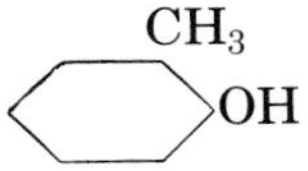

$$\langle\ \rangle\text{—OH}$$

with CH_3

and dinitro-*o*-cresol, the formula

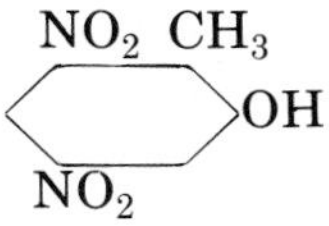

$$\langle\ \rangle\text{—OH}$$

with NO_2 CH_3 and NO_2

From the similarity of these compounds, it seems logical that the dinitro-*o*-cresol should be highly toxic, and experiments have proved that it is. Both picric acid and dinitro-*o*-cresol, which as a dye has the name "Victoria yellow," are low in solubility. In order to overcome this difficulty and prepare a derivative that may be readily dissolved in water, dinitro-*o*-cresol is treated with sodium hydroxide to give the corresponding sodium salt,

$$\underset{NO_2}{\overset{NO_2 \quad CH_3}{\bigcirc}}ONa$$

As mentioned above, one of the first substituted phenols to be introduced was sodium dinitro-*o*-cresyllate (Sinox). This material was for several years the leading selective herbicide for killing broadleaf weeds in cereals, peas, flax, grass, and onions. Later introductions were dinitro-*o*-cresol, dinitro-*o*-*sec*-butylphenol, dinitro-*o*-*sec*-amylphenol, and their amine and ammonium salts. Pentachlorophenol and its sodium salt are also used. The parent phenols are soluble in oils, and their amine, ammonium, or sodium salts are used in aqueous solution. The parent compounds serve as foliage-contact herbicides, the salts as selective weed killers. Studies on the toxicities of the dinitro compounds of the series phenol, methylphenol (cresol), ethylphenol, propylphenol, butylphenol, and amylphenol proved that toxicity increased with increasing length of the side chain up to the butyl compound, and then dropped off slightly with the amyl compound.

All side chains in this series were in the ortho position and, above the ethyl substitution, the chains were branched (iso compounds). Ortho chain substitutions are more toxic than meta or para.

CHLOROPHENOLS.

Another substituted phenol series showing increases in toxicity is phenol, chlorophenol, dichlorophenol, trichlorophenol, tetrachlorophenol, and pentachlorophenol. The last compound is about equal in toxicity to dinitromethylphenol (dinitrocresol). Dinitrobutylphenol is about three times as toxic as dinitrocresol and pentachlorophenol. The above two series of substituted phenols are oil-soluble compounds. The dinitrophenols increase in oil solubility with increasing length of the aliphatic side chain. The butyl compound is a dark, oily, crystalline substance that melts around 30°C; the amyl compound is a liquid at ordinary temperatures. Both compounds are oillike enough to dissolve in ordinary diesel fuel in the proportions used in common fortified-oil emulsion formulations (up to 1 lb per gal of oil). Pentachlorophenol is only slightly soluble in diesel fuel; aromatic oil of around 25 percent aromaticity is required to dissolve ½ lb per gal of oil; aromatic oil of 40 percent aromaticity is needed to hold 1 lb per gal. Tests on compounds with nitro and chloro substitutions show none so toxic as the dinitro-*o*-*sec*-butylphenol.

Pentachlorophenol is soluble in aromatic oils but not in water; to render it soluble, it is reacted with sodium hydroxide to form the sodium salt. Both PCP and sodium pentachlorophenate are employed in weed control, the former in fortified oil emulsion as a general-contact herbicide, the latter in aqueous solution as a soil-borne toxicant against annual weeds.

INTRODUCTION OF 2,4-D

The introduction of 2,4-D into the field of weed control brought about a revolution in agriculture that has changed not only weed-control methods, but the whole point of view of crop production. When it became apparent that this novel chemical could eliminate most annual weeds in cereal crops at rates of 1 lb per acre or less, it was obvious that organic chemicals of high potency could be found to perform many functions useful to the grower. Within a very short time it was discovered that 2,4-D translocated in the assimilate stream and would kill roots of perennial weeds to appreciable depths; it could be applied through the soil as a preemergence treatment; it killed emerged aquatic weeds; it could be used as a hormone to set fruits on pineapples; and it caused typical hormone responses that in some instances were deleterious to crops.

CHEMISTRY OF 2,4-D COMPOUNDS

The chemical 2,4-dichlorophenoxyacetic acid is a white crystalline substance, very slightly soluble in water or in aliphatic oil, fairly soluble in aromatic oil (1 percent in benzene), and very soluble in ethyl alcohol and similar organic solvents. In early formulations polyethylene glycol was used to make the acid compatible with water in aqueous sprays. Soon, however, the salts and esters were introduced, and now many 2,4-D compounds are available.

In treating the problems of toxicity, solubility, and compatibility of 2,4-D compounds, we encounter a number of opposing factors. Considering water solubility, the series 2,4-D acid, ammonium salt, potassium salt, sodium salt, and alkanolamine salts represents increasing solubility paralleled by increasing polarity of the compounds. Although the increase in polarity should indicate a decrease in cuticle compatibility, the differences in toxicity through this series are not great when they are compared on an acid-equivalent basis at commonly recommended dosages.

The esters of 2,4-D are all relatively nonpolar compounds, and they increase in oiliness with increasing length of the aliphatic chain. The methyl ester, for instance, is a crystalline solid; all the higher esters are oily liquids at ordinary temperatures. Toxicity of all the esters on an acid-equivalent basis is recognized to be distinctly higher than that of the acid and salts. The factor is in the neighborhood of two.

Table 10-4. Percentage Composition and Molecular Weights of 2,4-D Compounds

No.	Compound	Molecular weight	Acid, %	Pounds required to contain 100 lb 2,4–D acid
1.	2,4–D acid	220	100	100
2.	NH$_4$ salt	237	93	108
3.	Na salt	242	91	110
4.	Na salt monohydrate	260	85	119
5.	Isopropanolamine	296	74	135
6.	Morpholine	306	71	139
7.	Diethanolamine	325	68	147
8.	Triethanolamine	369	60	166
9.	Methyl ester	234	94	106
10.	Ethyl ester	248	89	112
11.	Isopropyl ester	262	84	119
12.	Butyl ester	276	80	125
13.	Isoamyl ester	290	76	132
14.	Butoxyethanol ester	320	69	146
15.	Isooctyl ester	332	66	152
16.	Propyleneglycolbutylether ester	334	66	152

From the testing done so far, there seems to be no distinct trend in toxicity of the 2,4-D esters from methyl through amyl. Increasing compatibility with increase in chain length may be offset by increasing molecular weight and hence dilution of the toxic group. Tests indicate that some of the low-volatile esters are distinctly superior to the lighter esters with respect to absorption and translocation. This is significant where these materials are being used to control perennial weeds and brush. Some of the higher esters that have been tested are butoxyethanol ester, polypropyleneglycolbutylether ester, pentasyl ester, octyl ester, tetrahydrofurfuryl ester, and polyethyleneglycol half ester. Others are undoubtedly undergoing screening. Table 10–4 gives the composition and molecular weights of some 2,4-D compounds.

Herbicides of the chlorophenoxy type penetrate the cuticle as the nondissociated parent acid molecule and are taken up by the living parenchyma cells of the mesophyll. Here, by movement along the symplast (interconnected system of living cells), the molecules reach the phloem and, upon entry into the sieve tubes, they move along with the assimilate stream from foliage to regions of growth and reproduction where foods are being actively utilized (Crafts, 1961). In these regions of active metabolism, the herbicide molecules are accumulated to toxic levels and they induce cell division, cell enlargement, callus and tumor formation, tissue crushing, and, if they are present in sufficient quantity, death (Fig. 10–8). In some susceptible species death may occur in a few days. In more resistant species weeks, months, or even years may be required; in the last case (prevalent in woody plants), fungi, bacteria, and termites may contribute to the delayed destruction.

ACTION OF 2,4-D THROUGH THE SOIL

Work by Anderson and Wolf (1947) and Anderson and Ahlgren (1947) proved that 2,4-D is effective as a preemergence treatment applied through the soil. Obviously 2,4-D is absorbed by roots as well as by foliage. In 1948, the author proposed that roots are adapted to the absorption of polar compounds, whereas leaves may take in apolar esters more readily (Crafts, 1948). In recent studies on the differential uptake of 2,4-D acid and its octyl ester by corn seedlings, Morre and Rogers (1960a) found that coleoptile sections took up more ester than acid, whereas roots absorbed more acid than ester.

While molecular structure has an important effect in 2,4-D uptake by roots, solubility also plays an important role. Crafts and Emmanuelli (1948) showed that 2,4-D acid was superior under conditions of high rainfall, whereas the sodium salt was best when rainfall was sparse. With the increasing use of preemergence methods of weed control, particularly since the introduction of granular formulations, 2,4-D is used on millions of acres of row crops each year.

Like other toxic chemicals, 2,4-D in small quantities in the culture medium produces a mild stimulation of plant growth. This, coupled with the fact that the chemical may be leached from the soil, indicates that there is little danger of accumulation in the soil in toxic quantities provided proper attention is paid to the rate and time of application and to subsequent management of the treated areas. In fact, Wort (1959) reports that 2,4-D, combined with iron and copper salts and applied in the form of dusts or sprays, may increase production of buckwheat, wheat, sugar beets, potatoes, corn, and beans. Arle (1954) has shown that 2,4-D in irrigation water will stimulate growth of cotton.

One group of chlorophenoxy compounds, the salts of chlorophenoxyethylsulfate and benzoate, is designed for use through the soil. These compounds (sesone, Methin, Sesin, and Natrin, sold under the Crag label) are activated by biological breakdown in the soil to the corresponding acids (2,4-D, 2,4,5-T, MCPA).

FIGURE 10-8.   A. Normal rice plants. B. Rice plants showing symptoms of rice injury. Panicles are reduced in size, abnormal in form, and many are unable to emerge from the sheaths.

SELECTIVITY OF 2,4–D COMPOUNDS

As is well known, the 2,4-D compounds are highly selective, being relatively low in toxicity to members of the grass family and, with a few notable exceptions, very toxic to other plant species. Like other selective herbicides, the specificity of 2,4-D is relative; at sufficiently high concentrations it will kill all species; at lower concentrations it will kill many of intermediate and low tolerance; some susceptible species are readily destroyed at concentrations as low as 500 ppm of the applied solution or at dosage rates as low as 0.4 lb per acre. Selectivity is not due to differential wetting but to protoplasmic tolerance resulting from inherent ability of certain plants to resist the toxic action of the chemical.

As with the dinitrophenols, the relatively nonpolar parent dichlorophenoxyacetic acid and its esters seem to be the most active compounds, followed by the amine salts, the ammonium salts, and the sodium salts. Differences between these various compounds have not been so prominent as with the dinitrophenols, possibly because the 2,4-D compounds have been used at dosages considerably above the threshold level and because temperature has such an important role in the speed of action.

SYMPTOMS OF 2,4-D INJURY

Application of 2,4-D to plants may result in several distinct responses. First, it causes a twisting or bending of the stems and leaves of some sensitive plants. This results from differential growth rates in petioles, pulvini, and elongating regions of the stem. Second, it causes a thickening of leaves and sometimes stems, accompanied by increase in turgor. Corn may bend until it lies flat on the ground and heavy winds at the time of extreme turgor of stems may break the plants off. There may also be pronounced changes in color, such as yellowing or reddening of leaves resembling autumnal coloration. Third, and most important, there is a cessation of growth, followed by death of tissues. This is followed by characteristic browning and drying of stems and leaves and often by decay of roots in the soil. All these are direct or primary symptoms of 2,4-D applied in herbicidal concentrations.

When 2,4-D is applied to or gets into plants in sublethal concentrations, an extremely interesting array of secondary growth responses may follow. Figure 10–9 and 10–10 show some of these, as exhibited by grapes and cotton. Such responses often serve as indicators of drift or volatilization of 2,4-D to sensitive crops. They may be only incidental to a complete recovery of the crop, or in some instances they may lead to severe crop loss. Examples are the production of seedless tomatoes that will not stand handling to the cannery, the reduced yield of cotton due to lowered leaf area and shedding of flowers, and the injury to

FIGURE 10-9.   Contact prints of Tokay grape leaves, showing leaf shapes and vein arrangements resulting from increasing doses of 2,4–D. Upper left, lowest dose; lower right, highest dose.

FIGURE 10-10.   Abnormal growth of cotton leaves resulting from exposure to 2,4–D. Upper row, right to left, shows recovery as succeeding leaves grow after the initial shock. Lower row left, four abnormal prophyls; right, two normal leaves.

cereals from crippled heads and empty florets. Most of these responses result from abnormal growth of young plant organs and reflect the hormone characteristic of 2,4-D. Common also are tumorlike proliferations of bud and root tissues, initiation of adventitious roots, and fasciation of stems, leaves, and flower parts. While some of these effects are caused by indoleacetic acid and other plant hormones,

2,4-D causes a greater variety and severity of symptoms than any of the other known growth regulators. On the other hand 2,4-D may be used to prevent preharvest drop of fluits (Avery et al., 1947), to ripen fruits (Mitchell and Marth, 1947), and to induce flower formation (van Overbeek, 1945).

FORMS AND ANALOGUES OF 2,4-D

Many formulations of 2,4-D are presently available for herbicidal use. Common 2,4-D compounds are listed below. Designating the dichlorophenoxy grouping

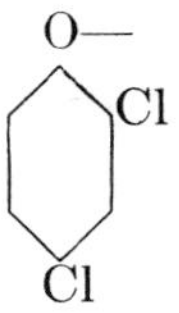

as R, examples of salts and esters of 2,4-D are as follows:

SALTS

Sodium salt, $R–CH_2COONa$
Potassium salt, $R–CH_2COOK$
Ammonium salt, $R–CH_2COONH_4$
Triethylamine salt, $R–CH_2COONH(C_2H_5)_3$
Triethanolamine salt, $R–CH_2–COONH(C_2H_4OH)_3$

ALKYL ESTERS

Methyl ester, $R–CH_2COOCH_3$

Isopropyl ester, $R–CH_2COOC\underset{\diagdown CH_3}{\overset{\diagup CH_3}{}}$

Butyl ester, $R–CH_2–COOC_4H_9$
Octyl ester, $R–CH_2–COOC_8H_{17}$

HEAVY OR LOW VOLATILE ESTERS

Butoxyethanol ester, $R–CH_2COOC_2H_4–O–C_4H_9$
Propyleneglycolbutylether ester,
$\quad R–CH_2COOCH_2(OH)CH_2–O–C_4H_9$

Tetrahydrofurfuryl ester $R–CH_2COO–\overset{H}{\underset{}{C}}\overset{O}{\diagup}\underset{}{CH_2}$
$\qquad\qquad\qquad\quad H_2–C-----C--H_2$

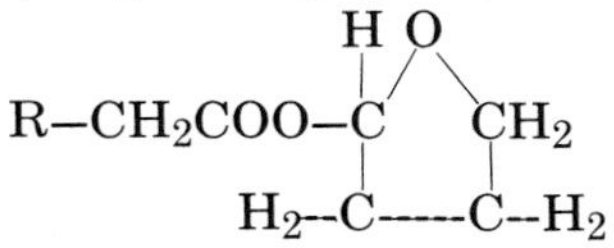

These examples represent only a few of the more common compounds that have been formulated and used in the field. Innumerable alkyl and alkanolamine salts may be synthesized; the same can be said of the esters. It should be apparent that the R in the above formulas could be, in addition to 2,4-D, the MCP

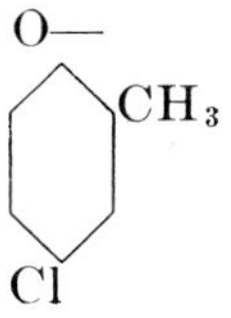

the 2,4,5-T

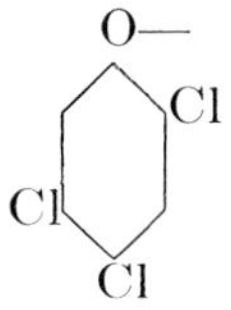

the 3,4-D

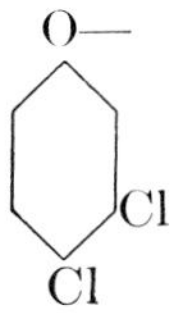

or the 4-chlorophenoxyacetic acid radical

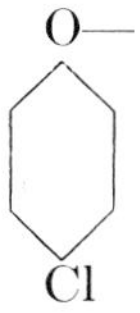

Finally, it should be pointed out that the phenoxypropionic, phenoxybutyric, and higher analogues may be substituted in place of the phenoxyacetic acids. The propionic acid series, i.e., 2(2,4-dichlorophenoxy)-propionic acid

$$\begin{array}{c} CH_3 \\ | \\ R{-}C{-}COOH \\ | \\ H \end{array}$$

are particularly potent against woody species of plants. The 2,4,5-T analogue, named silvex, is widely used in brush and tree control and it is also effective against certain aquatic weeds.

The straight-chain, even-numbered higher analogues, that is, butyric, hexanoic, octanoic, etc. series, have a special type of selectivity. They are toxic to plants that possess an active beta-oxidation enzyme system capable of degrading these compounds to 2,4-D. Some plants, among them certain crops, lack this active mechanism and hence are resistant to the herbicidal action of such compounds; examples are legumes, carrots, and celery. Formulations of the gamma butyric acid analogues are available on the market and are being used in the establishment of seedling legumes, in weeding legume pastures, and in certain vegetable crops.

An additional group of compounds related to 2,4-D, 2,4,5-T, and MCPA are the esters of the chlorophenoxy alcohols: sodium 2,4-dichlorophenoxyethyl sulfate, sodium 2-methyl-4-chlorophenoxyethyl sulfate, 2,4-dichlorophenoxyethyl benzoate, and sodium 2,4,5-trichlorophenoxyethyl sulfate. The commercial forms of these are known as sesone, Methin (MCPES), Sesin (2,4-DEB), and Natrin (2,4,5-TES), respectively. With these compounds should be mentioned tris(2,4-dichlorophenoxyethyl) phosphite (2,4-DEP, Falone).

These compounds have no direct contact action on plant foliage; when incorporated in soils, they are converted by microbial action to the corresponding acetic acids and hence are effective in controlling weed seedlings in the same way as the corresponding acetic compounds applied preemergence.

TOTAL ACTION OF 2,4-D

The 2,4-D compounds are unique weed killers with several herbicidal actions. For instance, they may kill leaves by contact as in the killing of prickly lettuce in barley to allow harvest by combining, or as in the treatment of mature cotton to allow mechanical picking. They have a selective action as in the control of mustard, radish, and fiddleneck in cereal crops. When applied to the foliage of deep-rooted perennials, they may be translocated into the roots and kill them. Finally, if applied to the soil, 2,4-D may be absorbed by the roots of weeds and cause their death. Such action may be selective because of differences in the tolerance of weed and crop plants to 2,4-D, or it may be due to differences in the location of the weed and crop-plant roots in the soil. True biochemical selectivity is the more dependable type to utilize, particularly in using 2,4-D as a preemergence treatment. The great herbicidal potency of 2,4-D often depends upon the fact that two or more of these actions may be effective at the same time.

REFERENCES

Akesson, N. B., W. E. Yates, and R. A. Fosse. 1960. Invert emulsions reduce unwanted drift. *Agrichemical West*, June, 1960.

Anderson, J. C., and D. E. Wolf. 1947. Pre-emergence control of weeds in corn with 2,4-D. *Amer. Soc. Agron. Jour.* 39:341–342.

——— and G. Ahlgren. 1947. Growing corn without cultivating. *Down to Earth* 3(1):16.

Anon. 1961. How surfactants affect herbicides. *Agr. Res.* 9(12):3–4.

Anon. 1974. *Herbicide Handbook of the Weed Science Society of America.* Geneva: W. H. Humphrey Press Inc.

Arle, H. F. 1954. The effect of 2,4-D on the growth and yield of cotton (Acala 44). *14th West. Weed Control Conf. Res. Prog. Rpt.* p. 84.

Avery, G. S., E. B. Johnson, R. M. Addoms, and B. F. Thomson. 1947. *Hormones and Horticulture.* New York: McGraw-Hill.

Crafts, A. S. 1948. A theory of herbicidal action. *Science* 108:85–87.

———. 1959. Further studies on comparative mobility of labeled herbicides. *Plant Physiol.* 34(6):613–620.

———. 1960. Evidence for hydrolysis of esters of 2,4-D during absorption by plants. *Weeds* 8(1):19–25.

———. 1961. *Translocation in Plants.* New York: Holt, Rinehart and Winston, Inc. 182 pp.

———. 1968. Water structure and water in the plant body. In *Water Deficits and Plant Growth*, ed. T. T. Kosloweki. New York: Academic Press Inc. pp. 23–47.

——— and A. Emmanuelli. 1948. Erradicacion de yerbajos en la cana de azucar. *Univ. Puerto Rico Agr. Expt. Sta. Bul.* 83.

——— and H. G. Reiber. 1948. Herbicidal properties of oils. *Hilgardia* 18(2):77–156.

Currier, H. B., and C. D. Dybing. 1959. Foliar penetration of herbicides—review and present status. *Weeds* 7(2):195–213.

Day, B. E., and L. S. Jordan. 1961. Spray retention by Bermudagrass. *Weeds* 9(3):351–355.

Dorschner, K. P., and K. P. Buchholtz. 1957. Interception of herbicidal sprays by oats and its relation to alfalfa stands. *Weeds* 5(4):342–349.

Dybing, C. D., and H. B. Currier. 1959. A fluorescent dye method for foliar penetration studies. *Weeds* 7(2):214–222.

——— and ———. 1961. Foliar penetration by chemicals. *Plant Physiol.* 36(2):169–174.

Ennis, W. B., Jr., R. E. Williamson, and K. P. Dorschner. 1952. Studies on spray retention by leaves of different plants. *Weeds* 1(3):274–286.

Gentner, W. A. 1973. Yellow nutsedge control with MBR-8251. *Weed Sci.* 21:122–124.

Jansen, L. L., W. A. Gentner, and W. C. Shaw. 1961. Effects of surfactants on the herbicidal activity of several herbicides in aqueous spray systems. *Weeds* 9(3):381–405.

Leopold, A. C., P. van Shaik, and M. Neal. 1960. Molecular structure and herbicide adsorption. *Weeds* 8(1):48–54.

Mitchell, J. W., and P. C. Marth. 1947. *Growth Regulators for Garden, Field, and Orchard.* Chicago: University of Chicago Press.

Morre, D. J., and B. J. Rogers. 1960a. Differential uptake of 2,4-D acid and its octyl ester by seedling corn roots and coleoptile sections. *Plant Physiol.* 35(3):324–325.

_____ and _____. 1960b. The fate of long chain esters of 2,4-D in plants. *Weeds* 8(3):436–447.

Szabo, S. S. 1963. The hydrolysis of 2,4-D esters by bean and corn plants. *Weeds* 11:292–294.

van Overbeek, J. 1945. Flower formation in the pineapple plant as controlled by 2,4-D and naphthalenacetic acid. *Science* 102:621.

_____, and R. Blondeau. 1954. Mode of action of phytotoxic oils. *Weeds* 3(1):55–65.

Wort, D. J. 1959. The foliar application of 2,4-D and other growth regulators with and without added minor elements. *4th Internatl. Cong. of Crop Prot. Proc.* 1:497–502. Hamburg, 1957. Pub Braumschweig, 1959.

11

Properties and Functions of Herbicides* (Continued)

For historical reasons the herbicidal properties of the dinitrophenols and the chlorophenoxy compounds have been treated in detail in Chapter 10. There are many other compounds that fill important niches in the over-all field of vegetation management; these will be considered now. Appendix Table 2 provides lists of the many compounds that have proven to be effective herbicides.

ACIDS

Of the acids listed, the arsenic compounds have been withdrawn from the market in most countries because of the hazards involved in their use as herbicides. Sulfuric acid is still used, mainly to control annual weeds in onions.

SALTS

Of the salts listed in Appendix Table 2, ammonium sulfamate (AMS), sold under the name of ammate, is used in brush and woody-plant control; it is applied in solution as a foliar spray, poured into frills, or sprayed onto stumps.

Boron salts are used in soil sterilizing mixtures, usually with sodium chlorate, triazines, or ureas.

---

*Much of the information reported in this chapter has been obtained from *1973 Pesticide Dictionary* published by Farm Chemicals, Meister Publishing Co., Willoughby, Ohio.

Calcium cyanamid is used mainly as a nitrogenous fertilizer.

Copper sulfate is used as an algaecide in irrigation ditches, ponds, and lakes.

Hexafluorate is a selective herbicide used to control prickly pear, dog cactus, and tasajillo on rangelands. It is absorbed by roots and translocated apoplastically.

Potassium azide is used as a soil fumigant; the sodium salt is used in the same way.

Sodium chlorate, while not as popular as formerly, is still used, mainly on nonagricultural soils to control perennial weeds.

Sodium pentaborate is a boron compound used in soil sterilization.

Tribonate is a postemergence contact herbicide used to control all vegetation on nonagricultural areas.

Tricalcium arsenate is used for preemergence treatment of turf and lawns to control crabgrass; it is also effective against bluegrass and chickweed.

The salts named in Appendix Table 2 which have not been mentioned above are not used in large quantities for controlling weeds at the present time; they have been used in the past.

Oils

The oils used for herbicidal purposes have been described in Chapter 10. Oils are still used in large quantities, but many former uses have been taken over by cheaper, less critical chemicals.

Aliphatics (See Appendix Table 2)

Acrolein or acrylaldehyde is an aquatic herbicide used mainly in irrigation canals and ditches. It is injected into the water at intervals along a canal and it kills by contact; the time of exposure multiplied by the concentration is a constant. Being hazardous to use, acrolein is applied only by licensed applicators.

Allyl alcohol is used to fumigate soils in forest tree nurseries. It kills weed seeds, weeds, and other pests.

Benzadox is a postemergence, soil-applied, selective herbicide.

Bidisin is used as a selective postemergence spray against wild oats; it is tolerated by wheat and barley, also beets and peas.

Chloropon is soil-applied, postemergence as a selective herbicide.

Chloropicrin is a soil fumigant used to control annual weeds in soils being planted to fruit trees, strawberries, or other high-value crops.

TCA (trichloroacetic acid) and dalapon (2,2-dichloropropionic acid) are two important herbicides in the control of grasses. In the field both are used as the water-soluble sodium salts. TCA is used through the soil; it is readily absorbed by roots and translocated via the transpiration stream into the foliage. At low dosage TCA produces pronounced formative effects. For killing Johnsongrass and Bermudagrass it is used at rates of from 80 to 100 lb per acre. For controlling barnyardgrass and crabgrass seedlings in cotton, sugar beets, and other row crops, dosages as low as 5 lb per acre have proved effective. TCA is the principal herbicide used to control quackgrass in Scandanavia.

TCA application must be timed for optimum absorption by roots. In regions of frozen soils, application in the spring just after the soil thaws is effective. In regions of frequent rainfall, early fall or early spring applications present the chemical in the root zone before the soil temperature becomes sufficiently elevated to promote rapid breakdown. In regions of winter rains and dry summers, winter or spring applications are favorable. Less rainfall is required to carry the chemical to the roots in sandy soils than in clay soils. Midsummer application, even in regions of summer rains, is not effective because TCA is subject to rapid breakdown in warm, moist soils.

Dalapon is used primarily by spray application to foliage; it is readily absorbed and translocated in the phloem via the assimilate stream; applied to roots, it is absorbed and translocated in the transpiration stream but it is not so effective as a soil-borne herbicide. Figure 11–1 illustrates the effectiveness of dalapon applied preplant to control Johnsongrass in soybeans. Figure 11–2 shows the results of an autumn treatment with dalapon at 20 lb per acre in controlling quackgrass in maize the following summer.

As noted, the chlorinated aliphatic acids cause formative effects, growth inhibition, leaf chlorosis, leaf necrosis, and eventually death. They interfere with the meristematic activity of root tips and apical meristems; wax formation on leaf surfaces is reduced and cell membranes are altered. These compounds are very resistant to degradation by higher plants. TCA is essentially nondegradable; dalapon undergoes slow degradation yielding pyruvic acid through dechlorination, hydroxylation, and dehydrogenation. The primary toxic action of dalapon is associated with alteration of protein structure, possibly conformational changes that could alter enzymes and change membrane integrity. A rather specific action of dalapon appears to be an increase in ammonia. In susceptible species the formation of amides seems insufficient to prevent accumulation of toxic levels of ammonia, possibly due to changes in amide-forming enzymes.

DBA is a preemergence, preplant, translocated material.

Glytac is a grass killer used to control Johnsongrass, Bermudagrass, quackgrass, and similar weeds. It is mixed with oil and applied as a directed spray avoiding crop plants.

HCA is a nonselective herbicide and crop desiccant used on alfalfa.
Methylbromide is a volatile soil fumigant.
Monoxone is an herbicide and crop defoliant and desiccant.
Orga 3045 is a grass-killer used to control rice weeds in Japan.
Tridex is a preemergence, soil-borne herbicide.

AMIDES

There are twenty-three compounds listed in Appendix Table 2 as amides. Evidently at least two modes of action are represented because

FIGURE 11-1.   Control of Johnsongrass in soybeans by preplant application of dalapon at 10 lb per acre. Treated area on left. (Photograph by courtesy of the Dow Chemical Co.)

some six of these compounds are applied to foliage; the remaining ones are preplant or preemergence materials applied through the soil; some require incorporation.

Alachlor, butachlor, carbetamide, CDAA, and CDEA are all soil-borne herbicides applied preplant or preemergence to control seed-

FIGURE 11-2.   Control of quackgrass by fall application of dalapon. Top, corn growing in quackgrass-infested soil; bottom, corn growing in soil treated the previous fall with dalapon at 20 lb per acre. (Photographs by courtesy of the Dow Chemical Co.)

ling weeds at the time of or soon after germination. CDAA is recommended for use in vegetable crops on muck soils.

Chlorthiamid, cypromid, dicryl, monalide, pronamide, propanil, and solan all have herbicidal properties when applied to foliage. Chlorthiamid and pronamide also act through the soil.

Cyprazole, delachlor, dinitramine, diphenamid, karsil, MCAA, napromide, naptalam, oryzalin, propachlor, and profluralin are all soil-borne materials.

CDAA (Randox) and CDEA are compounds of strong herbicidal activity; they are used preemergent and are particularly effective against grasses. They inhibit root elongation by stopping cell division in susceptible species.

Propachlor also inhibits root growth, probably by regulating protein synthesis; it degrades rapidly in maize and soybeans.

Alachlor inhibits growth of both shoots and roots; it is reported to be active against nutsedges.

Diphenamid allows seeds to germinate but kills the seedlings prior to emergence. Tomatoes tolerate diphenamid whereas most annual weeds succumb to its toxicity; grasses are the most susceptible weeds. Diphenamid applied as a foliar spray responds to high humidity and low light with increased toxicity.

Naptalam acts as an antigeotropic reagent; roots grow against the force of gravity and in a humid situation the tips may emerge from the soil. Naptalam has proven very useful on cucurbit crops; it is also used in soybeans, peanuts, and vine crops. Combined with chlorpropham, it is used in cranberries.

Pronamide causes cell enlargement and necrosis on quackgrass rhizome apices. It is used against Bermudagrass, annual grasses, and nightshade; incorporation aids effectiveness.

Propanil, applied by spraying, controls barnyardgrass in rice. At sublethal dosage it causes chlorosis; at lethal dosage, necrosis and collapse occur. Propanil is absorbed more rapidly by barnyardgrass than by rice in bioassay tests but its rapid breakdown in rice may be involved. Propanil has proved to be highly toxic to prune trees, even by drift from neighboring rice fields; its use is prohibited by law in parts of California.

Solan and dicryl are foliar herbicides; shoot growth stops soon after application but leaf symptoms are slower to appear. Solan is used as a directed spray in tomatoes; dicryl was used on cotton but is principally employed in certain vegetable crops.

Napromide is proving effective for controlling annual weeds preemergence in tree crops; it persists in the soil and holds weeds in control for a whole growing season.

Delachlor offers promise as a preemergence herbicide in sugar beets, peanuts, potatoes, soybeans, and peas. It is effective against both dicots and monocots, particularly barnyardgrass, crabgrass, bristlegrasses, and *Panicum* species.

ARSENICALS

Inorganic arsenical herbicides, principally sodium arsenite, have been used for a hundred years or more; some arsenates and arsenic pentoxide were tried. Because of the great mammalian toxicity of sodium arsenite and because when applied to green vegetation it is attractive to animals, its use resulted in a tremendous number of animal deaths; many people, including children, were poisoned. Now these materials are prohibited by law in many countries. Hexaflurate is used as a postemergence contact spray.

The organic arsenical herbicides have become widely used within the past decade and, except for the fact that arsenic is nondegradable in soils, they offer help in controlling perennial grasses that have not been possible to control in the past.

Cacodylic acid (hydroxydimethylarsine oxide) was one of the first of the organic arsenicals to be introduced. Cacodylic acid and its sodium salt are used in forest management to control weedy or unwanted trees, usually by injection into the trunk using a tool designed for the purpose. Hand frilling and application with a pressure oil can may be used where only a few trees are being killed.

Cacodylic acid is also used in lawn and pasture renovation, to control weeds in orchards and vineyards, and by directed spray in row crops, including cotton. Calciumpropanearsenate (No-Crab) is used preemergence to control crabgrass in turf. Pencal (calciumarsenate) has a similar use.

The salts and esters of monomethylarsinicacid are being used as translocated herbicides in controlling Johnsongrass, quackgrass, Dallisgrass, nutsedge, goosegrass, barnyardgrass, sandbur, cocklebur, ragweed, and puncturevine. The sodium acid salt (MSMA), the disodium salt (DSMA), the monoammonium salt (MAMA), and some amine salts have been used. Addition of surfactants, combinations with 2,4-D and mixtures with other herbicides have proved effective in some situations. In turf, these materials have been used against the above-named weeds plus bahia grass, chickweed, and wood sorrel. Dandelion, plaintain, and other turf weeds yield to the triethanolamine salt. To broaden the spectrum of weeds controlled, a mixture of MSMA, sodium cacodylate, and cacodylic acid has been formulated; it is used as a general, postemergence herbicide to provide a quick burn on annual weeds while retaining the systemic properties essential to controlling perennials. Many of the traditional organic arsenical formulations are now being offered in new, highly concentrated formulations for convenience and economy (Anon., 1970a, b).

Benzoic Acid Derivatives

Among many substituted benzoic acids that have been tested, six have come into use in economic quantities. These are bifenox, 2,3,6-TBA, (2,3,6-trichlorobenzoic acid), dicamba (3,6-dichloro-o-anisic acid), tricamba (3,5,6-trichloro-o-anisic acid), chloramben (3-amino-3,5-dichlorobenzoic acid), and PCA (polychlorobenzoic acids). Pointed out as early as 1942 as growth regulators, benzoic acid derivatives have been in use for over two decades for controlling weeds: 2,3,6-TBA, and PCB as translocated herbicides against a host of perennial weeds; dicamba, tricamba, bifenox, and chloramben as selective pre- or directed postemergence herbicides in field crops. Dicamba is effective postemergence against broadleaf herbaceous weeds in lawns and turf, established grass crops, winter wheat, fall barley, oats and wheat, field corn, and on noncropland. Tricamba is similar in properties to dicamba, possibly a bit more persistent in soils.

Chloramben has been most successful for preemergence application in soybeans where it has proved effective in controlling annual weeds throughout a single growing season. It has also been used in asparagus, field corn, mung beans, peanuts, sunflowers, and sweet potatoes.

The substituted benzoic acid compounds vary in their persistence in plants and soils. 2,3,6-TBA is quite stable in plants and there is no experimental evidence that it actually breaks down; one or more conjugates may be formed. Likewise, this compound is very persistent in soils and in pots, flats, and other greenhouse hardware; for this reason it must be carefully handled; pots in which it is used should be discarded.

Magalhaes and Ashton (1969) found evidence for cell membrane disruption as a possible mode of action of dicamba. Dicamba degradation rates vary with species or soils. Dicamba breakdown takes place more rapidly in wheat than in wild buckwheat which probably explains its success as a selective spray in wheat. Chloramben is complexed with naturally occurring compounds in soybeans, carrots, and other crops. An N-glucosyl chloramben conjugate has been isolated from soybean; a second conjugate, designated as chloramben-X, has shown up in chromatographic studies of extracts of chloramben-treated soybean plants. N-glucosyl chloramben and chloramben-X are both less toxic than chloramben, the glucose conjugate is the least toxic of the three.

THE CARBAMATES

The carbamate herbicides were introduced in 1945 when propham (IPC) was announced by Templeman and Sexton (1945). Being a grass killer, propham became popular for weeding such crops as soybeans, kidney beans, cowpeas, sunflowers, radishes, turnips, and sugar beets. A weakness of this product was its volatility and its ready breakdown by soil microorganisms. Chlorpropham proved to be longer lasting; applied in spring, it would last through the growing season of the crop. One producer of propham and chlorpropham has found a chemical which, applied with these herbicides, reduces microbiological breakdown so that they give longer lasting results. This compound, termed PCMC, is p-chlorophenyl N-methycarbamate. It has been tested and found to be effective; it is now being included in marketed formulations of propham and chlorpropham. Kaufman and Plimmer (1972) have found that PCMC is readily degraded in the soil by microorganisms.

There are some fifteen carbamates available as herbicides (see Appendix Table 2).

ASULAM, ASULOX

Asulam is a selective, preplant or postemergence herbicide that has been on test since 1965. It has little action on red clover or annual bluegrass but is very potent against broadleaf dock (*Rumex obtusifolius*), particularly when applied postemergence. Asulam inhibits cell division and growth of meristems. Since postemergence treatment followed by discing gives complete control at 2.0 to 4.0 lb per acre, it seems that absorption by leaves and stems excedes uptake by rootstocks. Asulam is being tested on a range of weeds in an attempt to broaden the spectrum of weed candidates for treatment. It is effective in controlling Johnsongrass in sugar cane, bracken fern in forests, wild oats and mustard in flax seed, and many weeds in cucurbits. It has been reported to be very effective for controlling bracken fern at dosages which make application by air possible.

BARBAN, CARBYNE

Barban is a selective, postemergence herbicide used to control wild oats in wheat, barley, flax, peas, and sugar beets. It inhibits growth of the shoot apices, causes development of a bluegreen coloring and brittleness of leaves, and, if properly used, causes death or loss of competitive ability. Applied at low volume to oats in the 1¼ to 2½-leaf stage by spraying, it causes destruction of apical meristems in oats but has little or no effect on wheat. Barley is less tolerant, flax even less than barley. If oats attain the 3-leaf stage they may not be killed but remain stunted (Fig. 6–4).

CARBASULAM

Carbasulam is a selective, preemergence carbamate for hard to control weeds.

CHLORBUFAM, BiPC, CHLORINATE

Chlorbufam, also called BiPC or Chlorinate, is a chlorophenyl carbamate used in combination with OMU to make alipur, a mixed preemergence herbicide, to control both monocots and dicots in onions, carrots, beans, spinach, and beet crops. Mixed with pyrazon it makes alicep, another formulated herbicide commonly used in sugar beets.

CHLORPROPHAM, CIPC

Chloropropham, known in the early literature as CIPC has had a long record as a successful herbicide in alfalfa, beans, berry crops, carrots, ladino clover, garlic, seed grass, peas, peppers, rice, onions, peas, spinach, sugar beets, tomatoes, safflower, soybeans, gladioli, and woody nursery stock; it also inhibits sprouting of potatoes. There is evidence that this herbicide is sufficiently volatile to kill dodder seedlings by vapor contact when granules are applied to moist soil (Slater et al., 1969).

CYCLOATE, RO-NEET

Cycloate is a preplant weed killer used to control annual grasses in sugar beets; also nutgrass, shallow-rooted perennial grasses, and many broadleaf weeds are controlled.

DESMEDIPHAM

Desmedipham is a selective, postemergence, soil-applied herbicide effective against a variety of weeds.

DICHLORMATE, ROWMATE

Dichlormate kills young seedlings after germination by causing chlorosis. It has been tested and found useful in soybeans, peanuts, potatoes, beans, garlic, peas, and ornamentals. Treated when 2 in. to 4 in. high, barnyardgrass and other grasses as well as many broadleaf weeds in rice are held in control until shaded out by the crop.

ETHIOLATE

Ethiolate is a selective, preemergence, soil-applied herbicide.

KARBUTILATE, TANDEX

This chemical is a broad-spectrum weed and brush killer used on nonagricultural land. It is recommended in the control of both annual and perennial broadleaf and grassy weeds, brush and vines, on railroad, utility and pipe-line rights-of-way, on drainage ditches, and industrial sites. Soil-borne, karbutilate is readily absorbed by roots and translocated apoplastically.

PHENMEDIPHAM, BETANAL

Phenmedipham is a postemergence herbicide, effective in sugar beets. It is used to control lambsquarters, shepherdspurse, dogfennel, wild turnip, common chickweed, wild radish, ragweed, kochia, wild buckwheat, green foxtail, nightshade, and field pennycress. Since this weed killer acts through foliar absorption, rain falling soon after application may lower its effectiveness. Norris (1972) found that crystallization of this chemical in the spray tank depends upon temperature and dilution. When temperature of the solution is below 40°F and dilution greater than 1:25, the chemical crystallizes, clogging screens and stopping flow.

Phenmedipham breaks down rapidly in the soil. Kossman (1970) found half-lives for this chemical in soils to vary from 28 to 55 days. Phenmedipham is strongly fixed in soil; only very little was found below a depth of 5 cm in field plots on which it was used.

PROPHAM, I.P.C.

This original carbamate herbicide is a mitotic poison, a growth inhibitor, and a specific toxicant on certain grasses. Freed (1951) found that, in treating quackgrass, oil was needed in the formulation and that the chemical required intimate mixing in the soil to injure the rhizomes in disced sod.

PROXIPHAM

Proxipham is a preplant or preemergence herbicide used against both monocot and dicot weeds in beets, onions, and carrots.

SWEP

This carbamate herbicide is a popular material in Japan where rice is an important food crop. The use of swep allows planting of dry-field, direct-seeded rice, eliminating the laborious hand transplanting. Also it conserves water at a time when the supply is limited for weed control in the transplanted paddies; flooding is avoided where swep is used. Swep is presented as a wettable powder, in a granular form, and mixed in granules with MCPA. The granules may be applied by hand, by mechanical spreader, or, in California, by air in flooded rice.

TERBUTOL, AZAK

Terbutol is selective, preemergence herbicide used to control crabgrass in turf; it is absorbed by roots from the soil; it inhibits growth of roots and rhizomes at the terminal meristems; it is low in solubility and leaches slowly; it is not fixed on soil colloids.

THE DIPYRIDILIUMS

Three dipyridilium compounds are in use as herbicides; they are diquat (6,7-dihydrodipyrido[1,2-a:2′,1′-c] pyrazinediium ion), paraquat (1,1′-dimethyl-4,4′-bipyridinium ion), and morphamquat (1, 1′-*bis*-(3,5-dimethylmorpholine-carboxymethyl)-4,4′-dipyridilium dichloride). These compounds, related to the quaternary ammoniums, occur in solution as ions. They are general contact-spray materials used on nonagricultural lands and to control all vegetation on lands that are not in crop. Available since the mid-1950s, these compounds have found wide use for controlling weeds on roadsides, ditchbanks, etc., on industrial areas, and firebreaks, and for eliminating all vegetation in nontillage programs. They are useful in pasture renovation, for killing annual weeds in perennial crops, where the latter will not be permanently injured, for seasonal control of weed growth in orchards and vineyards, and for controlling aquatic weeds in certain situations. Diquat has been shown to translocate apoplastically if applied in the evening and then exposed to light on the next day; apparently, for translocation to take place, the compound must have time in the dark for penetration; upon being exposed to light it forms free radicals, the form in which it is strongly phytotoxic. If applied in strong light, the free ions are formed immediately, killing the leaf tissues before sufficient accumulation of the chemical. Translocation is apoplastic, that is, through the xylem. In the light, the dipyridilium herbicides cause rapid desiccation of foliage; wilting is an early symptom. At the cellular level, they destroy membrane integrity; light, molecular oxygen, and chlorophyll are required for maximum development of phytotoxicity. When these are present, the free radicals are reoxidized, producing peroxide which some workers consider to be the actual toxicant. Others however believe that the free radicals are the toxic agents. Turner (1969) found that repeated applications of paraquat over a period of 60 days reduced carbohydrate reserves in rhizomes of quackgrass to about 50 percent of the level obtained with the same number of hand clippings. Possibly, some paraquat translocated into the rhizomes increased respiration, causing depletion of carbohydrates.

The availability of paraquat to plants by absorption from the soil and by direct physical contact with sprayed plant materials has been studied by Damanakis et al. (1970). They found that this herbicide is much more available from peat soils than from clay soils; paraquat sprayed at usual dosage on peat was absorbed by rye grass seedlings, if not incorporated. Paraquat on litter of sprayed plants was available to plants by root uptake and by contact with living leaves.

Seth (1971) found that application of paraquat at 0.56 kg/ha in 112 liters per acre followed in 2-3 weeks by a second application at half the above dosage provides complete and lasting control of *Mikania cordata*, a serious weed in the tropics, in oil palm, tea, and rubber.

NITRILES

There are four nitriles that serve as herbicides: bromoxynil, dichlobenil, diphenatrile, and ioxynil. Three are selective foliar sprays used to control those weeds which tolerate 2,4-D and MCPA. Dichlobenil is used preemergence.

BROMOXYNIL, BROMINAL, BUCTRIL

Bromoxynil is a postemergence herbicide applied as a spray on weeds in cereal crops. It is recommended for use against blue mustard, fiddleneck, corngromwell, cow cockle, field pennycress, green smartweed, groundsel, lambsquarters, London rocket, shepherdspurse, silverleaf nightshade, tartary buckwheat, tarweed, tumblemustard, wild buckwheat, and wild mustard.

DICHLOBENIL, CASORON

Used preemergence, dichlobenil is recommended for weed control in cranberries, nurseries, vineyards, citrus and deciduous fruit trees, and in granules for aquatic-weed control in lakes and ponds. Recent tests have shown that dichlobenil will suppress field bindweed when treated by means of the sprayblade; it is volatile enough to stop growth at the chemical layer; the tests show inhibition for a full season.

DIPHENATRILE, DIPAN

Diphenatrile is used postemergence to control seedling grasses in turf.

IOXYNIL, ACTRIL, BANTROL, CERTROL

Ioxynil is a postemergence herbicide used to control seedlings of bindweed, buttercups, chickweed, cornflower, dandelion, fat hen, groundsel, mayweeds, mustards, plantains, shepherdspurse, and speedwell in cereals and turf. Douglas fiddleneck, tartary buckwheat, hempnettle, bedstraw, kochia, pineappleweed, and prostrate knotweed are also controlled.

THE NITROANILINES

There are eleven dinitroaniline herbicides in use; trifluralin, the first, was introduced in 1960 (Alder et al., 1960); the others have been discovered since. The dinitroanilines are orange colored compounds, low in water solubility, and somewhat volatile. They have generally been used as selective, preplant, soil-incorporated herbicides applied just before or at planting time. Trifluralin is now being used by the sprayblade method for controlling field bindweed, and by thorough soil incorporation against Johnsongrass. In this method the rhizome system of the Johnsongrass should be cut up into small pieces by discing so that each piece comes into contact with the chemical. Trifluralin is available as an emulsifiable concentrate or as granules.

BUTRALIN, AMEX-820

Amex-820 is a nitroaniline that has appeared among a number of dinitroanilines introduced after trifluralin proved to be so effective in controlling weeds. Amex-820 has proved effective in controlling many common weeds in tomatoes and peppers; it will probably find use in many more crops.

BENEFIN, BALAN

Benefin differs from trifluralin by having an ethyl and a butyl substitution in place of two propyl substituents on the nitrogen. It has the CF_3 group. It is recommended for control of annual grasses and broadleaf weeds in peanuts, direct-seeded lettuce, established turf, seeded alfalfa, red clover, birdsfoot trefoil, ladino clover, and transplant tobacco. It may be soil incorporated as much as 10 weeks before planting.

CHLORNIDINE

Chlornidine is a selective, preemergence herbicide. It requires incorporation for activation.

DINITRAMINE

Dinitramine is another of the dinitro herbicides that has been introduced. It requires extensive testing before its full herbicidal potential is known.

DIPROPALIN

Dipropalin has been tested as a preemergence herbicide against seedling grasses, such as crabgrass, in turf.

FLUCHLORALIN

Fluchloralin is a new herbicide now under test.

ISOPROPALIN, PAARLAN

Isopropalin is a selective, preemergence herbicide to be soil-incorporated for control of grasses and broadleaf weeds in direct-seeded and transplant tomatoes; it is under test in transplant tobacco and peppers, both direct seeded and transplant.

MODERN WEED CONTROL

224

NITRALIN, PLANAVIN

Planavin differs from trifluralin by having a methylsulfonyl group in place of the CF_3 substituent. It is a selective, preemergence material recommended for weed control in cotton, soybeans, safflower, peanuts, alfalfa, and some vegetable crops.

ORYZALIN, RYZELAN, SURFLAN

Oryzalin is a selective, preemergence, surface-applied herbicide for weed control in soybeans, established alfalfa, fruit trees, nut trees, vineyards, and ornamentals. It has a melting point of 141-142°C, compared with 49°C for trifluralin; it would be less volatile, hence the suggested surface application instead of incorporation.

All of the dinitroanilines are growth inhibitors; those that have been investigated are mitotic poisons.

TRIBONATE

Tribonate is a selective, postemergence, contact herbicide.

TRIFLURALIN, TREFLAN

Trifluralin is characterized by having a CF_3 substitution para to the nitrogen on the toluidide structure. It has been widely used as a selective treatment in cotton. Its toxic action is to inhibit growth of the entire plant, but particularly the growth of secondary roots. The cotton plant escapes this action, to a large degree, by sending down a strong tap root that very soon develops lateral roots below the depth of incorporation of the toxicant. Shallow-rooted annual weeds germinate in this layer and die as soon as the roots extend into the treated soil. Trifluralin shows no evidence for translocation in vascular tissues in plants. Saghir and Abu-Shakra (1971) report that this herbicide inhibits germination and tube growth of *Orobanche ramosa* seeds in stimulation fluid; 1000 ppm prohibited germination.

PHENOLS AND PHENYLETHERS

There are fifteen substituted phenols that are herbicides. DNOC was the first to be used; the sodium salt was introduced into the United States in 1937 under the name of Sinox. It is a postemergence, selective herbicide that was used against annual weeds in cereal crops. When it was discovered that Sinox could be activated by adding 3 lb of ammonium sulfate to the spray tank, great interest was aroused. It soon become apparent that this activation resulted from the fact that the undissociated cresol molecules in the activated solution penetrated the plant cuticle more rapidly than did the ions of the sodium salt. It was then discovered that any acid or acid salt could be used to activate this herbicide, that the ammonium and amine salts could be used without activation, and that the parent dinitro cresol in an oil carrier is an excellent general contact herbicide. The parent compound could be used to fortify spray oils of low inherent phytotoxicity; the parent compound in an aromatic oil carrier could be emulsified with added detergent and thus extended.

Further screening of substituted phenols brought the dinitro-o-secondary butyl and amyl compounds into use: the parent compounds as general contact toxicants, the ammonium salts as selective contact herbicides, and the amine salt of dinitro-secondary butylphenol as a preemergence material for use to control weeds in cotton. Thus the substituted phenol herbicides played an important role in ushering in the chemical revolution in agriculture.

BROMOPHENOXIM, FANERON

Bromophenoxim is an effective contact herbicide used selectively to control broadleaf weeds, particularly phenoxy-resistant ones such as bedstraw, dogfennel, and fiddleneck, in cereal crops. It is available as a 50 percent wettable powder.

DINOSAM, DNAP, CHEMOX GENERAL

The principal use of this compound has been as an adjunct to dinoseb in formulating these two parent dinitrophenals as a general contact, postemergence material, for use as a preplant spray against common weeds in preparation of land for seeding, as a general contact, broad-spectrum spray in nontillage programs, and on nonagricultural lands.

DINOPHENATE

Dinophenate is a postemergence, selective contact spray being tested.

DINOSEB, DNBP, MANY TRADE NAMES

Dinitro secondary butyl phenol proved to be the most toxic of a number of dinitro substituted phenols tested for phytotoxicity (Crafts, 1945). It soon found three uses in weed control: (1) the ammonium salt as a postemergence, selective spray in flax, beans, peas, leek, potatoes, coffee, vineyards, and orchards; also a desiccant in potatoes and legume crops for seed; (2) the parent phenol in oil as a general contact spray; and (3) the alkanolamine salt named Premerge was used to kill germinating seeds in the top-soil layer; also in early postemergence and directed sprays.

DINOSEB-ACETATE, ARETIT

There are three acetic acid esters of the dinitrophenols; dinoseb-acetate is one, the acetate of 2-*sec*butyl-4,6-dinitro phenol. It is used as a selective herbicide for controlling annual broadleaf weeds in peas, beans, potatoes, clover, alfalfa, corn, and cereal crops.

DINOTERB-ACETATE

This compound, differing from the former dinitro-acetate by having a tertiary instead of a secondary butyl substituent on the phenol ring, is used preemergence for controlling broadleaf weeds in sugar beets, legumes, and cereals. It is used postemergence to control witchweed (*Striga* sp.) in maize, sorghum, and alfalfa.

DMPA, ZYTRON

This compound may be used in solution as a spray, or in granular form to kill crabgrass, knotweed, nimblewill, and other annual weeds of turf. Its toxicity is not high so that the recommended dosage is 15 lb per acre.

DNOC, SINOX

The sodium salt of dinitro-o-cresol, activated with ammonium sulfate or sodium bisulfate was the first selective spray for killing annual weeds in cereal crops to become popular. Used at the rate of 1 gal of activated compound in 80-100 gal per acre it controlled wild mustards, wild radish, and other easy-to-kill annuals in wheat and barley crops. By doubling the concentration of the spray solution, such weeds as vetch, corn cockle, hunger weed, fiddleneck, sunflower, and black nightshade could be controlled; the cereals are burned by the spray but they recover.

ETINOFEN

Etinofen is a dinitrophenol having a 2-ethoxymethyl substitution in the place of the methyl group in DNOC. This gives it special selectivities against hard-to-kill weeds.

FLUORODIFEN, PREFORAN

Fluorodifen is a preemergence, broadcast or band treatment material used to control annual grass and broadleaf weeds in soybeans, cotton, maize, rice, strawberries, and a number of vegetable crops. Seedling alfalfa and some vegetable crops are sensitive to fluorodifen.

MEDINOTERB-ACETATE, MC1488

This dinitrophenol has a methyl group in the number 5 location on the phenyl ring. It is used preemergence to control broadleaf weeds in sugar beets, cotton, leguminous crops; postemergence in cereals. It is combined with urea in granules for *Striga* control.

M0338, M0500

These nitroethers resemble nitrofen and fluorodifen in chemical structure. They are used principally to control annual weeds, particularly grasses in rice, cotton, and some vegetable crops.

NITROFEN, TOK-E25

This phenylether compound is used preemergence on a number of vegetable and field crops to control grasses and broadleaf weeds. It may be applied as a postemergence spray on cabbage, peanuts, soybeans, and potatoes. It has been used to control barnyardgrass in rice, being a popular herbicide in paddy rice in Japan.

PCP, PENTACHLOROPHENOL

PCP, first introduced as an activator for sodium chlorate weed killers, soon proved to be an effective toxicant in its own right. Dissolved in an aromatic oil and containing a surfactant, it can be emulsified and used as a general contact spray against common annual weeds. Sodium pentachlorophenate may be activated and used as a selective spray. In Hawaii the emulsified PCP has been metered into water used in furrow irrigation of sugar cane; it kills annual weeds until the cane closes in.

PHENOXY COMPOUNDS, 2,4-D, 2,4-DB, 2,4,5-T, MCPA, MCPB, SILVEX, ETC.

Because of the great historical importance of the chlorophenoxy herbicides, they have been described in detail in Chapter 10 (pages 199–207). It suffices here to point out the facts that 2,4-D was the first herbicide having such toxicity that it may be effective in some situations at 4 oz per acre; that the heavy ester formulations are effective translocated herbicides used in controlling deep-rooted perennial weeds; that 2,4,5-T and Silvex are excellent agents in the control of brush and weedy trees; and that 2,4-D was the first preemergence herbicide to be used successfully by application through the soil. Although its use in this way has been largely replaced by the triazine, urea, and uracil herbicides, its early use through the soil is a milestone in the progress of chemical weed control.

The butyric acid analogues of 2,4-D have found a valuable place in the herbicide field being selective toward crop species that lack the beta-oxidation mechanism.

2,4-D

As shown in Chapter 3 (Table 3–9), worldwide production of 2,4-D is 100 million pounds or more per year; it must still be the most used single chemical in the field. (Fig. 11–3).

2,4-D is a selective postemergence herbicide used to control annual weeds in cereal crops. It has been used as a preemergence material applied to soil for absorption by the roots of seedlings as they emerge from the germinating seeds. The amine salt formulation of 2,4-D is used undiluted in cuts through the bark of trees.

2,4,5-T

2,4,5-T in its many formulations is used as a killer of woody plants. It may be used either as an amine salt in water or as an ester in oil or oil

FIGURE 11-3. Control of wild mustard with 2,4–D. This photo shows plots upon which low-volume trials were made. Volumes as low as 5 gallons per acre were as effective as over 100 gallons, a result possible only with a translocated herbicide.

emulsion. The aqueous and emulsion sprays are used on foliage; in oil the ester formulations are used as basal sprays.

MCPA, METHOXONE

This analogue of 2,4-D is used as a selective, postemergence herbicide against broadleaf weeds. It is less toxic against certain crops, notably rice and is widely used to control broadleaf weeds of aquatic habit in that crop. It is also more selective on cereals, legumes, and flax.

MECOPROP, MCPP

Mecoprop formulations are broadleaf-weed killers useful in controlling chickweed, clover, and plantain in turf. Also inhibited are knotweed, dichondra, pigweed, ragweed, lambsquarters, and ground ivy. Schmidt (1972) found that the full activity of mecoprop involves both foliar effects and absorption from the soil when postemergence foliar application is followed by precipitation.

SILVEX, PHENOPROP

Silvex is 2(2,4,5-trichlorophenoxy) propionic acid. It is more effective than 2,4,5-T for control of certain woody plants, oaks in particular. It is also used against chickweed, clover, henbit, and yarrow in turf; also in sugar cane and other crops.

Chlorophenoxyethyl Esters

The sodium salts of 2,4-D ethyl sulfate, MCPA ethyl sulfate, 2,4,5-T ethyl sulfate, and the 2,4-D ethyl benzoate and phosphite have been formulated and tested in a wide variety of weed situations. These compounds have little or no direct phytotoxicity to plants in their original state; when incorporated in soils they are converted by microbial action to the corresponding alcohols, which enter young seedlings by root absorption. These compounds, named sesone, Methin, Natrin, sesin, and Falone, are used preemergence in strawberries, peanuts, tomatoes, and other crops. They are available in granular form for convenience of application.

Pyridazones

BROMPYRAZONE

Brompyrazone is a pre- and postemergence herbicide, selective in cereals and toxic to both monocotyledonous and dicotyledonous weeds.

CHLORAZON

Chlorazon is a selective, pre- and postemergence herbicide useful against most common weeds.

DIMETHAZONE

Dimethazone is a selective, preemergence, soil-applied material that is undergoing tests.

NORFLURAZON

Norflurazon is a newly discovered, selective, preemergence chemical applied through the soil.

OXAPYRAZON

Oxapyrazon is a selective, pre- and postemergence herbicide useful against common weeds in sugar beets, table beets, stock beets, maize, and sorghum.

PYRAZON

Pyrazon is a popular pre- and postemergence herbicide selective in beets and onions against both monocot and dicot weeds. It has proved to be temperature sensitive and there has been crop damage under very unusual temperature extremes. Koren and Ashton (1973) found that pyrazon conjugation was the same at 35° and 18.3°C. They concluded that susceptibility of beets at high temperatures results from increased absorption and translocation which is not accompanied by its conjugation.

REFERENCES

Alder, E. F., W. L. Wright, and G. F. Soper. 1960. Control of seedling grasses in turf with diphenylacetonitrile and a substituted dinitroaniline. *Proc. North Central Weed Control Conf.* 17:23–24.

Anon. 1970a. Weeds controlled by Broadside. Form No. C7091. Marinette, Wis.: The Ansul Company.

Anon. 1970b. Ansar 170 H.C.; Ansar 8100; Broadside. Marinette, Wis.: The Ansul Company.

Crafts, A. S. 1945. A new herbicide, 2,4-dinitro, secondary butyl phenol. *Science* 101:417–418.

Damanakis, M., D. S. H. Drennan, J. D. Fryer, and K. Holly. 1970. Availability to plants of paraquat adsorbed on soil or sprayed on vegetation. *Weed Res.* 10:305–315.

Freed, V. H. 1951. Some factors influencing the herbicidal efficacy of isopropyl N phenyl carbamate. *Weeds* 1:48–60.

Kaufman, D. D. and J. R. Plimmer. 1972. Biodegradation of p-chlorophenylmethylcarbamate. *WSSA Abstr.* 188, 1972.

Koren, E., and F. M. Ashton. 1973. Influence of temperature on absorption, translocation, and metabolism of pyrazon in sugar beets. *Weed Sci.* 21:241–245.

Kossmann, K. 1970. Uber Abbaugeschwindigkeit und Verteilung von Phenmedipham in Boden. *Weed Res.* 10:349–359.

Magalhaes, A. C., and F. M. Ashton. 1969. Effect of dicamba on oxygen uptake and cell membrane permeability in leaf tissue of *Cyperus rotundus* L. *Weed Res.* 9:48–52.

Norris, R. F. 1972. Factors controlling crystallizing-out of phenmedipham in the spray solution. *West. Soc. Weed Sci. Proc.* 25:33–34, 1972.

Saghir, A. R., and S. Abu-Shakra. 1971. Effect of diphenamid and trifluralin on the germination of *Orobanche* seeds *in vitro*. *Weed Res.* 11:74–76.

Schmidt, R. R. 1972. Bekämpfung von *Galium aparine* mit Mecoprop in Abhängigkeit von Vershiedenen Bodenarten. *Weed Res.* 12:174–181.

Seth, A. K. 1971. Control of *Mikania cordata* (Burm. f.) B. L. Robinson in plantation crops using paraquat. *Weed Res.* 11:77–83.

Slater, C. H., J. H. Dawson, W. R. Furtick and A. P. Appleby. 1969. Effects of chlorpropham vapors on dodder seedlings. *Weed Sci.* 17:238–241.

Templeman, W. G., and W. A. Sexton. 1945. Effect of some arylcabamic esters and related compounds upon cereals and other plant species. *Nature* 156:630.

Turner, D. J. 1969. The effects of shoot removal on the rhizome carbohydrate reserves of couch grass (*Agropyron repens* (L.) Beauv). *Weed Res.* 9:27–36.

12

Properties and Functions of Herbicides (Continued)

THIOCARBAMATES*

There are ten thiocarbamate compounds used in weed control. They are listed in Appendix Table 2.

BENTHIOCARB, SATURN, BOLERO

Benthiocarb is used to control a great variety of weeds, particularly grasses. It is recommended for controlling barnyardgrass, sedges, and spikerush in rice.

BUTYLATE, SUTAN

Butylate is a selective, preplant, soil-incorporated herbicide used against grassy weeds and nutsedges in maize. It should not be used in milo, sorghum, or hybrid-seed corn. It will kill seedlings of Johnsongrass and quackgrass; also lambsquarters, redroot pigweed, purslane, annual morningglory, velvetleaf, and Florida purslane.

CDEC, VEGEDEX

This herbicide is a dithiocarbamate used mainly on commercially grown vegetable crops. It kills most of the common annual weeds in a wide variety of crops. It has a slight vapor pressure; it is applied as a spray or as granules to the soil surface and immediately incorporated, mechanically or by sprinkling.

*Much of the information reported in this chapter has been obtained from *1973 Pesticide Dictionary*, published by Farm Chemicals, Meister Publishing Co., Willoughby, Ohio.

DIALLATE, AVADEX

Diallate is applied preplant, soil-incorporated for control of wild oats in alfalfa, alsike clover, barley, maize, flax, lentils, peas, potatoes, red and sweet clovers, and sugar beets. It is usually used in the spring but it can be applied before the soil freezes in the fall for spring wild oats control.

EPTC, EPTAM

EPTC is effective in controlling annual grassy weeds and nut-sedges, also seedlings of perennial grasses and some broadleaf weeds. It may be applied pre- or postemergence. It is used in maize, beans, peppers, tomatoes, and many other crops. Although it will not eradicate nutsedge, a spring treatment will permit development of a crop free of competition. For best results EPTC should be incorporated into the soil to a depth of 2 to 3 inches immediately after application. It may be metered into irrigation water.

Two chemicals have been discovered that protect maize from injury by incorporated EPTC. One (1,8-naphthalic anhydride) is named Protect, the other (N,N-diallyl-2,2-dichloroacetamide) carries the code R25788. Protect was used in 1969 and 1970, R25788 in 1971, and both were employed in 1972 in trials (Rains and Fletchall, 1973); injury to maize both from seed treatment and when used as a tank mix was greatly reduced.

METHAM, VAPAM

Metham is a water-soluble salt which breaks down in moist soil to form methyl isothiocyanate, a toxic vapor that kills plant roots as well as fungi, bacteria, and insects. Metham is applied in solution by spraying in the plow furrow, by mechanical soil incorporation, or by surface application followed by rain or sprinkle irrigation. Rolling is recommended after incorporation. Metham is used as a fumigant against deep-rooted perennials and against weed seeds and other pests in potting and bedding soils, in ornamental and tobacco seedbeds, nursery soils, and propagating beds.

MOLINATE, ORDRAM

Molinate is used for controlling barnyardgrass in rice. It is applied and immediately incorporated with a disc or spiketooth harrow before flooding for planting of water-seeded rice; also it may be applied by airplane after water-seeded or drilled rice is flooded and after the rice is from 2 to 5 inches in height; the seedlings should be at least two-thirds submerged.

PEBULATE, TILLAM

This widely advertised herbicide is used as a preemergence selective reagent which inhibits nutsedge growth and kills seedlings of crabgrass, foxtail, barnyardgrass, wild oats, henbit, hairy nightshade, lambsquarters, purslane, pigweeds, and nettleleaf goosefoot. It is recommended for use in sugar beets, tomatoes, tobacco, table beets, peppers, and strawberries.

TRIALLATE, AVADEX BW, FAR-GO

Triallate is a pre- or postplant, soil-incorporated herbicide used to control wild oats in peas, barley, and durum and spring wheats.

VERNOLATE, VERNAM

Vernolate is a selective preemergence material that should be incorporated immediately after application as an emulsion. It is used in soybeans, peanuts, tobacco, and sweet potatoes. It controls crabgrass, barnyardgrass, foxtails, goosegrass, nutsedge, and seedlings of perennials grasses. Applied to dry soil, it may be incorporated by sprinkler irrigation.

TRIAZINES

The chloro-substituted triazines are all limited to soil application by their lack of phloem mobility. They are readily absorbed from soils by roots and translocated via the xylem to the foliage where they inhibit oxygen evolution in photosynthesis. There are some twenty-four triazines recognized as weed killers; among these there are compounds that break down rapidly for use in crops, others that are long-lasting on nonagricultural soils. First used extensively in maize where the chlorine was found to be rapidly displaced by an OH group, thus detoxifying the molecule, triazines that are adapted to weed control in many crops have been screened. The triazine herbicides are listed in Appendix Table 2. Those molecules whose names end in "ine" are chloro substituted; those ending in "one" have a methoxy substitution; those ending in "yn" or "yne" have methyl mercapto substitutions. Bladex has chlorine in the normal position and a nitrile group on one of the amino substituents.

AMETRYNE, GESAPAX, EVIK

Ametryne is a selective material used to control common, broadleaf and grassy weeds in pineapples, sugar cane, and bananas. It has given promising results in citrus trees and as an aquatic-weed killer. It is not necessary to incorporate ametryne in regions of summer rains.

ATRATONE, GESATAMIN

Because of its methoxy grouping, this chemical is fifty times more water soluble than atrazine. It has been tested but has not offered any unique properties.

ATRAZINE, AATREX, GESAPRIM

Atrazine has probably become the triazine herbicide used in larger quantities and in more situations than any other of the soil-borne materials. It is used both pre- and postemergence in maize, sorghum, sugar cane, and pineapples. It is used preemergence in orchards, vineyards, forest-tree nurseries, Christmas-tree plantations, and grass-seed fields. It is becoming important in establishment and renovation of rangeland, in minimum and nontillage programs. Nontoxic oil is added to atrazine to control grass seedlings in maize and sorghum. Sugar beet, tobacco, oats and many vegetable crops are very sensitive to atrazine in soils and should not be planted in the year following its use. Atrazine may be applied by air on soils too wet to take ground machinery.

AZIPROTRYN, MESORANIL, BRASORAN

This methylthio triazine compound is used on peas, onions, sunflower, maize, and on cole crops, with the exception of cauliflower. It handles both monocot and dicot weeds. It can be applied preemergence to weeds in sown cole crops.

CYANIZINE, SD 15418, BLADEX

This herbicide combines a triazine group with a propionitrile side chain; thus it possesses two phytotoxic moieties. It is used in field maize and popcorn to control a wide spectrum of grassy and broadleaf weeds.

CYPROZINE, OUTFOX

Cyprozine, in a water emulsion is used as a postemergence herbicide in maize, sorghum, and sugar cane; it has proved to leave no toxic residue in soils in the year following use. It should be used before the maize crop is 10 inches high and the weeds 4 inches.

DESMETRYNE, SEMERON

This methylmercapto triazine is used in cole crops against a wide array of grasses and broadleaf weeds.

DIPROPETRYN

Dipropetryn is a recent addition to our arsenal of herbicides used to control troublesome weeds in cotton grown on sandy soil; it can be applied at or soon after planting before weeds and cotton emerge.

METHOPROTRYN, GESARAN

A methylmercapto triazine, methoprotryne has been screened as a preemergence herbicide for use against many annual weeds in wheat, barley, maize, flax, and alfalfa.

IPAZINE, METHOMETON, METHOPROTRYN

These are all selective, preemergence, soil-applied herbicides used in a number of field crops to control broadleaf and grassy weeds. Methoprotryn is used postemergence by directional spray.

METRIBUZIN

This complex, asymmetrical, triazine molecule characterizes a herbicide of diverse properties. It is used as a preemergence material and it is also used at layby for control of late weeds that interfere with mechanical harvest. It is proving effective for controlling weeds in soybeans, potatoes, and tomatoes, and in the control of algae. It controls grasses in winter cereals and many weeds in pineapples and sugar cane in the tropics.

NORAZINE, G30026

This triazine, having a methylamino and an isopropylamino substituent, resembles atrazine but is about four times as water soluble and over fifty times as soluble as simazine. Early tested, it proved very effective against weeds but was not so well tolerated by maize and grapes, possibly because it was rapidly leached into the root zone of these crops.

PROMETONE, GESATRAM, PRAMITOL

Prometone, about three times as water soluble as norazine, is a nonselective, pre- and postemergence herbicide used to control many annual and perennial weeds on nonagricultural land.

PROMETRYNE, CAPAROL

This methylmercapto triazine is used to control many annual grasses and broadleaf weeds in cotton, in bluegrass grown for seed, and in celery. It also looks promising in peas and soybeans and on industrial areas. Application may be made preemergence, postemergence directed, or at layby in cotton. In arid regions it should be incorporated. In celery it can be used as an overall spray.

PROPAZINE, MILOGARD, GESAMIL

Propazine is used for selective, preemergence control of annual weeds in milo or sorghum. Application should be made at planting or immediately after; it can be done by ground rig or by airplane.

PRYNACHLOR

Prynachlor is used to control weeds in cabbage, cauliflower, and kohlrabi.

SEBUTHYLAZINE

Sebuthylazine is a selective, preemergence, soil-borne herbicide of recent origin.

SIMAZINE, PRINCEP, GESATOP

Simazine is the triazine that displaced chlorazine and became the principal selective, preemergence herbicide in maize. Being soluble in water only to 5 ppm, it is very persistent in soils. When it became evident that soil residues of simazine were a real problem, use in maize and many other crops was shifted to atrazine, which has a water solubility of 33 ppm. Simazine, meanwhile, became one of the principal nonselective herbicides used on thousands of miles of highways, irrigation canals, firebreaks, industrial sites, and other places that are kept free of all vegetation for fire protection. Applied suspended in water in autumn or winter, it stops growth of all seedlings soon after germination. When contact action for killing weeds postemergence on highways is required, aminotriazole is used in the formulation.

Simazine is used preemergence in established alfalfa, in orchards and vineyards, caneberries, cranberries, nut trees, ornamental and tree nurseries, and turf-grass seed or sod production; Norway spruce tolerates simazine. Allott (1969) found that, when simazine is applied at a rate of 2.0 lb per acre to undisturbed soils, degradation takes place annually to about 80 percent. Caneberries in Ireland have not suffered from this application rate after 7 to 8 years in the absence of cultivation.

Much interest has been aroused in the possible increase in nitrogen uptake by plants as influenced by micromolar concentrations of s-triazines in the soil. Ries and Gast (1965) found that simazine at 2×10^{-8}M applied to maize growing under low nitrogen increased the nitrogen concentration of the leaves by 90 percent. The same concentration of simazine applied to roots of 10-day-old barley seedlings growing in nutrient culture increased the water-soluble protein content when grown at 30°C days and 15°C nights with 3mM nitrate nitrogen. In a time-course study, simazine increased ^{14}C-leucine incorporation into protein (Pulver and Ries, 1973).

SIMETONE, GESADURAL

This methoxy triazine has somewhat greater water solubility than simazine but it is not sufficiently different to warrant further development.

SIMETRYNE, GY-BON

Simetryne is not sufficiently unique in phytotoxicity or selectivity to warrant development.

SUMITOL, ISOBUMETON

Sumitol has been tested and is on trial for use on established alfalfa. It is also promising for pre- and postemergence use on sugar cane; it has possibilities on citrus.

TERBUTHYLAZINE

Terbuthylazine is a new, selective, preemergence, soil-borne material.

TERBUTRYN, IGRAN, PREBANE

This methylmercapto triazine has been developed for the control of annual weeds in winter wheat, sorghum, peas, and winter barley and for short residual vegetation control on vacant lots.

TRIETAZINE, GESAFLOC

This analogue of simazine is used for selective, preemergence control of annual monocots and dicots in tobacco, potatoes, tomatoes, and peas.

TRIAZOLES

There are only two herbicides in this group, amitrole and amitrole-T.

AMITROLE, AMIZOL

Amitrole is a general, postemergence, translocated herbicide used to kill perennial broadleaf weeds in nonagricultural areas. It is used to control quackgrass before planting maize. It is used in the control of certain woody species, notably poison ivy and poison oak. It is effective in the control of cattails and some aquatic weeds in marshes and drainage ditches. It is mixed with simazine to control mixed weed growth on highways (Amizol).

AMITROLE-T, CYTROL

This material is a mixture of aminotriazole and ammonium thiocyanate. It is very mobile in plants and is used against Canada thistle, quackgrass, and water hyacinth on noncrop areas. It is also used for spot treatment on perennial weeds on cropped lands after harvest or in locations not used for growing food crops.

Aminotriazole in any form is prohibited from use on any food crops in the United States by the EPA. Amitrole and amitrole-T are used in large quantities combined with triazine and urea herbicides for vegetation control along highways, city streets and country roads, and fence lines. The purposes of this use are fire protection, increased visibility, and general esthetics.

URACILS

Three substituted uracils that are effective weed killers are in wide use. The nucleus of these uracil compounds is the same for all, the substitutions differ.

BROMACIL, HYVAR X

Bromacil is used for general weed and brush control in noncrop areas; it is especially effective against perennial grasses. It is widely used along highways, on railway rights-of-way, and in scores of industrial weed situations. At controlled low dosage it can be used selectively in pineapple and citrus crops. By basal or broadcast application, it is adapted to brush control. Application with a root plow has proved effective in control of salt cedar.

LENACIL, VENZAR

Lenacil lacks the bromine of bromacil and has a cyclohexyl substitution in place of the secondary butyl. It is suggested as being selective against annual weeds in beets and spinach when used at the proper dosage.

TERBACIL, SINBAR

Terbacil differs from bromacil by having a chlorine substitution in place of bromine, and a tertiary butyl in place of the secondary butyl. It is used to control annual weeds and seedlings of perennial grasses in apples, peaches, citrus, mint, and sugar cane. It should be applied while the weeds are still small. It can be used against perennial grasses which should be thoroughly disced before treatment. On sugar cane and mint, preemergence application may be made by aircraft.

Terbacil is quite effective in the control of nutsedge.

UREAS

The urea herbicides constitute one of the most important groups of compounds used for weed control. Although several urea compounds were described as potential herbicides as early as 1946, the announcement of CMU in 1951 by Bucha and Todd initiated a phase of weed-control activity that has revealed hundreds of chemicals of herbicidal possibilities. A number of the available ones will be described.

Like the triazines and uracils, the substituted urea herbicides lack phloem mobility and therefore are used primarily as soil-borne materials; some have sufficient contact toxicity to be used as general postemergence reagents. And, at low dosage rates, many are used as selective, pre- or postemergence herbicides in crops. Residual soil toxicity varies greatly among them; where special susceptibilities exist, the cropping program must take them into consideration. Eventually all urea herbicides break down to CO_2, H_2, NH_3, NO_2, and common organic constituents of decaying vegetation.

MONURON, TELVAR, CMU

Monuron was first introduced as a soil-borne herbicide of broad-weed spectrum, used to control all weeds on railroad rights-of-way, highway verges, firebreaks, and other noncrop areas. At the end of the first year of field testing it was found to be ineffective in controlling deep-rooted perennials, such as perennial rye, wild licorice, Russian knapweed, and others. Soon, formulations combining monuron with sodium chlorate, boron compounds, 2,4-D, 2,3,6 TBA, and amitrole were devised. These were more successful in controlling general weed growth on noncrop areas.

It was found that, at carefully observed low dosage rates, monuron could be used selectively in cotton, sugar cane, pineapple, asparagus, and citrus. It may be applied as a suspension in water or in granular form; it requires rainfall or irrigation to wash it into the soil horizon where weed seeds are germinating. Monuron is preferred on medium to heavy soils; it tends to leach from sandy soils.

DIURON, KARMEX

Diuron has two chlorines on the phenyl ring; it is less soluble than monuron; it is used at dosages of 4 to 16 lb per acre for general weed control of annuals, at 16 to 48 lb per acre against perennials. It is applied as a suspension in water with continuous agitation in the spray tank to avoid settling out. Application by means of a root plow has been effective in controlling salt cedar.

At dosages ranging from 0.6 to 6.0 lb per acre, it is used selectively for controlling weeds in cotton, sugar cane, pineapples, orchards and vineyards, and alfalfa, especially alfalfa for seed. Like monuron, diuron is sold in mixtures with other chemicals, particularly translocated materials, to handle deep-rooted perennial weeds.

FENURON, DYBAR

Fenuron is about five times as soluble in water as monuron; it is used as a soil-borne herbicide against woody plants and deep-rooted perennials. For convenience in the woods, fenuron is formulated as pellets. It requires rainfall or irrigation to leach it into the proper soil layer where it kills weed seedlings soon after germination.

FENURON-TCA, MONURON-TCA

These two combinations are nonselective herbicides used in non-crop areas to control general weed growth. The TCA leaches to affect perennial weed roots.

NEBURON, KLOBEN

Neburon differs from diuron in having a butyl group in place of one of the methyl substituents. This makes neburon about seven times less soluble in water than diuron. It is used selectively for weed control in nursery plantings of woody ornamentals, annual weeds in dichondra, and grassy weeds in wheat; its selectivity results from its low solubility and its location in the top-soil layer.

These four substituted urea compounds appeared in quick succession; in the meantime, many more modifications of the general pattern laid down by these original compounds were tested. These will now be described.

ANISURON

Anisuron is a new urea herbicide for selective preemergence used to control hard-to-kill weeds.

BENZOMARC

Benzomarc has a benzoyl group on the same nitrogen as the dichlorophenyl group in diuron. It is a selective, preemergence herbicide used to kill annual weeds in wheat, rice, cotton, fruit trees, vineyards, soybeans, and flax.

BENZTHIAZURON, GATNON

This urea herbicide is selective in sugar and fodder beets. It controls seedlings when used preplant or preemergence. It is safer in beets than pyrazon.

BUTURON, ARISAN, EPTAPUR

This compound has a propynyl ($-C \equiv CH$) group giving it unique selectivity. It is suggested for use on cereal crops and maize, also in carrots.

CHLORBROMURON, MALORAN

Chlorbromuron has a bromine substituent on the phenyl group and a methoxy on the 1 nitrogen. It is useful for eliminating annual weeds in maize and soybeans. It is also promising in wheat, potatoes, carrots, celery, cotton, asparagus, and sugar cane.

CHLOROXURON, TENORAN

This urea compound has a p-chlorophenoxy phenyl group on the 3 nitrogen. It controls annual weeds applied preemergence and is tolerated by soybeans, strawberries, carrots, onions, celery, lentils, caneberries, and ornamental bulb crops. It is used postemergence on soybeans, dry-bulb onions, strawberries, and carrots.

CHLORTOLURON

Chlortoluron is a selective, preemergence, soil-borne herbicide still being tested for use against special weeds.

CYCLORON, ALIPUR

Cycloron is selective for annual weeds in sugar and fodder beets, spinach, carrots, peas, beans, and it is effective in nursery weed control.

DIFENOXURON, PINORAN

Difenoxuron has a methoxy-phenoxy group in the usual phenyl position on this substituted urea herbicide. It is selective postemergence in field-seeded onions.

FLUOMETURON, COTORAN

A CF_3 substitution on the meta position on the phenyl group of this urea herbicide gives it selectivity in a number of crops. Use is indicated for cotton, asparagus, grain sorghum, sugar cane, citrus, and ornamental bulb crops. It may be applied preemergence on the soil surface, preemergence incorporated, post planting, and postemergence. It may be mixed with DSMA or MSMA for Johnsongrass control in cotton.

ISONORURON

This herbicide, having a hexahydromethanoindanyl group on one nitrogen, is selective in sugar cane, cotton, wheat, barley and rye; annual weeds are controlled.

KARBUTILATE, TANDEX

This molecule combines a carbamate group on the phenyl substituent of the substituted urea making it a combination of two toxicants. It is used to control annual and perennial broadleaf weeds and grasses, brush, and vines. It is useful on railroad, utility, and pipe-line rights-of-way, firebreaks, drainage-ditch banks, and industrial sites.

LINURON, LOROX, AFALON

Linuron differs from diuron in having a methoxy group in place of one of the methyl substituents. It is used preemergence to control annual weeds in winter-sown and spring-sown wheat. Autumn treatments have proved better than spring treatments.

METHABENZTHIAZURON, TRIBUNIL

This urea compound has a benzothiazoyl substitution in place of the phenyl group. It is used preemergence to control annual weeds in winter-sown and spring-sown wheat. Autumn treatments have proved better than spring treatments.

METHIURON

Methiuron is a selective, preemergence, soil-borne herbicide.

METOBROMURON, PATORAN

Metobromuron has a bromine substituent in the para position on the phenyl ring and a methoxy group on the other nitrogen. It is effective in controlling annual weeds in beans, potatoes, tobacco, and safflower.

METOXURON, DOSANEX

This urea compound has a methoxy group in the para position on the phenyl substituent. It is recommended for postemergence treatment of annual weeds in winter wheat and winter barley, pre- and postemergence in carrots.

MONOLINURON, ARESIN

Monolinuron is used pre- or postemergence on potatoes, dwarf beans, asparagus, cereals, ornamentals, grapes, berries, and trees for control of many species of annual weeds.

SIDURON, TUPERSAN

Siduron is used preemergence for controlling annual grassy weeds, such as crabgrass, foxtail, barnyardgrass, in newly seeded or established plantings of bluegrass, fescue, redtop, smooth brome, perennial ryegrass, orchard grass, and some bentgrasses, namely Pencross, Seaside, Highland, Astoria, Nimisila, C-1, C-7, and C-19. It is not to be used on other bentgrasses nor on Bermudagrass turf.

TEBUTHIURON, SPIKE, EL-103

Tebuthiuron is a pre- and postemergence, selective herbicide that controls many woody plant species. It is available as a wettable powder and as pellets. It is recommended in reforestation programs, and for pasture and range renovation. It also provides effective weed control in plant and ratoon sugar cane. Dosage rates vary according to plant species and soil type.

TRIMETURON

Trimeturon is a new pseudourea introduced in Europe by Bayer. It is still under test. Should it prove to have unique selectivities, it may be useful against hard-to-kill weeds.

UNCLASSIFIED HERBICIDES

BANAIR

Banair is a postemergence, selective herbicide applied to growing weeds after tillering of the crop; clover is one weed controlled.

BANDANE, HALTS

Bandane is a crabgrass killer used on turf; also used in preemergence band treatments to control annual grasses in row crops.

BENAZOLIN, CORNOX

Benazolin is a postemergence herbicide used as the potassium salt or the ethyl ester in water. It is used principally in mixtures with chlorophenoxy compounds for broad-spectrum weed control in clover mixtures and also mixed with dicamba and 2,4-D. It is designed to handle weed problems where 2,4-D fails.

BENOXAZOLE

Benoxazole is a selective, preemergence material for application via the soil.

BENSULIDE, BETASAN

Bensulide is used to control crabgrass, annual bluegrass, redroot pigweed, barnyardgrass, lambsquarters, shepherdspurse, goosegrass, and dead nettle in dichondra and grass turf. It is used preemergence. On grass turf it should be applied preplant or at planting time. In established dichondra, it should be applied preemergence to weeds. Bensulide is fixed in the surface soil layer; it requires rainfall or sprinkling to wash it in and it provides long-lasting control.

BENTAZON, BASAGRAN

Bentazon is a preemergence material used to control 2,4-D tolerant weeds, such as cocklebur, pineapple weed, velvet leaf, chrysanthemum, smartweed, mayweed, pricklysida, and bedstraw, in barley, wheat, rye, oats, maize, sorghum, rice, soybeans, potatoes, and pasture grasses.

BENTRANIL

Bentranil is a postemergence herbicide used to control annual weeds in cereal crops, maize, and rice.

BENZAZIN, BAS 1700 H

Benzazin is used postemergence to control dicotyledonous weeds in barley, wheat, rice, potatoes, maize, and sorghum.

CHLORFLURAZOL

This benzimidazole, postemergence herbicide has been tested against broadleaf weeds in wheat and barley.

CHLORFLURENOL, MAINTAIN

Chlorflurenol is used as a growth retardant to inhibit excessive growth of a wide spectrum of herbaceous and woody species and to control broadleaf and grassy weeds, It is freely mobile in plants and tends to accumulate in buds and growing points.

DAZOMET, MYLONE

The chemical tetrahydro-3,5-dimethyl-2H-1,3,5-thiadiazine-2-dione has proved to be an effective soil fumigant against annual weeds in seed beds and potting soils when applied preemergence to the weeds and incorporated into the soil and sealed by sprinkling. It has killed purslane, crabgrass, and Bermudagrass, and it kills germinating seeds, nematodes, and fungi. Foret (1959) used it to sterilize potting soil by spraying the moist soil in 6-in. layers, adding more soil, and spraying successively until his pile was complete; then he covered the pile with polyethylene sheeting and left it for three weeks. This treatment eliminated a wide array of annual weeds and killed most of the nutsedge.

The breakdown of dazomet in moist soil results in release of methyl isothiocyanate, formaldehyde, hydrogen sulfide, and monomethylamine. These interact at or near the site of release to kill most living organisms. Soil pH seems not important in this process but temperature is; warm soil temperatures are favorable to rapid and complete action and dissipation of the toxic products. Three weeks are required for complete elimination of phytotoxicity in treated soils.

DCPA, DACTHAL

DCPA is a selective, preemergence herbicide used to control broadleaf and grassy weeds on turf, ornamentals, strawberries, vegetable transplants, cotton, soybeans, and field beans. Having an average half-life in soils of 100 days but little tendency to leach, it is effective in controlling weed seedlings through the normal growing season for many crops.

DECAZOLIN, BAS 3490H

This unique herbicide has been tested and shown effective against barnyardgrass, crabgrass, foxtails, millet, and nutsedges, as well as common broadleaf weeds, in maize, potatoes, beets, and rice.

DESTUN

Destun is a selective, preemergence material useful against annual broadleaf weeds, grasses, and nutsedges in many field and vegetable crops.

DICHLONE, PHYGON

This chemical is an active fungicide commonly used as a seed protectant and soil fumigant. It is available as a dust or a wettable powder.

DIMEXAN

Dimexan is a selective, contact, foliar herbicide of recent introduction.

ENDOTHALL, AQUATHOL, HYDROTHOL

Endothall is a preemergence or postemergence herbicide and desiccant. It is used in sugar beets, red beets, and spinach, as a turf weedkiller, and as an aquatic herbicide.

EXD, DEX, SULFASAN

This sulfur-containing herbicide is useful as a pre- or postemergence application on onions and snap beans; also useful as a preharvest desiccant.

FENAC, TRIFENE

Fenac is used as a preemergence, season-long herbicide in sugar cane against Johnsongrass seedlings. It also has wide application against general weed growth on noncroplands. It is effective against submerged aquatic weeds when applied to soil before flooding or as granules which sink to the bottom of the ditch or lake.

FLUMEZIN

Flumezin is a selective, preemergence, soil-borne chemical of recent introduction.

FLURENOL, FLURECOL

Flurenol is a systemic, postemergence herbicide used to kill such weeds as pineapple weed, camomile, bedstraw, and hempnettle in wheat, barley, rye, and oats.

FLUROMIDINE

Fluromidine has a trifluoromethylimidazo pyridine structure. It is still being tested.

GLYPHOSATE, ROUNDUP

Glyphosate is a translocated herbicide effective against both broadleaf weeds and grasses. It is proving very effective in controlling Johnsongrass, Bermudagrass, bullgrass (*Paspalum fasiculatum*), bindweed, and many other perennial weeds. As a directed spray it can be used in corn, cotton, soybeans, and in tree and vine crops. It will kill witchweed and its host plants.

HALOXIDINE

Haloxidine has a dichloro, difluoro, hydroxypyridine structure. It is selective for preemergence soil application.

METHAZOLE, PROBE, BIOXONE

Methazole is a pre- and postemergence herbicide useful against a wide range of broadleaf and grassy weeds. It is useful on field crops, fruit trees and vines, and on vegetable crops.

MH, MALEIC HYDRAZIDE

MH is a growth retardant and a herbicide. It is used to retard growth of turf, shrubs, and trees, and if dosage is controlled it is harmless to existing foliage.

At higher dosage MH is used to control wild onions, garlic, and quackgrass in maize, potatoes, tomatoes, beans, peas, and beets. In this latter usage MH is applied in spring when quackgrass is 4 to 10 inches tall; after 4 to 8 days the sod is plowed, disced and harrowed, and prepared for planting. MH has been used to control Bermudagrass but dalapon has proved to be more effective.

NOA

NOA is a postemergence herbicide, used to control such 2,4-D tolerant weeds as mayweed, pineapple weed, and dogfennel in wheat, rye, barley, and oats. Mixed with 2,4-D or MCPA it controls these weeds plus those ordinarily handled by the phenoxy compounds.

NORTRAN AND NORTRON

These two dissimilar molecules, recently introduced by Fisons of England, are selective, preemergence herbicides useful against hard-to-kill weeds.

OXADIAZON, RONSTAR

Oxadiazon is a pre- and postemergence, selective material used to control both monocots and dicots, particularly annual grasses in soybeans, cotton, rice, sugar cane, peanuts, vegetable and flower crops, orchards, and vineyards.

PICLORAM, TORDON

Picloram is a postemergence, translocated herbicide useful against perennial weeds, brush, and trees. Most grasses are tolerant as are cruciferous crops. This herbicide is very mobile in plants; when applied to foliage it penetrates and is transported symplastically from foliage to roots; when applied to roots through the soil it is readily absorbed and moved apoplastically to the leaves. Picloram is an extremely potent growth regulator and should be used with care to avoid drift in places where susceptible, nontarget species are growing.

Picloram is used in forestry to kill weedy tree species; it is used along rights-of-way to control brush and perennial weeds. It proved effective in controlling skeleton weed in wheat and lime bush in the forests of Australia. It is available as a water-soluble material for aerial application and in pellets for hand or machine application.

PMA, PMAS, AGROSAN

PMA, phenylmercury acetate, is used as a postemergence, selective herbicide to control crabgrass in turf. Its main use is as a granular formulation suitable for machine application. Protective gloves should be worn if spread by hand.

RHIZOBITOXINE

The bacterial toxin rhizobitoxine (2-amino-4-[2-amino-3-hy-droxypropoxy]-*trans*-3-butanoic acid) has, in common with amitrole, the property of causing chlorosis when applied to leaves. In tests on a number of plants, Owens (1973) found rhizobitoxine to be as toxic as amitrole; phytotoxicity varied; sorghum was very susceptible, large crabgrass was moderately sensitive, and wheat was tolerant; Kentucky bluegrass was very tolerant.

TCBC, RANDOX-T

Trichlorobenzyl chloride is an adjunct to CDAA in formulating Randox-T. This latter herbicide is used preemergence to control weedy annual grasses in onions, cabbage, sweet potatoes, tomatoes, celery, sugar cane, and white potatoes.

TH-1568A, ACNQ

This compound is a selective, postemergence spray used in Japan against weeds in rice.

TRI-PE

Tri-PE is a selective, preemergence material for use on row crops and as a desiccant in onions.

VORLEX, DI-TRAPEX

This mixture of methyl isothiocyanate and chlorinated C_3 hydrocarbons is used as a soil fumigant. It is applied preplant to kill weed seeds, fungi, insects, and nematodes.

REFERENCES

Allott, D. F. 1969. The persistence of simazine applied annually in the prolonged absence of soil cultivation. *Weed Res.* 9:279–287.

Foret, J. A. 1959. Sterilizing potting soils with Mylone. *Sta. to Sta. Res. News* 5:3–4. Union Carbide Chemicals Co.

Owens, L. D. 1973. Herbicidal potential of Rhizobitoxine. *Weed Sci.* 21:63–66.

Pulver, E. L., and S. K. Ries. 1973. Action of simazine in increasing plant protein content. *Weed Sci.* 21:233–237.

Rains, L. J., and O. H. Fletchall. 1973. Chemicals used to protect corn from EPTC injury. *WSSA Abstr.* 13. 1973.

Ries, S. K., and A. Gast. 1965. The effect of simazine on nitrogenous components of corn. *Weeds* 13:272–274.

13

Combinations of Herbicides

Two or more herbicides may be used in combination; in fact many modern herbicide formulations involve combinations of toxicants. There are many reasons for using mixtures of herbicides.

1. A mixture can be used to broaden the spectrum of herbicidal action in order to kill a greater variety of weeds. Many mixtures are formulated for this purpose, for example, 2,4-D plus IPC, dalapon plus amitrole, MCPA plus 2,3,6-TBA, CDAA plus TCBC (Randox-T), MCPA plus TCA, etc.

2. A mixture can be used in the hope of producing a synergistic action and hence an increase in the effectiveness of the treatment. An example of this is the mixture of amitrole and ammonium thiocyanate sold as amitrole-T. There is evidence that the thiocyanate used in this formulation prevents the rapid uptake and drastic contact action of amitrole, allowing for a steady prolonged uptake and translocation. This is important in the control of perennial weeds.

3. An additive can be used to prevent the rapid detoxification of the more active toxicant of a formulation. Stone and Rake (1955) attribute the effectiveness of mixtures containing boron to its inhibition of microorganisms in the soil which break down the organic component.

4. One constituent of a mixture may be used to inhibit some deleterious action of another. For example, in the acid-arsenical mixture the sodium arsenite greatly reduced the corrosive action of the sulfuric acid on iron or steel parts of the application machinery. In borate-chlorate mixtures, whereas the borate constituents are them-

250

selves phytotoxic, they also reduce the tendency of chlorates to ignite and burn vigorously in contact with organic materials.

One further type of mixture is that which contains a pesticide plus a fertilizer. In the constant search for means of reducing production costs, many people have mixed herbicides with plant nutrients to eliminate one application operation. Before mixing a herbicide into a liquid fertilizer, their compatibility should be tested, for some such mixtures will form precipitates. In the hands of experienced operators, herbicide-fertilizer mixtures may be used with considerable savings. They cannot be recommended for use by inexperienced farmers.

Klingman of North Carolina State College of Agriculture and Engineering recommends treatment after one cultivation when corn is 10 to 12 in. high. He suggests 80 to 120 lb of nitrogen as ammonium nitrate plus ⅛ to ¼ lb of low-volatile ester of 2,4-D plus ⅓ lb of surfactant in about 18 gal total mix. Apply as a directed spray; a second or third application may be made as needed to handle late-germinating weeds.

Among the many organic herbicides being used, certain combinations have proved very effective. 2,4-D has been a remarkably effective material when used straight, but the very property that makes it so valuable as a selective herbicide, namely, the variation in susceptibility of different plant species, militates against its use on resistant plants. Resistant brushy species, a good many of which belong to the rose family, have proved susceptible to 2,4,5-T and, where a variety of plants is being treated, combinations of 2,4-D and 2,4,5-T are used. A number of so called "brush killers" are formulations of these two chemicals, and varying proportions of the two have been prepared. Some commercial preparations have equal parts of each, some are one-third 2,4,5-T and two-thirds 2,4-D; others are formuated in other proportions. Practically, it is best to apply each chemical at the dosage rate required to kill the individual species demanding the highest dosage of that chemical and to apply the mixture only where species requiring both are growing together.

One large group of plants, the grasses, are all relatively resistant to 2,4-D and its analogues; search has brought out a number of grass killers. The first of these, IPC, has proved effective principally when applied through the soil to roots of annuals during the winter. Combinations of 2,4-D and IPC are effective in temporarily sterilizing the soil against seedlings of grasses and broadleaf weeds. Because IPC is effective only through the soil, it is advisable to use a mixture of finely ground IPC and 2,4-D acid when this combination is called for. Emulsifiable IPC could be combined with 2,4-D salt or ester for liquid application, but this combination would be considerably more subject to loss by leaching. Under conditions of limited rainfall following application, it might prove more effective than the solid forms. Where longer lasting results are desired, 2,4-D acid plus CIPC should be used; granular formulations are useful.

Combinations of TCA with 2,4-D and 2,4,5-T have proved effective in providing temporary soil sterilization against mixed weed populations, including perennial grasses. This mixture is effective in controlling weeds on railroad rights-of-way (Bogle, 1949).

A combination spray containing 10 lb of TCA, 2 lb of 2,4-D, and 1 pt of wetting agent is valuable in the control of cattails and tules in irrigation ditches.

Sodium TCA in combination with sodium chlorate has been tried for the control of Bermudagrass and Johnsongrass with marked success in the southeastern states (Bogle, 1949). Sodium TCA has also been combined with pentachlorophenol. Because the latter is simply a contact killer, this combination was better in the fall when there was little natural regrowth.

At least one situation has been described where a combination of 2,4-D with the contact killer, pentachlorophenol, has been found effective (Crafts and Emanuelli, 1948). In Puerto Rico, grasses and broadleaf weeds occur in cane fields. Day lily is a rather succulent, broadleaf weed that is highly susceptible to 2,4-D but relatively tolerant of the fortified oil emulsion used on the grasses. Because killing of day lily by the general contact material is slow, there is ample time for absorption and translocation of 2,4-D before the plants are severely injured by the fortified oil emulsion. By combining 2,4-D in the fortified-oil emulsion formula, it was possible to kill both grasses and broadleaf weeds with maximum efficiency of the spraying operation.

A chemical can produce a combination treatment if it has contact action on the foliage when applied as a spray and then kills root tissue when washed into the soil. Such combined action is the basis for many successful herbicidal treatments, and it can be used to advantage where frequent summer rains or sprinkler irrigation provides the washing action. Sodium chlorate, sodium arsenite, sodium pentaborate, ammonium sulfamate, 2,4-D, dalapon, amitrole, and TCA all act on both foliage and roots and can be applied so as to have the double action where rainfall or sprinkling is available.

Combinations of modern herbicides may take many forms; some involve combination molecules. Examples are sesone and its analogues where the sulfate, benzoate, or phosphite entity simply modifies the molecule rendering it nontoxic until it is decomposed by the soil microflora and the toxic 2,4-D molecule is released. Other examples are Urox, which combines monuron with TCA; Urab, which combines fenuron and TCA; and erbon, which combines the toxic groups of

2,4,5-trichlorophenoxyethyl alcohol and 2,2-dichloropropionic acid (dalapon).

Sackston (1958) sprayed young flax with MCPA (sodium salt), TCA (sodium salt), and mixtures of these two herbicides in an attempt to handle broadleaf weeds and grasses; the latter became increasingly aggressive where hormonelike weed killers were used to eliminate the broadleaf weeds. MCPA was used at 3 oz acid equivalent per acre, TCA at 5.8 lb acid equivalent per acre. Combination sprays used both of these at the above dosages; volume rate was 35 gpa. Prostrate knotweed (*Polygonum aviculare*) and large crabgrass (*Digitaria sanguinalis*) were the principle weeds.

MCPA gave fair control of the knotweed, and TCA reduced crabgrass to below 50 percent of control plots; weights of all weeds in grams for the various plots were: control, 272 g; TCA treatment, 99 g; MCPA, 103 g; and TCA + MCPA, 36 g. The values given are averages of five replicates. Sackston concluded that the combination gave better control of knotweed than either chemical alone.

Sheets and Leonard (1958) studied the herbicidal action of combinations of amitrole with dalapon, monuron, several aliphatic acids, and chlorinated aliphatic acids in an effort to find useful formulations for weed control where 2,4-D cannot be used because of the hazards involved. Amitrole plus dalapon gave marked reduction in fresh weight of barley and kidney beans. The effects of the two compounds applied as a mixture appeared to be additive. The addition of sublethal dosages of the sodium salt of 2,2-dichloropropionic acid (dalapon) to amitrole solutions decreased the immediate development of chlorosis in primary (treated) leaves while increasing chlorosis of the trifoliate leaves. This would seem to indicate that dalapon exerts a sparing action on the primary leaves, making for greater uptake and translocation of the amitrole. Ammonium thiocyanate, employed in the mixture amitrole-T, appears to have this same effect.

In studies of the interaction of amitrole and dalapon using barley, bean, and barnyardgrass, Sheets and Leonard found additive effects only. Mixtures of amitrole and monuron gave results indicating greater-than-additive toxicities. Since all three species gave indications of these enhanced toxicities, it seems possible that synergism is displayed by this combination.

In studies using Bermudagrass, amitrole-dalapon mixtures gave no greater effects than dalapon alone; that is, amitrole did not seem to add to the toxicity of dalapon. Typical amitrole chlorosis did not appear on leaves sprayed with amitrole solution containing any appreciable quantity of monuron. Monuron chlorosis and abscission, however, occurred from treatments with as little as 1/10 lb per acre, and these symptoms appeared whether amitrole was present or not. As mentioned, amitrole chlorosis was inhibited when dalapon was included in the spray solution. Thus amitrole chlorosis in bean appears to be blocked by monuron or dalapon; the latter was required in equimolar concentration with amitrole, but lesser quantities of monuron had the same effect.

Indyk (1957) found that mixtures of sodium salt of PCP with CDEC and with 2,4-D gave excellent control of broadleaf weeds and grasses in soybeans with little injury to the crop. Hay (1961) used CDAA and DNBP with success. Chloramben has been used successfully in soybeans for years; combined with 2,4-DB it handles heavy weeds like cocklebur and sunflower.

Maestri and Currier (1958) investigated the interaction of MH and endothall. They found that in foliar application of the mixture, MH enhances penetration and contact toxicity of endothall. At certain concentrations endothall prevents the systemic distribution of MH, probably by injuring the phloem tissue. MH is an inhibitor, endothall a stimulator of respiration; that follows from the acute toxicity of endothall in contrast to the slow, systemic, dormancy-inducing action of MH.

One finds many reports on the practical use of herbicide mixtures in agricultural literature. For example, from Oregon comes the report that 1 lb of amitrole applied as a spray on Canada thistle followed 1 day later by a 1-lb per acre spray application of 2,4-D provides a very effective treatment for this difficult perennial weed. Mixing the two will not work, for they react to form a less active salt. And applying the 2,4-D before the amitrole results in a distinct antagonism; the 2,4-D apparently affects the plants in such a way that the amitrole fails to translocate.

Where monuron or simazine are used postemergence, inclusion of 2,4-D at ½ to 1 lb per acre in the spray solution will kill most emerged weeds, while the soil-borne ingredients handle germinating seedlings (Fig. 13–1). In row crops such mixtures require careful application, for 2,4-D may injure most crops. Directed sprays are required on crop species that are at all susceptible to 2,4-D.

Amitrole and 2,3,6-TBA are recommended for controlling field bindweed, Canada thistle, coltsfoot, dock, foxtails, crabgrass, barnyardgrass, and combinations of these weeds.

Diuron plus amitrole has been used as a postemergence spray for handling growing weeds and germinating seeds.

Fenac plus 2,4-D has proved successful in control of perennial weeds; 2,4-D kills foliage and translocates to the roots; fenac has a slow contact action on foliage, and it is absorbed from the soil by roots. Rainfall or irrigation following within a week after application will result in the greatest effectiveness of this combination.

Dalapon, at 4 lb per acre, plus 2,4-DB, at 2 to 3 lb per acre, have been used in establishing alfalfa and birdsfoot trefoil in weedy soils in regions of summer rainfall. Dalapon plus amitrole, in combination or applied separately as occasion demands, is used in New Zealand in pasture establishment. Dalapon, applied preplant combined with a postplant application of Premerge, is effective in controlling both quackgrass and broadleaf weeds in corn. Eptam plus 2,4-D has been used to handle both broadleaved weeds and grasses in corn.

FIGURE 13-1. A mixture of diuron at 3.2 lb (actual) and 2,4–D amine at ¼ lb per acre was used on the sprayed area in this vineyard. Both broadleaf weed and grasses were controlled.

Since these relatively early experiences with mixed herbicides, many publications have appeared describing great numbers of combination treatments. The addition of diquat and paraquat has contributed greatly to the list of successful combinations. And each time a new chemical appears on the market, new publications describe its use alone and in combination with other herbicides.

Much energy has been expended in attempts to rationalize various theories of the synergism of herbicides. In an early paper Crafts and Cleary (1936) presented results of experiments where arsenic, borax, and sodium chlorate were used two at a time in combinations; they used a simple graphing method to analyze their results, assuming that an arithmetic treatment would adequately express their results.

Zemanek (1969) used NaTCA plus pyrazon, dalapon plus pyrazon, NaTCA plus lenacil, and dalapon plus lenacil in sugar beets and found that the susceptibility of the beets to phytotoxicity did not parallel that of the weeds; hence selectivity was not reduced. The combinations controlled both mono- and dicotyledonous weeds.

Studying weed control in soybeans, Parochetti et al. (1972) found that preemergence applications of trifluralin, nitralin, vernolate, or linuron, followed by chloroxuron postemergence resulted in higher soybean yields than any single herbicide treatment.

Sterrett et al. (1972) recorded an antagonistic effect between picloram and bromacil on oats; this combination inhibited both transpiration and root growth.

Using barnyardgrass as a test plant, Hagimoto and Yoshikawa (1972) found synergism between benoxazole and either chlorbromuron or simetryne; other combinations involving benthiocarb, MCPA, MCAA, or swep gave a high degree of growth inhibition. The writers postulate a "growth-dilution" response to explain the rapid increase with age of the tolerance of barnyardgrass for photosynthesis inhibitors. Growth inhibitors in combination with photosynthesis inhibitors gave evidence for synergism under their test conditions.

Ludwig (1973) reports that a mixture of 2,4-D amine with atrazine was more effective than either material applied alone for controlling weeds in maize in Britain.

MIXTURES OF HERBICIDES WITH FERTILIZERS

Although discovery of the activation of sinox with ammonium sulfate resulted from an attempt of a farmer to apply sinox with a nitrogen source, little attention was paid to applying herbicides and fertilizers together until the mid 1950s when solid fertilizers were impregnated with liquid pesticides. Since then the use of mixtures of herbicides with fertilizers applied as solutions or slurries has increased rapidly until now hundreds of thousands of acres of maize and soybean crops are so treated. Meyer et al. (1973) made field studies to evaluate the compatibility of atrazine with suspension fertilizers on maize (Pioneer 321). Preplant incorporation gave better fertilizer availability than preemergence treatments.

ANALYSIS OF HERBICIDE ACTION

In two excellent papers, Gowing (1959, 1960) has called into question the direct arithmetic analysis used in arriving at the conclusions as to herbicide interaction cited by Crafts and Cleary (1936). As Gowing points out, when differing mechanisms of action result in differing types of dosage-response curves, it is difficult to compare compounds on an arithmetic basis, and at best only rough approximations are given. Gowing (1960) describes several methods for graphing results and points out the advantages of curves where the response as percent inhibition on a probability scale (probits) is plotted against the logarithm of dosage. This has the effect of straightening the usual sigmoid curve to a straight line. Gowing also stresses the advantages of comparisons at the 50 percent inhibition value. This is the steepest part of the curve, and hence deviation is at a minimum, making for the greatest validity of comparisons.

The criticisms of the earlier methods of analysis of herbicide response are justified and, as the number of compounds being used in combination increases, the need for critical comparative methods increases. It seems desirable, however, to emphasize here a number of limitations of analyses of experimental results of herbicide interaction. Certainly, probit analysis (Bliss, 1935; Finney, 1952) is justified and useful in comparing groups of compounds having a common mode of action, for example the analogues of 2,4-D, the phenylcarbamates, the substituted ureas, the symmetrical triazines, etc. However, if one is seeking synergism, he is more likely to find it in mixtures of compounds having dissimilar modes of action, and here one must be cautious in selecting his combinations, for too great dissimilarity may obviously lead to failure. For example, contact herbicides may be profitably compared with combinations as may systemic toxicants. But a combination of strong contact reagent with a systemic material may well lead to failure because the former may destroy the mechanism responsible for transport of the latter.

In a similar way, if two chemicals depend upon absorption by roots for their toxic action, means must be provided for them to be leached into the zone of absorbing roots. This may be made difficult by differences in solubility, fixation, or mode of absorption by roots. And if the mode of action of two compounds differs widely, the mixture may fail because one eliminates the action of the other. For example, there seems to be little reason to combine a substituted urea or triazine herbicide with one that prevents germination or kills seedlings before they emerge, for the blocking of photosynthesis cannot take place, and the compound that acts in this way would be wasted.

Where broadening of the spectrum of action is desired, different principles are involved and different methods are required. For example, tests on the spectrum of individual chemicals should be made first, and combinations should be designed to cover known susceptible species. Synergism can hardly be expected to emerge from such tests; detection of antagonism would logically be the main object of such studies.

In spite of the many advances in methods of analysis of toxicity

Table 13-1. **Mixture of Herbicides**

Name	Ingredients
Aatram	Atrazine + propachlor
Alanap plus	Naptalam + chlorpropham
Amadon 101	Picloram + 2,4–D
Amilom WP	Chloramben + linuron
Amizine	Amitrole + simazine
Ancrak	Naptalam + dinoseb
Aquathol plus	Endothall + silvex
Atratol 8P	Atrazine + NaClO$_3$ + borax
Atratol 8pW	Atrazine + prometone
Bonus Type B	Dicamba + 2,4–D
Bonus Super	Diphenamid + neburon + carbaryl
Borocil IV	Bromacil + boron comp.
Broadside	MSMA + sodium cacodylate
Brominal plus	Bromoxynil + MCPA
Bronate	Bromoxynil + MCPA
Brushkiller 155	Dichlorprop + 2,4–D + 2,3,6–TBA
Brushkiller 170	Dichlorprop + 2,4–D
Caparol + MSMA	Prometryne + MSMA
Chipcoturf Kleen	Mecoprop + 2,4–D
Chlorax	NaClO$_3$ + metaborate
Chlorea	NaClO$_3$ + metaborate + monuron
Chlorvar	Bromacil + NaClO$_3$ + metaborate
Crab-E-Rad Super	Octylammonium + Dodecylammonium methanearsonates
Dal-E-Rad + 2	DSMA + 2,4–D
Ded-Weed	2,4–D + 2,4,5–T
Dinoxol	2,4–D + 2,4,5–T
Dowpon C	Dalapon + TCA
Dyanap	Naptalam + disoseb
Emulsamine brushkiller	2,4–D + 2,4,5–T
Emulsavert	2,4–D + 2,4,5–T
Enide dinitro EC	Dinoseb + diphenamid
Envert–DT	2,4–D + 2,4,5–T
Eradicane	EPTC + antidote
Esteron Brush killer	2,4–D + 2,4,5–T
Fenac plus	Fenac + 2,4–D
Fenamine	Fenac + atrazine + amitrole
Fenavar	Fenac + bromacil + amitrole
Fenavar Granular	Fenac + bromacil
Fydulan	Dichlobenil + dalapon
Hibor C	NaClO$_3$ + metaborate + bromacil
Instemul DTA–66	2,4–D + 2,4,5–T
Kansel	2,4–D + dicamba
Kleer-lot	Amitrole + linuron
Knoxweed	EPTC + 2,4–D

Table 13-1. Mixture of Herbicides (Cont.)

Name	Ingredients
Krovar I + II	Bromacil + diuron
Londax	Linuron + propachlor
MAD	MSMA + 2,4–D
MBC	NaClO$_3$ + metaborate
Mecopar	Mecoprop + 2,4–D
Methar Super	Octylammonium + Dodecylammonium methylarsonate
Monex	MSMA + diuron
Monobor-chlorate	NaClO$_3$ + metaborate
Mor-Cron	Naptalam + chlorpropham
Ontrak	Prometone + PCP
Phytar 560	Cacodylic acid + sodium salt
Plus 2	Dicamba + 2,4–D
Polybor-chlorate	NaClO$_3$ + octaborate
Pramitol 5PS	Prometone + simazine + NaClO$_3$ + metaborate
Premerge 21	Dinoseb + chloramben
Primaze 80W	Atrazine + prometryne
Proturf	2,4–D + dicamba
Pyramin plus	Pyrazon + dalapon
Rack Granular	Fenac + atrazine
Rad-E-Cate 25	Sodium cacodylate + dimethyl arsinic acid
Randox–T	CDAA + TCBC
Solo	Naptalam + chlorpropham
Spot Weeder	Dicamba + 2,4–D
Tank Mix	Alachlor + 2,3,6–TBA
Turf Builder + 2	2,4–D + mecoprop
Turf Builder + 3	Diphenamid + carbaryl
Turf Builder + 4	2,4–D + dicamba + bensulide + chlordane
Ureabor	Bromacil + NaClO$_3$ + metaborate
Urox 379	Bromacil + hexachloracetone
Vegabate	AMS + MSMA
Verton	2,4–D + 2,4,5–T
Vi-Par	Mecoprop + 2,4–D
Weedar Amine brush-killer	2,4–D + 2,4,5–T
Weedaway brushkiller	2,4–D + 2,4,5–T
Weed Blitz	NaClO$_3$ + metaborate
Weed-E-Rad + W	MSMA + cacodylic acid
Weed Free BC	NaClO$_3$ + tetraborate + bromacil
Weed Free BT	Bromacil + TBA
Weed Free G	Bromacil + diuron + TCA + 2,3,6–TBA
Weed Free SW	MSMA + diuron
Weed Free 235	MSMA + surfactant
Weed Free HC 1.6	Metaborate + NaClO$_3$ + bromacil
Weedone Brushkiller	2,4–D + 2,4,5–T

data, there are no substitutes for straight toxicity testing using dosage series designed to run from zero to complete inhibition or death of the assay plants. There is no substitute for knowledge of the leaching and fixation of soil-borne chemicals in many soils. There is no substitute for accurate knowledge of the formulation, the application method, and the primary mode of attack of the chemical on the plant. And finally, there must be sound judgment in combining these various types of information into a logical scheme for testing herbicide mixtures. For example, the writer questions the logic in testing PCP, a contact herbicide, 2,4-D and dalapon, two systemic growth regulators, amitrole, a systemic enzyme inhibitor, and monuron, a soil-borne herbicide that blocks the photolysis of water in plant foliage, by a foliage dipping procedure (Gowing, 1959). Certainly, search for a "unifying theory on the nature of herbicide activity," in view of the great number of mutually exclusive modes of phytotoxic action that are recognized, would be a waste of time. Studies to distinguish the various modes of phytotoxic action, to relate each to the physiology of susceptible plants, and to use all logic and ingenuity at our command to fit the formulation and application methods to specific requirements would be much more useful.

Table 13–1 gives a list of mixtures that have been used in various aspects of weed control. Some of these mixtures are concocted for convenience of handling and storage, some to aid in application, some to broaden the spectrum of species controlled, and some to handle specific situations. In fact, many of the newer mixed formulations, such as that containing triazine, uracil, and urea herbicides are aimed at specific weed situations, and this type, comparable in a sense with a physician's prescription, is being put out in ever increasing quantity. Many of the advances in chemical weed-control technology may involve mixed formulations designed to meet specific weed problems. In fact not only herbicides and fertilizers but insecticides and fungicides are being applied in mixtures. In this technology more and more attention will have to be paid to the nature of the ingredients, their compatibility, their interactions, the residue problems they create, and their over-all effectiveness in meeting the prescribed requirements. And these demands, in turn, will increase the need for basic information on the chemical, physical, and physiological nature of the chemicals being used.

REFERENCES

Bliss, C. I. 1935. The calculation of the dosage-mortality curve. *Ann. Appl. Biol.* 22:134–167.

Bogle, R. H. 1949. Efficient and Economical Herbicides for Railroad Weed Control. An industrial report. Alexandria, Va.: R. H. Bogle Co.

Crafts, A. S., and C. W. Cleary. 1936. Toxicity of arsenic, borax, chlorate and their combinations in three California soils. *Hilgardia* 10:401–413.

————— and A. Emanuelli. 1948. Combinations of 2,4-D with fortified oil-emulsion contact herbicides. *Bot. Gaz.* 110(1):148–154.

Finney, J. D. 1952. *Probit Analysis*. 2d ed. New York: Cambridge Univ. Press. pp. 1–318.

Gowing, D. P. 1959. A method of comparing herbicides and assessing herbicide mixtures at the screening level. *Weeds* 7(1):66–76.

—————. 1960. Comments on tests of herbicide mixtures. *Weeds* 8(3):379–391.

Hagimoto, H., and H. Yoshikawa. 1972. Synergistic interactions between inhibitors of growth and photosynthesis. I. The "growth-dilution hypothesis." *Weed Res.* 12:21–30.

Hay, J. R. 1961. Pre-emergence weed control in soybeans with mixtures of two herbicides. *Weeds* 9(1):117–123.

Indyk, H. W. 1957. Pre-emergence weed control in soybeans. *Weeds* 5(4):362–370.

Klingman, G. C. 1961. *Weed Control: As A Science*. New York: John Wiley Sons Inc. 421 pp.

Ludwig, J. W. 1973. The use of a low dosage of atrazine alone and in mixtures with other herbicides in the maize crop. *Weed Res.* 13:12–18.

Maestri, M., and H. B. Currier. 1958. Interactions of maleic hydrazide and endothal. *Weeds* 6(3):315–326.

Meyer, L. J., L. S. Murphy, and O. G. Russ. 1973. Atrazine and suspension fertilizer compatibility. *Weed Sci.* 21:217–220.

Parochetti, J. V., R. W. Feeny, and S. R. Colby. 1972. Preemergence herbicides plus postemergence chloroxuron on soybeans. *Weed Sci.* 20:548–553.

Sackston, W. E. 1958. Control of weeds in late sown flax plots with MCPA and TCA. *Weeds* 6(4)399–405.

Sheets, T. J., and O. A. Leonard. 1958. An evaluation of the herbicidal efficiency of combinations of ATA with dalapon, monuron, and several other chemicals. *Weeds* 6(2):143–151.

Sterrett, J. P., J. T. Davis, and W. Hurtt. 1972. Antagonistic effects between picloram and bromacil with oats. *Weed Sci.* 20:440–444.

Stone, J. D., and R. W. Rake. 1955. Effect of borate additives on herbicides. *Agr. Chem.* 10(5):36–38, 123–125.

Zemanek, J. 1969. Interaktion zwischeneinigen herbiziden bei vorsaatund vorauflaufbehandlung in Zuckerrüben. *Weed Res.* 9: 265–271.

14

*Weed Control in Field Crops**

Field crops were the first in which selective, chemical weed control was practiced; it was here that 2,4-D first proved its great value. Weed control in a number of field crops was discussed in the Technical Papers of the FAO International Conference on Weed Control in 1970. Weed control was described in rice (Matsunaka, 1970; Smith, 1970), wheat, oats, and barley (Hay, 1970; Nalewaja and Arnold, 1970; Mukula, 1970), and in maize and sorghum (Nieto-Hatem, 1970; Meggitt, 1970; Phillips, 1970). Weed control is reported in cotton by Buchanan and McWhorter (1970), in soybeans (Knake, 1970), and in sugar crops (Orsenigo, 1970; Millhollon, 1970; Schweizer and Dawson, 1970). These reports cover research on weed control in field crops up until June, 1970.

The chemicals described in the preceding four chapters will control most of our troublesome weeds in a wide variety of situations, both in crops and in noncrop areas. The following chapters describe the various uses of herbicides but, because of the many variables involved such as weed and crop species, soil properties, weather conditions, and application methods, it is impossible to be specific as to dosages, times of treatment, and detailed warnings. Since much of this information is printed on the labels and is also available from county agents, service personnel, and agri-business dealers, the user is advised to take advantage of this wealth of knowledge in making out his weed-control

---

*Information presented in Chapters 14 through 19 has been obtained from *1973 Weed Control Manual and Herbicide Guide* published by Farm Technology and Agri-fieldman, Meister Publishing Co., Willoughby, Ohio.

program. Commercial pesticide applicators usually have local experience that may be invaluable in determining a logical and safe course of procedure. Again, local agencies who are familiar with soils, weather, weed species, and crops grown should be consulted wherever available. And with new chemicals and new weed-crop situations one should procede with caution, putting on experimental trials where possible.

And finally, residues, soils, climates, and weed and crop species are so intimately interrelated that only experience is of value in making judgments. One should observe all precautions on the label at all times.

Because registrations differ so in time and locality, they are not considered in this book. Local agencies must be sought out to advise in such matters.

Weed control in the following crops will be treated in this chapter:
Alfalfa (*Medicago sativa*)
Barley (*Hordeum vulgare*)
Beans (*Phaseolus sp.*)
Beets (*Beta vulgaris*)
Clovers (*Trifolium sp.*)
Cotton (*Gossypium sp.*)
Flax (*Linum sp.*)
Legumes (lespedeza) (*Lespedeza sp.*)
Trefoils (*Lotus corniculatus*)
Maize (*Zea mays*)
Mint (*Mentha sp.*)
Oats (*Avena sativa*)
Peanuts (*Arachis hypogaea*)
Peas (*Pisum sativum*)
Rice (*Oryza sativa*)
Rye (*Secale cereale*)
Safflower (*Carthamus tinctorius*)
Sorghum, crop and seed (*Sorghum sp.*)
Soybeans (*Glycine Max.*)
Sugar cane (*Saccharum officinarum*)
Sunflower (*Helianthus annuus*)
Tobacco (*Nicotiana tabacum*)
Wheat (*Triticum aestivum*)
Weeds of fallow lands

Alfalfa (lucerne)

Weed control is used in several ways in alfalfa: preplant, preemergence at seeding time; selective postemergence during establishment and between successive crops; pre- and postemergence in established alfalfa.

Benefin is used at seedbed preparation. It may be applied and incorporated as much as 10 weeks prior to seeding. It controls seedling grasses and many broadleaf weeds. 2,4-DB in ester or amine salt form may be applied postemergence but while the weeds are still small (2–5 leaf stage). It is selective against broadleaf weeds.

Chlorpropham is used for dodder control. Granules are applied after cutting and before dodder emerges.

Dinoseb is commonly used on dormant alfalfa to kill annual broadleaf weeds; it may also be used selectively in small seedling alfalfa being grown for seed. The general formulation is used on dormant alfalfa, the selective on seedlings.

Diuron has been used to control annual weeds in established alfalfa, particularly in seed field where alfalfa may be planted in rows or hills. Used at a heavy dosage it controls not only annual weeds but alfalfa seedlings as well; this is desirable in fields of improved strains of alfalfa for seed production.

Southwood (1971a) found diuron or atrazine more effective than linuron or dalapon plus paraquat for controlling barley grass in alfalfa in southern Australia. Kapusta (1973) controlled common chickweed in the first alfalfa cutting with sumitol, cyanazine, simazine, and terbacil.

EPTC is used as a preplant, incorporated herbicide against most annual weeds.

EPTC, in a liquid formulation, may be metered into irrigation water in established alfalfa to kill annual weeds. Application must be preemergence to the weeds for full effect.

Metribuzin is an effective preemergence herbicide when used on dormant alfalfa.

Propham is used postemergence after the alfalfa has 3–5 leaves to control grasses or volunteer cereals. Soils should still be cool.

Nitralin or trifluralin may be used in established alfalfa. These herbicides should be applied while the alfalfa is dormant or just following cutting; they must be incorporated. The use of a springtooth harrow or rolling cultivator minimizes injury to the alfalfa crowns.

Sumitol has proved to be an excellent weed killer in alfalfa. Applied preemergence to the weeds during the winter dormancy of the crop, this triazine shows remarkable selectivity and not excessive persistence. If it is used in the year prior to plowing out the alfalfa, a triazine-tolerant crop such as maize or sorghum should follow.

Terbacil is useful when applied preemergence to weeds on dormant alfalfa.

BARLEY

Barban is used as a postemergence spray to control wild oats which should be in the 2–2½ leaf stage for best results.

Bromophenoxim or bromoxynil plus MCPA may be sprayed on spring barley in the 2-leaf stage to control chickweed, tarweed, fiddleneck, purple mustard, chrysanthemum, gromwell, fumitory, and other broadleaf weeds that are tolerant to 2,4-D.

Dicamba is used as a spray in the 2–3 leaf stage of the barley to control wild buckwheat, smartweed, and other broadleaf weeds.

2,4-D and MCPA are used to control most broadleaf weeds in barley. They are available in ester or amine salt forms and should be applied from the 3–4 leaf stage up to boot. Legumes should not be underseeded.

Triallate is used pre- or postplant incorporated to control wild oats in spring barley.

BEANS

Dry lima, and pole beans for feed or seed will be treated here. An array of soil-borne herbicides are used in bean crops depending upon the weeds present and the crop species and variety.

Chlorpropham is used preemergence to kill many broadleaf and grassy weeds; beans should be planted at least 1 inch deep.

DCPA is incorporated prior to planting to control annual grasses and broadleaf weeds; lima beans are not tolerant.

2,4-D has been successfully used as a directed spray in field beans to control field bindweed. Use low-pressure nozzles and shields.

Dinoseb is used preemergence or in the very early seedling stage to kill many broadleaf and grassy weeds. Dinoseb should not be used on very light, sandy soils.

Fluorodifen may be applied broadcast or in bands, preemergence with no incorporation. It controls grasses and broadleaf weeds. Do not follow this herbicide with anything but large-seeded legumes.

Trifluralin may be used as a selective, preemergence, incorporated herbicide to control annual grasses and most broadleaf weeds.

BEETS (SUGAR AND FODDER)

Barban is used as a postemergence spray to control wild oats; the oats should be in the 2-leaf stage and beets should be less than 30 days old.

Cycloate is used preplant incorporated, 3 to 4 inches deep in bands to control weeds on medium textured to heavy soils. Cycloate controls annual grasses, nutsedge, black and hairy nightshade, and other broadleaf weeds.

Cycloate plus diallate are used preplanting to control wild oats, annual grassy weeds, and a wide spectrum of broadleaf weeds. This mixture is available as an emulsifiable concentrate and as granules.

Cycloate plus R-11913, another carbamate, will control kochia in sugar beets in the intermountain states.

Dalapon is used postemergence of beets (1–7 leaves) to kill seedling grasses. Directed sprays have been safer than overall sprays.

Diallate is used preplant to control wild oats; it should be incorporated; not for use on sandy soils.

Eptam may be used preplanting with incorporation to kill annual grasses and broadleaf weeds; it may be metered into irrigation water where bed planted; it is used in the autumn in planted beets in some northern states.

Nitrofen is used preemergence at seeding to control annual weeds in beets in hot, dry regions; furrow irrigation should be used during or soon after emergence of crop—rainfall may result in loss of the crop.

Paraquat is a contact material used on weeds during seedbed preparation. Application to beds may be by ground or aerial spray. Apply only to soils having some clay content.

Pebulate is widely used to control many weeds in beets.

The mixture pebulate plus diallate is used preplanting to kill wild oats, other annual grasses, and certain broadleaf weeds. It is available both in liquid and granular formulations. Dosage should be scaled to the textural grade of the soil; it should not be used on light, sandy soils.

Phenmedipham is used postemergence to beets past the 2-leaf stage; weeds should be in cotyledon to 4-leaf stage. This material controls a wide variety of broadleaf weeds that commonly infest sugar beets; redroot pigweed, and some grasses are not controlled.

Propham has been used against grassy weeds in beets preplanting, incorporated immediately before seeding. It can also be used as a postemergence directed spray with shields to protect the beets. Beets should be well rooted and irrigation should follow the propham application.

Pyrazon is a preemergence, selective herbicide used to control most broadleaf, annual weeds in beets; it should be sprayed over the beds or shallow incorporated where no rains occur. Pyrazon with a wetting agent may also be used postemergence when beets have 2 true leaves and weeds are small. Where grasses abound, dalapon postemergence or TCA preemergence may be included in the pyrazon treatment.

TCA preemergence may be included in the pyrazon treatment. TCA preemergence is excellent against certain grasses; rainfall or sprinkler irrigation is required to incorporate it to a depth where weed seeds are germinating.

Trifluralin, emulsifiable or granular, may be used when beet plants are 2–6 inches tall. It controls summer weeds until harvest time. Trifluralin must be incorporated but does not require rain or irrigation to activate it if the soil is moist.

CLOVERS (ALSIKE, LADINO, RED, SUBTERRANEAN, AND LESPEDEZA)

Dinoseb is commonly used on these crops when they are dormant in the winter to kill annual weeds; the temperature should be above 5°C (40°F) for satisfactory results, 10–15°C (50–60°F) is better.

Eptam may be used to control most annual, broadleaf and grassy weeds. It can be applied preplant during preparation of the seed bed, or postemergence to crop but preemergence to weeds by metering it into irrigation water.

Chlorpropham is used to control chickweed, downy brome grass, and other annual weeds in clover. It is usually applied in fall or early winter. In pelleted form it can be applied to growing crops and irrigated in. Propham may be applied in fall, winter, or early spring to control chickweed and most annual grasses. 2,4-D and MCPA may be used on dormant crops to kill sensitive broadleaf weeds, but care must be taken to avoid treating plants which have green foliage exposed.

Southwood (1971b) conducted 5-year trials on the control of broomrape in subterranean clover in New South Wales. He found that superphosphate, which greatly increased growth of the clover, reduced the broomrape population; 2,4-DB application in spring was less effective. Spring grazing of broomrape before flowering killed many of the plants; superphosphate in autumn followed by spring grazing reduced broomrape density.

Brock (1972) finds trifluralin, carbetamide, and asulam effective in controlling broadleaf dock in newly sown red clover. All three gave good control of dock from seed. Asulam gave the best control from rootstocks. Annual bluegrass was controlled by trifluralin and carbetamide but not by asulam.

COTTON

Bensulide is used preplant or preemergence incorporated to kill annual grasses and broadleaf weeds, the latter in semiarid irrigated localities.

Dalapon is used to control Johnsongrass in cotton. It may be applied preplant and then the grass plowed or deep disced. Dalapon is also used postplant in spot treatments; annual grasses and Bermudagrass are controlled.

DCPA may be used preemergence to weeds by applying at seeding time; shallow incorporation is desirable. Annual grasses, Johnsongrass seedlings, and some broadleaf weeds are controlled. DCPA may also be used as a layby treatment; rainfall or irrigation is required.

Dinitramine is used preplant incorporated in cotton.

Diphenamid is used in cotton by applying preemergence to weeds on prepared seedbed at planting time; annual grasses and broadleaf weeds are controlled.

Diuron can be used at several times during the season for weed control in cotton. It is used preemergence, postplanting, as a postemergence directed spray when cotton is 6 inches or more in height, or by directed spray at layby. Diuron is effective against most annual weeds of cotton.

DSMA is used postemergence as a directed spray against Johnsongrass, nutsedge, Dallisgrass, cocklebur, barnyardgrass, ragweed, sandbur, and puncturevine. MSMA is used in the same way against the same weeds.

EPTC is used in cotton as a broadcast subsurface treatment in established stands. On nonirrigated cotton it is applied by injection keeping at least 4 inches from the drill row.

Fluometuron may be used on cotton pre- and postemergence, broadcast or in bands. It may be directed or sprayed over the tops of plants from 3 inches tall to layby. It is effective against most weeds of cotton, both grasses and broadleaf.

Linuron is used at low dosage as a directed spray when cotton is at least 15 inches tall, but weeds must still be small. It kills most annual broadleaf weeds and grasses. Not for use on Pima cotton.

Methazole has been used either pre- or postemergence to many weeds in cotton. It is approved for experimental use on seed cotton only.

Monuron has been used at layby as a directed spray against most annual weeds and grasses of cotton.

Nitralin is used to kill most weeds in cotton. It may be applied from preplanting until 90 days before harvest. Layby application should be by directed spray.

Paraquat is used to control all weeds during seedbed preparation and before seeding the cotton. At proper dosage, paraquat may be applied by airplane to kill volunteer cereal at the time of seedbed preparation. There should be a minimum of disturbance of the soil in planting to avoid bringing new weed seeds to the surface.

Prometryne may be used preplanting, preemergence, postemergence, or as a directed spray at layby. This material must be incorporated by rainfall, sprinkler irrigation, or mechanically during seedbed preparation; it should not contact the cotton seedlings.

Pigweeds and Russian thistle can be controlled by dipropetryn, a new, cotton herbicide.

Trifluralin should be applied and incorporated prior to planting, during planting, or immediately after planting. It kills most annual grasses and broadleaf weeds of cotton. Trifluralin is available in liquid and granular formulations.

Most of the chemicals listed in Appendix Table 2 under the nitroanilines are being tested on cotton. Individually and in mixtures they are proving effective against most cotton weed pests.

FLAX

Barban is used as a selective spray to control wild oats in flax. The application should be made while the oats are in the 2–2½ leaf stage; the flax should be less than 12 inches high.

EPTC is used preplant incorporated to control wild oats, other annual grasses, and broadleaf weeds. The flax should be planted within 10 days of EPTC incorporation.

MCPA amine salt is used as a postemergence spray when flax is 3–6 inches tall to control mustard, amsinckia, and other broadleaf weeds. Dalapon may be added to control grasses.

LEGUMES

When legume crops are being used for hay or seed production, they can be treated preemergence when they are seeded, they can be sprayed with selective sprays when small (weeds must also be small), and they can be treated while dormant to eliminate the winter annual weeds that often infest the first cutting of hay or contaminate the seed crop.

EPTC is a safe material to use preemergence in legume crops; it may also be metered into irrigation water at the time of the first irrigation. Dinoseb selective is used to handle small weeds when the crop plants have 2 or more leaves. When the crop plants are dormant, dinoseb amine (Premerge) chlorpropham, propham, planavin, or trifluralin should be incorporated.

Diquat or dinoseb selective may be applied to seed crops preharvest as desiccants.

MAIZE, CORN

Alachlor is an important herbicide in maize. It is used preemergence or preplant incorporated to control most annual grasses and broadleaf weeds. It is effective under a wide range of soil and moisture conditions and can be applied with liquid fertilizers.

Ametryne will kill most annual broadleaf and grass weeds. It is applied postemergence as a directed spray when corn is 12 inches or more high. It is useful in field, sweet, and popcorn.

Atrazine is probably the most widely used herbicide in maize and sorghum. It may be applied preplant, at planting, or postemergence but before weeds are 1½ inches tall. It kills most annual weeds and at high dosage is used to control nutsedge. Against quackgrass, split applications are made, one before plowing and one at planting. Dosages used against nutsedge and quackgrass leave residues and atrazine-tolerant crops should follow. To kill late-emerging grass, atrazine plus an emulsifiable, phytobland oil is used as a directed spray.

Butylate is used preplanting incorporated against grasses and nutsedge. Mixed with atrazine, most weeds are controlled.

CDAA kills most annual broadleaf and grassy weeds when used preemergence. The mixture involving TCBC, termed Randox-T, is the preferred formulation.

CDEC is used against most weeds in maize, applied as a spray or in granules after planting but before weeds emerge; rainfall or sprinkler irrigation is needed.

Chloramben is useful for controlling most weeds of maize applied during or immediately after planting; not to be used on sandy soils.

Chlorbromuron kills most annual weeds of maize, including fall panicum, foxtail, smartweed, jimsonweed, and velvetleaf, if applied preemergence to the crop and the weeds. Alachlor may be added to broaden the weed spectrum.

Cyanazine may be applied as a spray before planting, at planting, or after planting but before the crop has emerged; also postemergence by directed spray. This herbicide is effective against a great number of grassy and broadleaf weeds.

Cyprazine is used as a postemergence spray when weeds emerge until they attain a height of 2 inches; directed spray using drop nozzles may be used when maize is 12 inches high.

Dalapon is used against quackgrass and Johnsongrass by spraying in spring, plowing 4 days later, and planting 1 to 4 weeks after plowing. Other grasses are also controlled. (Fig. 11–2).

Diallate is used preplanting or preemergence incorporated against wild oats and foxtail.

Dicamba is effective against annual, broadleaf weeds, including some that are resistant to 2,4-D. Only one postemergence application should be made per season. Dicamba plus alachlor are used to control a wider array of weeds. They should be applied preemergence.

Dinoseb may be used preemergence or postemergence to young seedling maize. Many annual weeds are controlled.

2,4-D was the first preemergence material introduced in maize culture. The ester formulation kills grasses as well as broadleaf weeds as they emerge from seeds. Postemergence 2,4-D ester or amine is used when weeds are small and maize 2–8 inches high or later; after maize is 10 inches tall or over, the use of drop nozzles is desirable.

EPTC, combined with protectants (Protect, R27588), is used by application and incorporation immediately after planting to handle wild cane, Johnsongrass seedlings, and other weeds in maize. To control nutsedge and attendant weeds, a higher dosage is applied 7 to 10 days before planting with immediate incorporation. If R27588 or Protect is included in the formulation, injury to maize is minimized.

Linuron is used as a postemergence directed spray when maize is at least 15 inches tall and weeds no more than 5 inches; most annual weeds are controlled.

Paraquat is applied as a preplant spray to control growing weeds in preparing to plant maize; seeding should be carried out with minimum disturbance of the soil. Paraquat may be combined with alachlor and atrazine to control existing weeds and give residual control through the growing season where nontillage is being practiced. A surfactant adds to the effectiveness of paraquat.

Propachlor may be applied as a liquid spray or as granules to control a wide range of weeds; it should go on preemergence or early postemergence; nitrogen fertilizer may accompany the herbicide.

Simazine was the first triazine herbicide extensively used in maize. It can be used in the fall to control quackgrass; the land should be plowed and planted to maize for 2 consecutive years. To kill annual weeds including grasses, simazine may be applied preplant or at planting time. The most serious problem with simazine is the soil residue that requires planting a tolerant crop on the following year; the shift to atrazine has been made because, being more water soluble, this triazine presents less of a residue problem.

Maize is being grown in increasing quantities on nontilled land. Triplett and Lytle (1972) have shown that maize may be grown with no tillage for 7 years or more with yields equal to those of the cultivated crop if weeds are controlled. They found, in Ohio, that paraquat plus simazine gave the most consistent weed control. There were shifts in the weed population with fall panicum and dogbane becoming more prevalent.

MINT

Dinoseb in the form of an alkanolamine salt is used preemergence to control most annual weeds, both broadleaf and grassy, in mint.

Terbacil is applied in spring after the last cultivation to handle annual weeds preemergence. It presents a residue problem so that replanting should be done only with tolerant crop species.

Trifluralin is used on dormant, established peppermint and spearmint to control all annual weeds preemergence to the weeds. Incorporate by springtooth harrow.

Oats

Bromoxynil is used by incorporation for control of amsinckia in oats.

Dicamba may be used postemergence to control wild buckwheat, smartweed, and other weeds in spring oats. Mixed with MCPA, dicamba will control a wide spectrum of spring, annual weeds.

In fall-sown oats, dicamba may be applied after winter dormancy to kill dogfennel, corn cockle, cow cockle, knawel, fiddleneck, and gromwell. Addition of 2,4-D or MCPA to the dicamba spray widens the spectrum.

Diuron may be applied in fall or spring to control a great variety of weeds in winter oats.

Terbutryn has been used pre- or postemergence to control most annual weeds in winter oats. There should not be more than one application in a single year.

Triallate is used pre- or postplant incorporated to control wild oats and some other grasses. Consult local authorities as to the varieties of oats that tolerate this chemical.

2,4-D ester or amine salt is used postemergence after the crop is well-tillered to control annual and perennial broadleaf weeds.

Peanuts

Alachlor, preplant and postplant incorporated or surface applied, is used in peanuts to control a number of annual weeds and perennial weed seedlings; it is effective over a wide range of soil and moisture conditions.

Benefin may be incorporated as early as 10 weeks before planting up to planting time to kill a wide variety of annual weeds. Benefin must be incorporated but it does not need rain or irrigation to activate it if the soil is moist; it resists leaching. Vernolate may be mixed with benefin to handle nutsedge and a broad spectrum of grasses as well as broadleaf weeds.

Chloramben is used at planting time as a broadcast or band preemergence herbicide against most annual weeds of peanuts.

Dinoseb may be applied preemergence at planting, at soil cracking, at early or at late postemergence. After the crop plants are up they must be shielded. Most weeds of peanuts are controlled.

Diphenamid is used preemergence to weeds at planting; a wide variety of annual weeds is controlled. Dinoseb may be used with diphenamid from cracking to 7 days later to broaden the spectrum of weeds controlled.

Naptalam plus dinoseb are used preemergence at cracking time to

control cocklebur, annual morning glory, teaweed, jimsonweed, sandbur, foxtail, barnyardgrass, and goosegrass. This mixture is commonly
used as 12-inch bands on 36-inch rows.

Nitralin, preemergence from 6 weeks prior to planting until
planting or immediately thereafter, will control most broadleaf weeds
and grasses in peanuts.

Sesone, which breaks down in the soil to release 2,4-D, may be
applied preemergence, at cracking time, or postemergence to control
most weeds.

Trifluralin, granular or liquid, may be applied preplant, at planting, or immediately after planting to kill annual broadleaf and grassy
weeds.

Vernolate will kill annual grasses, such as crabgrass and goosegrass, and some broadleaf weeds in peanuts. It may be applied preplant, at planting, or immediately after.

Hauser and Parham (1969) found that weeds may reduce yields of
peanuts as much as 50 percent. They applied a combination of
2,4-DEP and dinoseb at cracking time; this treatment controlled
Florida purslane and large crabgrass and produced maximum yields;
weed knifing from 2 to 5 times during the growing season also gave high
yields. Deep cultivation injured roots, reducing yields. Cultivation
which moved the soil into contact with the plants increased incidence
of southern blight, also reducing yields.

Hauser et al. (1973) describe two systems for using herbicides plus
cultivation for peanut culture. One combines a preplant incorporated
treatment with benefin, an incorporation of vernolate at planting, and
a layby cultivation 5–6 weeks after planting. The second system involves injection of vernolate at planting, application of dinoseb at
cracking, and 2,4-DB as a layby spray followed by cultivation. Peanut
yields were increased.

PEAS (FIELD)

Sinox was used soon after its introduction to control broadleaf
weeds in field peas. The ammonium salt of dinoseb replaced Sinox
because it was more selective and the amine salt was soon introduced
as a preemergence treatment. Meanwhile, propham was introduced to
handle annual grasses, and was largely displaced by chlorpropham
when it became available.

In soils having wild oats, barban was found to be useful for their
control; later, diallate as a preemergence treatment became popular.
EPTC has been used, particularly where there are infestations of
nutsedge; annual grasses are controlled. MCPB is useful where Canada thistle abounds; other broadleaf weeds are controlled. More re-

cently, nitralin, propachlor, and trifluralin have come into use as preemergence herbicides. The latter may be used by the sprayblade method for spot treatment where bindweed occurs.

RICE

Potassium azide is used in a granular form to control seedlings of certain aquatic weeds in rice. Application should be 15 to 20 days after permanent flooding; the rice should be at least 6 inches in height and flood water should be maintained for 2 weeks.

Benthiocarb and butachlor, applied 6–8 days after planting, have controlled barnyardgrass and water lilies in trials in the Philippine Islands.

2,4-D should be sprayed on well-established rice, late postemergence and before the boot stage, to control coffeeweed, curly indigo, mud plantain, red stem, and sedges. Rice is sensitive to 2,4-D in early seedling, boot, and early-heading stages.

MCPA is preferred over 2,4-D for killing broadleaf weeds of rice, including arrowhead, water plantain, red stem, sedge, nutsedge, and bulrush. The application should be made 50–60 days after seeding when rice is well established.

Molinate is used to control barnyardgrass, the principal weed in rice. It is applied preplant soil-incorporated soon after land preparation. Molinate may also be used postemergence when the grass is less than 3 inches high and two-thirds submerged at time of spraying by airplane. A granular formulation is available for application by air or ground equipment.

Propanil is used as a postemergence spray by air on flooded rice to control barnyardgrass, sedges, indigo, and croton. Drift of propanil from the target area onto prune trees in northern California has led to banning this chemical in areas where prunes are grown.

2,4,5-T is applied 2–3 weeks after flooding when rice is fully tillered to control curly indigo, Mexican weed, and other broadleaf weeds.

In the Philippines it has been found that the isopropyl ester of 2,4-D applied to contact the emerging seedlings of barnyardgrass will kill them without injuring the rice. This treatment may be used at a fraction of the cost of other chemicals.

RYE

2,4-DB is used postemergence in rye when weeds are less than 3 inches tall to kill many 2,4-D susceptible, broadleaf weeds; amine or ester forms are available.

Dinoseb will kill most weeds in young rye. It is applied while the weeds are small and tender and the grain is 3–6 inches tall.

MCPA is more selective than 2,4-D. It kills most broadleaf weeds when applied in 3-leaf to boot stage of the rye without injury to the crop.

SAFFLOWER

Barban is the preferred wild-oat herbicide for safflower. It is applied at the 2-leaf stage of the oats and not after the 8-leaf stage of the crop.

Chlorpropham is used preplant incorporated within 3 days before planting; rainfall or irrigation soon after application is essential. Volunteer grains, wild oats, stinging nettle, nightshade, and other weeds are controlled.

EPTC, preplant incorporated immediately, is used to kill annual weeds, grasses, and nutsedge.

Nitralin is used preplant as much as 6 weeks before planting, at time of planting or immediately after to kill most annual weeds of safflower.

Propham may be applied preemergence from 3 days before to 2 days after planting to control grassy weeds, stinging nettle, and nightshade.

Trifluralin, liquid or granular, may be used preplant incorporated to control many annual grasses and broadleaf weeds.

SORGHUM

Atrazine is used preemergence, applied preplant, at planting, or postplanting, to control most annual broadleaf and grassy weeds. Dosage must be adjusted to soil type, and rainfall or irrigation is required for activation.

Dicamba may be used on grain sorghum applied 10 to 25 days after emergence to control annual broadleaf weeds including pigweeds, lambsquarters, sunflower, purslane, and annual morning glory.

MCPA may be applied after the crop is 6 inches high but before flowering to control broadleaf weeds.

Paraquat may be used to kill all weedy growth before land preparation for seeding. If planting is to be on beds these should be formed in the fall and weeds allowed to grow. In seeding, disturb the soil as little as possible to avoid turning up fresh seed.

Propachlor is used preplant incorporated or preemergence to control most of the annual broadleaf and grassy weeds common to agricultural soils. Atrazine may be included in the spray to broaden the array of weeds controlled.

Propazine, preplant or preemergence, will control most annual weeds in sorghum; it is not preferred on sandy soils. Cotton or maize may be planted in the year following propazine use; other crops than sorghum should be planted only in the second year.

Terbutryn has proven useful for preemergence weed control in sorghum.

2,4-D applied after the crop is 6 inches tall but before heading will control most broadleaf annual weeds. Drop nozzles are preferred to avoid crop damage.

SOYBEANS

Alachlor is a safe chemical to use in soybeans; it leaves no soil residue. Used preemergence or preplant incorporated it handles a long list of annual grasses and broadleaf weeds. When mixed with linuron, annual morning glory, buttonweed, cocklebur, and mustard may be added to the list of weeds controlled. Mixed with chlorpropham, complete control of annual grasses is accomplished.

Barban is used to control wild oats in the 2-leaf stage, but not after 14 days from crop emergence.

Bentazon is an effective preemergence herbicide in soybeans. Bromoxynil applied postemergence has proved effective in the control of cocklebur and wild sunflower.

Chloramben applied immediately after planting kills most annual broadleaf and grassy weeds. It presents no soil residue problem. It is available in both liquid and granular forms. Use of 2,4-DB as a followup will handle cocklebur and sunflowers.

Chlorbromuron for weed control in soybeans is used preemergence on bands or broadcast to handle most annual weeds; soil should contain 1 percent or more organic matter; a 6-months residue problem attends use of this chemical. Alachlor may be mixed in to broaden the weed spectrum.

Chloroxuron is used postemergence, over-the-crop or directed, after soybean trifoliate leaves appear, to control such annual weeds as cocklebur, jimsonweed, pigweed, velvetleaf, smartweed, and lambsquarters. When a nonphytotoxic oil is included the spray should be directed.

Chloropropham applied preemergence is useful to control smartweeds, mustards, carpetweed, foxtail, crabgrass, barnyardgrass, and other annuals. Incorporated piggyback over trifluralin or nitralin, it aids in the control of nightshade, jimsonweed, morning glory, pigweeds, and lambsquarters. Soybeans should be planted at least 1 inch deep; rain or sprinkler irrigation is required. Alachlor may be included with chlorpropham to broaden the spectrum of weeds controlled.

Dalapon is used preplant to kill established Johnsongrass; the treated patches should be plowed or deep disced after 3 days. (Fig. 11–1).

DCPA applied at planting time and lightly incorporated will control annual grasses, Johnsongrass seedlings, and some of the common, broadleaf weeds.

Dinitramine is a preplant incorporated herbicide that is finding use in soybeans.

Dinoseb preemergence, or postemergence as a directed spray, is used to kill cocklebur, morning glory, and many other annual weeds. Repeat application may be necessary.

Diquat is used as a weed and crop desiccant sprayed about 7 days before harvest.

Diphenamid, used at planting time with linuron or chlorpropham, will control most annual weeds. Incorporated with dinoseb amine, diphenamid preemergence will kill a wide array of annual weeds.

Fluorodifen applied preemergence at planting time, broadcast or on bands, is useful in controlling annual grasses and broadleaf weeds including jimsonweed, smartweed, and foxtail. Rainfall is essential to activate the chemical.

Linuron, preemergence or directed postemergence when soybeans are 12 inches or more in height, will kill most annual weeds.

Metribuzin is an effective preemergence herbicide to control sicklepod and other difficult weeds in soybeans.

Naptalam with dinoseb used preemergence from planting until just prior to emergence kills most annual weeds; not to be used on sandy soils.

Nitralin used early preplant, at planting, or soon after and incorporated 1–1½ inches kills many annual weeds.

Oxadiazon is proving to be an excellent soybean herbicide. It is effective against a wide variety of broadleaf and grassy weeds in diverse soil types.

Oryzalin is giving full-season control of annual weeds.

Paraquat is used in the minimum or nontillage method. It is sprayed over the beds before or at planting time; planting with minimum disturbance is required to prevent bringing new weed seeds to the surface. It should not be used preplant or preemergence on soils lacking clay minerals.

Propachlor is used preemergence only on the seed crop.

TCA in the oil-soluble ester formulation may be used in an oil carrier as a directed basal treatment when weeds are up to 12 inches tall to kill annual grasses, Johnsongrass, coffeeweed, and other common weeds, and volunteer maize; it should not be used after seed pods are formed.

Trifluralin, liquid or granular, is used preplant incorporated to kill annual grasses and broadleaf weeds. At double the normal dosage it may be used to control established Johnsongrass. It must then be discincorporated to 4 inches depth and used in two consecutive years.

Vernolate used preplant incorporated gives seasonal control of most annual weeds. Nutsedge is inhibited during the crop season. Leaf crinkle may appear on primary leaves; it is only temporary.

2,4-DB postemergence, 7 to 10 days before soybean bloom, by directed spray will control cocklebur and inhibit redroot pigweed and annual morning glory.

SUGAR CANE

Sugar cane is a major world crop that has yielded to modern mechanization and chemicalization; herbicides are used on sugar plantations around the globe. Sodium arsenite was the traditional weed killer in cane until the introduction of pentachlorophenol and dinoseb in the Hawaiian Islands. With the appearance of 2,4-D, the parade of new chemicals started; some nineteen will be considered here.

Ametryne, a pre- and postemergence herbicide, is used to control both grassy and broadleaf weeds in cane. It may be applied broadcast to seed cane or directed after growth is under way.

Asulam is a pre- and postemergence material used on both broadleaf and grassy weeds; control is season-long. Atrazine and diuron are the standards by which all new herbicides are judged.

CDAA is used preemergence at planting time to control broadleaf and grassy weeds.

Dalapon has been the principal herbicide used to control Johnsongrass in cane fields. Glyphosate may possibly displace it.

Diuron is the preferred urea herbicide in cane, especially on light soils; it has lower solubility than monuron. It is used preemergence or postemergence depending on conditions.

Fenac kills many common weeds, including puncturevine. Application should avoid high concentrations in the root zone of the cane.

Glyphosate is a promising new herbicide against perennial weeds, particularly Johnsongrass. It may displace TCA and dalapon, the presently used chemicals in sugar cane.

MCPA is a more selective material than 2,4-D for controlling common broadleaf weeds by spray treatment.

MSMA is a translocated arsenical herbicide effective in controlling Johnsongrass. Because it leaves an arsenic residue in soils it should not be used repeatedly in cane.

Paraquat is an excellent contact material to kill existing weeds. Its weakness compared with diuron and atrazine is that competing weeds must be allowed to grow before they can be controlled; an advantage on sloping sites is that the dead weeds decay, leaving a humus covering and a porous soil condition from decaying roots that minimizes erosion.

Silvex is a herbicide that has followed 2,4-D and 2,4,5-T in controlling the succession of surviving weeds in cane.

Simazine, the first of the triazine herbicides, is still used on light soils but has been largely displaced by atrazine, which has somewhat less residue hazard.

2,4,5-T was used when the weeds tolerant of 2,4-D tended to take over. It has now been succeeded by silvex.

2,3,6-TBA is used as a translocated herbicide where perennial vines and herbaceous weeds abound.

TCA is a soil-applied grass killer used against Johnsongrass, Bermudagrass, and other weedy grasses in cane.

Terbacil is used both pre- and postemergence to kill most annual weeds in sugar cane. It is the only uracil herbicide tolerated by cane.

2,4-D has been used since its introduction in 1945 to control commelina and other succulent weeds in sugar cane. It later was used preemergence but has since been largely displaced by more effective, wide-spectrum materials.

Peng and Yeh (1970) determined the varietal tolerances of six sugar-cane varieties to diuron and atrazine. Although differences in tolerance were great, any residual effect, even at 20 kg/ha, on cane plants was insignificant 5 months after applications.

SUNFLOWER

Barban is used postemergence to control wild oats in sunflowers. Spray should be applied at the 2-leaf stage of the wild oats and before 14 days from emergence of the crop.

Chloramben is applied preemergence lightly incorporated to control annual grasses and broadleaf weeds. Best results are obtained if rainfall or sprinkler irrigation occurs 3–5 days after application.

EPTC applied and immediately incorporated before planting will handle most annual weeds.

Trifluralin incorporated preemergence will control all annual grasses and most annual broadleaf weeds in sunflowers.

TOBACCO

Most tobacco is grown in seedbeds and transplanted into the field. The seedbeds are usually fumigated with a strongly phytotoxic, volatile chemical.

Allyl alcohol, applied as a surface drench and watered in to 2–4 inches, will control most annual weeds as they germinate.

Benefin, used before transplanting, controls grasses and many broadleaf weeds.

Dazomet, applied in October and leached into the soil at least 4 weeks before seeding, will control weed seeds, soil insects, fungi, and nematodes.

Diphenamid, applied preemergence at seeding time, controls a wide variety of annual weeds.

Isopropalin is used incorporated pretransplant to control grasses and many broadleaf weeds in tobacco beds.

Metham applied at least 3 weeks before planting to smooth, well-prepared seedbeds controls all seedling weeds, fungi, nematodes, and insects.

Methyl bromide, a very volatile liquid, is applied beneath a gas-proof (plastic) covering. Exposure below the cover should last for 24–48 hours; the beds should be aerated 2–4 days before seeding. Most soil-borne organisms, including weed seeds, are destroyed.

Pebulate applied pretransplant controls grasses, many broadleaf weeds, and nutsedge.

Vorlex is injected 4 to 6 inches deep with chisels 8 inches apart in the tobacco beds. Rolling, rainfall, or sprinkling aids in holding in the fumes. This material may be used in the fall or in spring. It controls weed seeds and soil-borne organisms.

WHEAT

Barban is used in spring wheat to control wild oats; application by spraying should be made when the weeds are in the 2-leaf stage and less than 14 days after their emergence.

Bromoxynil is applied postemergence to weeds in spring when wheat is in the 3-leaf to boot stage. It controls tarweed, fiddleneck, purple mustard, gromwell, wild buckwheat, fumitory, bedstraw, and other 2,4-D-resistant weeds. MCPA may be mixed with it to broaden the spectrum of weeds controlled.

Dicamba may be used in wheat preplant to control perennial weeds. Wheat may be planted 30 to 60 days after application. Combined with 2,4-D or MCPA, dicamba may be applied postemergence to wheat after winter dormancy to control annual weeds such as dogfennels, gromwell, fiddleneck, and other spring weeds.

Dinoseb is used to spray small weeds in wheat underseeded with legumes; it kills practically all spring annual weeds; the wheat should be 3–6 inches tall and tillered.

Diuron is used in the northwestern U.S. to control gromwell, dogfennels, and most annual weeds in fall wheat. Application should be made soon after planting; dosage should be carefully considered; the residue may require a year to dissipate.

Linuron is used in the Northwest to control a wide array of spring annual weeds in wheat not underseeded; weeds should be small (under 2 inches) at time of treatment. Residue may last 6 months or more.

MCPA may be used postemergence in winter wheat against perennial weeds; a 3-year program should be planned to handle these weeds. In spring wheat a postemergence spray may be used from tillering until early boot to control broadleaf annual weeds.

Terbutryn is used in winter wheat not underseeded. It should be applied either pre- or postemergence in late fall or spring. Dosage should be carefully scaled; the residue may last 9 months. Eshel (1972) found terbutryn effective in controlling canarygrass in a semi-drawf cultivar; yield was increased 56 percent by preemergence, 29 percent by postemergence treatment.

Triallate may be used pre- or postplant and incorporated by discing 2 inches deep and cross-harrowing to control wild oats. There is no residue problem.

Trifluralin is used preplant in winter wheat; application should be followed by springtooth harrowing in two directions to incorporate it into the topsoil. Seed should be planted below the chemical zone; trifluralin controls most annual weeds.

2,4-D may be used in late spring or in wheat stubble in autumn to control perennial weeds. It is also used to spray spring weeds after the wheat has tillered but before the boot stage. Either ester or amine formulations are used against annual weeds; heavy esters are preferred against perennial weeds.

2,4-DB is used postemergence when weeds are less than 3 inches tall to control 2,4-D-susceptible weeds in wheat underseeded with leguminous crop plants.

WEEDS OF FALLOW LANDS

Most field crops are grown through part of one year; some may occupy the land for more than a single year, for example pineapples, alfalfa, and sugar cane. On the other hand, most cereal crops are harvested in the spring and summer, leaving the land fallow for some time before replanting. During the fallow period, annual weeds may grow; these may be controlled by tillage or use of paraquat. Perennial weeds usually make lush growth on fallow lands and this provides an opportunity to put them under control.

MCPA, liquid or granular, may be used to control fall bindweed, artichoke thistle, and other less difficult to control perennial weeds.

2,4-D is used to control many perennial weeds on fallow land. At medium dosage, Canada thistle, field bindweed, whitetop, sowthistle, and Texas blueweed may be inhibited; after 2 to 3 years treatment they may be eliminated. At high dosage, Bur ragweed, dogbane, leafy spurge, Russian knapweed, and White horsenettle may be controlled.

2,3,6-TBA is used on fallow land to control serious infestations of perennial weeds. This chemical is effective as a translocated spray and as a soil-borne herbicide; it is very persistent in soils and should not be used repeatedly on soils needed for cropping.

REFERENCES

Brock, J. L. 1971. The control of broad-leaved dock (*Rumex obtusifolius* L.) in newly-sown red clover (*Trifolium pratense* L.) with trifluralin, carbetamide and asulam. *Weed Res.* 12:310–315.

Buchanan, G. A., and C. G. McWhorter. 1970. Weed control in cotton. *F.A.O. Internatl. Conf. on Weed Control.* Davis, Calif., p. 163–183.

Eshel, Y. 1972. Selective action of triazines for control of wild canary grass in wheat. *Weed Res.* 12:301–309.

Hauser, E. W., and S. A. Parham. 1969. Effects of annual weeds and cultivation on the yield of peanuts. *Weed Res.* 9:192–197.

————, S. R. Cecil, and C. C. Dowler. 1973. Systems of weed control for peanuts. *Weed Sci.* 21:176–180.

Hay, J. R. 1970. Weed control in wheat, oats, and barley. *F.A.O. Internatl. Conf. on Weed Control.* Davis, Calif., p. 38–47.

Kapusta, G. 1973. Common chickweed control in established alfalfa. *Weed Sci.* 21:119–122.

Knake, E. L. 1970. Losses due to weeds, and methods of controlling weeds in soybeans. *F.A.O. Internatl. Conf. on Weed Control.* Davis, Calif., p. 284–304.

Matsunaka, S. 1970. Weed control in rice. *F.A.O. Internatl. Conf. on Weed Control.* Davis, Calif., p. 7–23.

Meggitt, W. F. 1970. Weed control methods, losses and costs due to weeds, and benefits of weed control in maize. *F.A.O. Internatl. Conf. on Weed Control.* Davis, Calif., p. 87–100.

Millhollon, R. W. 1970. Methods and benefits of weed control in sugar cane. *F.A.O. Internatl. Conf. on Weed Control.* Davis, Calif., p. 336–343.

Mukula, J. 1970. Weed control in cereal grains of Northern Europe. *F.A.O. Internatl. Conf. on Weed Control.* Davis, Calif., p. 68–78.

Nalewaja, J. D. and W. E. Arnold. 1970. Weed control methods, losses and costs due to weeds, and benefits of weed control in wheat and other small grains. *F.A.O. Internatl. Conf. on Weed Control.* Davis, Calif., p. 48–64.

Nieto-Hatem, J. 1970. The struggle against weeds in maize and sorghum. *F.A.O. Internatl. Conf. on Weed Control.* Davis, Calif., p. 79–86.

Orsenigo, J. R. 1970. Weed control in sugar crops. *F.A.O. Internatl. Conf. on Weed Control.* Davis, Calif., p. 318–335.

Peng, S. Y., and H. J. Yeh. 1970. Determination of the varietal tolerance of sugar cane to pre-emergence diuron and atrazine. *Weed Res.* 10:218–229.

Phillips, W. M. 1970. Weed control methods, losses and costs due to weeds, and benefits of weed control in grain sorghum. *F.A.O. Internatl. Conf. on Weed Control.* Davis, Calif., p. 101–108.

Schweizer, E. E., and J. H. Dawson. 1970. Weed control methods, losses and costs due to weeds, and benefits of weed control in sugar beets. *F.A.O. Internatl. Conf. on Weed Control.* Davis, Calif., p. 344–356.

Smith, R. J., Jr. 1970. Weed control methods, losses and costs due to weeds, and benefits of weed control in rice. *F.A.O. Internatl. Conf. on Weed Control*. Davis, Calif., p. 24–37.

Southwood, O. R. 1971a. The chemical control of barley grass in dryland lucerne. *Weed Res.* 11:231–239.

————. 1971b. The effect of superphosphate application, 2,4-DB and grazing on broomrape (*Orobanche minor* SM.) in a subterranean clover pasture. *Weed Res.* 11:240–246.

Triplett, G. B., Jr., and G. D. Lytle. 1972. Control and ecology of weeds in continuous corn grown without tillage. *Weed Sci.* 20:453–457.

15

Vegetable Crops

Vegetable crops represent the most diversified group of plants in which herbicides are used. Considering all aspects of vegetable production, probably almost every known herbicide can find a niche in which it fits. Thirty-eight individual species or varieties of vegetable crops are covered in the following treatment; some are treated in groups, which reduces the number to twenty-six. These will be discussed in alphabetical order.

Romanowski (1970) gives an excellent review of weed control in vegetable crops.

ARTICHOKES

Diuron is used in late fall or early winter to control preemergence winter annual weeds in artichokes.

Paraquat may be used to knock down annual weeds at any time in or around artichoke plantings.

Simazine is used as directed spray after the last fall tillage to handle winter and spring weeds.

ASPARAGUS

Chloramben is used preemergence at seeding time to control germinating spring annual weeds in direct-seeded asparagus. Activated carbon in a band over the row allowed use of linuron plus nitralin, chlorbromuron, and chloramben in asparagus.

Dalapon is applied postemergence as a spot spray or a directed spray to control established and seedling grasses.

Diuron is used preemergence to the weeds in the beds up until a few days before the spears appear. Rainfall or sprinkler irrigation or soil incorporation is needed; most annual grass seedlings and broadleaf weeds are controlled.

Paraquat may be used to kill annual weeds in middles or around edges of the field; it must be kept off the spears.

Sesone is used preemergence or after harvest to kill small weeds before they become established.

Simazine is applied preemergence to the weeds after the cutting season to kill most annual broadleaf and grassy weeds.

2,4-D is used during and after harvest to control field bindweed and other summer broadleaf weeds. It should be kept off the crop at harvest time; later, drop nozzles may be used to cover weeds and avoid the crop foliage. The sodium salt is usually used.

Beans (dry, lima, pole, snap)

Bentazon controls many weeds in navy beans.

Chloramben is used preemergence at planting on snap beans to control annual weeds.

Chlorpropham, applied preemergence, controls most grasses and many broadleaf weeds in bean crops. Seed should be planted at least 1 inch deep.

DCPA may be applied preplant incorporated several days prior to planting or preemergence at planting; it should not be used on lima beans. Annual grasses and many broadleaf weeds are controlled.

Dinoseb in the amine form may be applied preemergence or at emergence to control all common annual weeds. This material is used in liquid or granular forms.

EPTC is soil incorporated before planting. Use only on dry and snap beans. It handles annual grasses, Johnsongrass seedlings, and most other spring and summer weeds.

Fluorodifen is applied broadcast or in bands at planting, preemergence to crop and weeds. Rainfall or sprinkler irrigation is required. Most annual weeds are controlled.

Nitralin applied preemergence gives control of a wide array of weeds.

Trifluralin, liquid or granular, is used preemergence incorporated to control most annual weeds. EPTC may be added to broaden the weed spectrum.

2,4-D may be used postemergence by directed spraying and shielded nozzles to control field bindweed and Russian knapweed.

Beets (table)

EPTC may be used preplant, soil incorporated to handle most annual weeds.

Phenmediphem is used postemergence when beets are past the 2-leaf stage and weeds are in the cotyledon to 4-leaf stage. Dilute as instructed on the label. Most annual weeds are controlled.

Pyrazon used both pre- and postemergence kills most broadleaf weeds and some annual grasses. Incorporation 1–1½ inches deep aids in the control.

CANTALOUPE

Bensulide used preplant or preemergence will control most of the annual broadleaf and grassy weeds. If mixed with naptalam, a broader spectrum of weeds will be brought under control.

CDEC is used preplant or preemergence to handle annual weeds. Requires rainfall or sprinkler irrigation. Use a low dosage on sandy soils.

The ester formulation of chloramben applied preemergence at planting time will control most annual weeds; dosage should be scaled to the textural grade of the soil.

DCPA is used postemergence when the cantaloupes have 4–5 true leaves; it will kill annual grasses and such broadleaf weeds as purslane, lambsquarters, and pigweeds.

Paraquat is used to control growing weeds on beds or on flat-planted fields. It should be used to kill vegetation preparatory to finishing the seedbed for planting. It can be used in a minimum tillage program; seeding should not disturb the top soil.

Trifluralin, liquid or granular, is used postemergence when cantaloupes have 4–5 true leaves; use directed spray to avoid foliage of the crop plants; most annual weeds are controlled.

CARROTS, DILL, PARSLEY, PARSNIPS

Stove oil and Stoddard solvent have been used since the middle 1940s to kill many annual weeds in carrots, dill, and parsley. Since that time many new herbicides have been introduced to handle this problem; the soil-borne ones prevent any weed competition and usually last throughout the growing and harvest season.

Bensulide is used preplant incorporated to kill most annual weeds.

Chloroxuron may be applied preemergence followed by rainfall or sprinkler irrigation within 2 days to kill most annual weeds including annual bluegrass, barnyardgrass, *Brachiaria*, crabgrass, goosegrass, and lovegrass. It also can be sprayed over carrots when true leaves have been formed.

Chlorpropham is used preemergence on carrots to handle annual weeds, especially grasses.

Linuron is used on carrots to control many annual broadleaf and grassy weeds; it may be applied preemergence after planting or postemergence when carrots are 3 inches or more in height; weeds should not exceed 2 in. in height. Stoddard solvent may be used 1 day before or 2 weeks after linuron application.

Nitrofen may be used preemergence at planting time or postemergence within 2 weeks after crop emergence. It does not require rainfall but adequate surface moisture must be present after application. Most annual weeds are controlled.

Stoddard solvent has been used for years and is still used on commercial carrots. Dill, parsley, and parsnips also tolerate this oil and may be sprayed for annual weed control. Nozzle pressure should not exceed 75 lb per sq in. The oil should be fresh.

Trifluralin is used preemergence incorporated against annual weeds in carrots.

CELERY (SEEDBEDS AND CROP)

Allyl alcohol has been used as a soil fumigant on celery seedbeds. It is applied as a surface drench with sufficient water to insure penetration from 2 to 4 inches. All weeds are controlled; a time interval after application of 5 to 10 days is required for the toxicant to disperse.

CDAA is used posttransplanting in the field to kill grasses. CDEC may be used with CDAA to include broadleaf weeds in the control.

CDEC is used 3 weeks postplanting in the field to kill annual weeds.

Chloropicrin is a soil fumigant used before seeding to control weeds, insects, and nematodes in celery seedbeds.

Chloroxuron is used postemergence over the young plants in the seedbed after the plants have 2 true leaves. Most annual weeds are controlled.

Linuron is applied posttransplant before the plants are 8 in. tall for general annual weed control.

Metham is used to kill seeds of most annual weeds in seedbeds. It is applied before seeding as a drench.

Nitrofen may be used preemergence just after seeding or postemergence within 2 weeks after crop emergence in celery seedbeds. It can also be used in the field. It kills an array of grasses and broadleaf annual weeds.

Stoddard solvent or mineral spirits may be applied as a spray over the seedbeds when the crop has its first true leaves and before the crown leaf cups are formed. It may also be used in the field but not later than 1 month from transplanting. Oil will not control nettles, ragweed, or galinsoga.

Trifluralin is used before transplanting or before direct seeding; it must be incorporated but does not need rain or irrigation. It kills both grasses and broadleaf weeds.

Vorlex may be used before seeding in celery seedbeds; the soil should be cultivated and kept moist 1 week before the treatment.

COLE CROPS (BROCCOLI, BRUSSELS SPROUTS, CABBAGE, CAULIFLOWER)

Bensulide is applied preplant preemergence to control many annual weeds. It should be incorporated 1 to 2 inches deep. Under irrigated conditions sprinkle thoroughly. It has an 18 month residue period.

CDEC, liquid or granular, may be used preemergence on direct seeding or preplant to setting plants in the field. It can also be used postplant followed by irrigation. CDAA may be combined with CDEC to broaden the spectrum; most annual weeds are controlled.

DCPA may be used preemergence at seeding time or posttransplant preemergence to weeds. High dosage is required on muck or peat soils. All common annual weeds are controlled.

Isopropalin has a low toxicity to broccoli.

Nitralin is used from 6 weeks prior to planting, at planting, or immediately after on transplanted cole crops. Incorporation 1–1½ inches deep needed. Most common annual weeds controlled.

Nitrofen may be used preemergence, at or soon after seeding time; also postemergence when transplants are established or 2 weeks after direct-seeded plants have emerged. Most common annual weeds are controlled.

Trifluralin, liquid or granular, should be applied and incorporated before transplanting; preemergence for direct-seeded cole crops. It kills all annual grasses and most broadleaf weeds.

CUCUMBERS

Bensulide is used preplant incorporated to kill common annual grasses; broadleaf weeds will be controlled only in semiarid, irrigated regions. Bensulide has an 18-month residue period. (Fig. 15–1.A).

CDEC will kill most common annual weeds when applied preemergence at seeding time; fluid and granular forms are available.

Chloramben ester is effective in controlling common annual weeds if applied preemergence at planting.

DCPA controls annual grasses and certain broadleaf weeds if applied postemergence when crop plants have 4–5 true leaves.

Dibutalin has a low toxicity rating in cucumbers.

Dinoseb may be applied preemergence, broadcast against most common annual weeds.

Trifluralin, fluid or granular, may be used postemergence when crop plants have 3–4 true leaves. Spray should be directed. Incorporation machinery should throw treated soil into the plant rows. All common weeds are controlled.

EGGPLANT

DCPA is recommended for use postplant, 4 to 6 weeks after transplanting, or when direct-seeded plants are 4–6 in. high. Paraquat may be used to free beds of weeds preparatory to setting plants in the field.

FIGURE 15-1. Selective preemergence weed control in vegetable crops. Upper left, bensulide on cucumbers; right, chlorpropham on garlic. Lower left, benefin on lettuce; right, diphenamid in tomatoes. (Photographs courtesy of Floyd Ashton.)

GREENS (COLLARDS, KALE, SPINACH, TURNIPGREENS)

Alachlor gives good overall weed control in spinach.

CDEC is used preemergence on direct-seeded greens to kill common annual weeds; rainfall or sprinkler irrigation is needed. Additional applications may be made on spinach if required. Fluid and granular formulations are available.

Chlorpropham may be used to kill wild oats in the 2-leaf stage in spinach.

Cycloate is used preplant incorporated on mineral soils. Dosage should be scaled to the soil type. Annual grasses, nutsedge, and annual broadleaf weeds are controlled.

DCPA may be used preemergence at seeding on all greens but spinach. Most annual weeds are controlled.

Lenacil is effective in spinach.

Trifluralin is used preemergence incorporated before planting. All common annual weeds are controlled.

HORSERADISH

Nitrofen may be used once per season preemergence after planting. If used postemergence, application should be about 5 weeks after emergence. Most annual weeds are controlled.

LETTUCE

Benefin is used preplant at any time from 10 weeks prior to planting until planting. It must be incorporated. Most annual weeds are controlled. Toxicity of benefin to lettuce is low. (Fig. 15-1.B).

Bensulide is used preplant incorporated on tops of beds with power-driven tillers to a 1-2 inch depth; rainfall or irrigation is required; a wide array of common weeds is controlled.

CDEC is used preemergence to control purslane in head lettuce; rainfall or irrigation is needed. For preplant application, use 2-inch incorporation with a power-driven rotary tiller. Many common annual weeds are controlled.

Chlorpropham is used preemergence to control annual weeds, particularly grasses.

Paraquat is used to clear the land of vegetative growth before seedbed preparation. In a tillage program, the seedbed should be prepared soon; in nontillage, drill seed directly into sprayed beds with minimum disturbance of the soil. Use only on soils having appreciable clay content.

Propham should be applied preemergence within 2 days after planting, postemergence when lettuce has 4 or more leaves, or preplanting incorporated. Incorporation should be shallow; irrigation or rainfall should follow all treatments. Grasses and some broadleaf weeds are controlled.

OKRA

Diphenamid is suggested for controlling most annual weeds; apply at planting time.

Profluralin was the least toxic of ten dinitroanilines to okra.

Trifluralin should be applied and incorporated before planting to control many annual grasses and broadleaf weeds.

Onions, Garlic

Bensulide is used preplant incorporated or preemergence surface application to kill certain grasses and broadleaf weeds. Soil residue may last 18 months.

CDAA is used to control many annual grasses and broadleaf weeds in onions. Liquid formulation is applied just as the onions emerge; there may be one later application. The granular form may be applied preemergence, with 3 postemergence treatments after 3 true leaves are developed. A wide array of annual weeds are controlled.

Chloroxuron may be applied postemergence over the tops of onions after they have 2–3 true leaves to kill small, annual weeds; there should be 1 percent or more organic matter in the soil. Chloroxuron should not be used closer than 30 days from harvest.

Chlorpropham is used preemergence or directed postemergence on small annual weeds before the onions or garlic are beyond the loop stage. (Fig. 15–1.C). Should not be used during the flag stage, not on sandy soils, and not within 1 month of harvest.

DCPA is used preemergence to seeded onions; apply immediately after setting transplants, or as layby treatment up to 2 weeks after planting. DCPA controls most annual broadleaf and grassy weeds.

EXD is used one to 2 days before emergence of seeded onions. It kills most annual weeds.

Monolinuron, propachlor, and desmetryne have proven effective in onions and leeks.

Nitrophen is used preemergence or postemergence when onions have 2–3 true leaves. It should not be incorporated but top soil should be moist; most common annual weeds are controlled.

A light aromatic oil may be used preemergence to the onions on small weeds or postemergence by directed spray on established plants. Almost all annual weeds are controlled.

Chloroxuron may be applied postemergence over the tops of onions after they have 2–3 true leaves to kill small, annual weeds; there should be 1 percent or more organic matter in the soil. Chloroxuron should not be used closer than 30 days from harvest.

Chlorpropham is used preemergence or directed postemergence on small annual weeds before the onions or garlic are beyond the loop stage. (Fig. 15–1.C). Should not be used during the flag stage, not on sandy soils, and not within 1 month of harvest.

DCPA is used preemergence to seeded onions; apply immediately after setting transplants, or as layby treatment up to 2 weeks after planting. DCPA controls most annual broadleaf and grassy weeds.

EXD is used one to 2 days before emergence of seeded onions. It kills most annual weeds.

Monolinuron, propachlor, and desmetryne have proven effective in onions and leeks.

Nitrophen is used preemergence or postemergence when onions have 2–3 leaves. It should not be incorporated but top soil should be moist; most common annual weeds are controlled.

A light aromatic oil may be used preemergence to the onions on small weeds or postemergence by directed spray on established plants. Almost all annual weeds are controlled.

PEAS

When peas are grown in a field that has been in cereal crops, wild oats can be a problem. Barban applied in the 2-leaf stage of the oats and less than 14 days from emergence will control this pest. Treatment must be not later than 10 days after emergence of the peas.

CDAA may be used preemergence at the time of planting to control annual grasses.

Chlorpropham applied preemergence at planting time kills most annual weeds. Seed should be planted 1 in. deep and dosage should be scaled to the textural grade of the soil. Annual grasses and some broadleaf weeds will be controlled.

Dalapon is used postemergence when peas are 2–6 inches tall but not within 25 days of harvest to control annual grasses. It may be used also by spot treatment to inhibit Johnsongrass and other perennial grasses.

Diallate is used preplant soil-incorporated to kill wild oats. It does not present a soil-residue problem.

Dinoseb in the amine salt formulation may be used preemergence at planting time to control a wide array of broadleaf and grassy weeds. At lower dosage it may be sprayed postemergence on plants 2–6 inches tall; the plants should be free of dew. Dinoseb should not be applied as a spray after flower buds are visible.

EPTC is used preplant incorporated for annual grass control. Nutsedges are inhibited.

Fluorodifen may be used once in a crop to kill most annual weeds. It is applied broadcast or in bands, preemergence to crop and weeds, and not incorporated; rainfall is required. It should not be used under irrigation agriculture in the western states.

MCPA is used to control broadleaf weeds soon after they emerge and before they are 3 inches high. Peas stressed from lack of water should not be sprayed. Canada thistle may be treated as buds appear.

MCPB is used to control Canada thistle and other broadleaf weeds when peas have 6–12 nodes but before the flowers open.

Nitralin is used preemergence incorporated from 6 weeks before planting to planting time or immediately thereafter. Incorporation should be 1–1½ inches deep and within 2 days of application; most annual weeds are controlled.

Propachlor is used preemergence to control a wide array of annual weeds; crop safety is excellent.

Triallate is used preplant soil-incorporated to kill wild oats.

Trifluralin is applied before planting; incorporation is required; annual grasses and many broadleaf weeds are controlled.

PEAS (SOUTHERN)

DCPA should be used preplant incorporated or at planting time on clean seedbeds; many annual weeds are controlled.

Fluorodifen can be used once per crop, applied broadcast or on bands preemergence to crop and weeds, but not incorporated; rainfall is required.

Nitralin is used preemergence from 6 weeks before planting to planting time or immediately thereafter to control many annual weeds. Incorporation 1–1½ inches deep is required but rainfall or irrigation is not.

Trifluralin is used preplant incorporated to control most annual weeds.

PEPPERS

Bensulide is used preplant or preemergence in seeded bell peppers. Incorporation 1–2 inches in depth is needed or application to bed surface and irrigation where rainfall does not occur. The period of residue persistance is 18 months; common annual weeds are controlled.

Chloramben may be used at transplanting time or at layby to control a wide array of annual weeds; avoid use on light, sandy soils.

DCPA is used 4 to 6 weeks after transplanting or at 4–6 inches height on direct-seeded peppers. Scale dosage to soil type; many annual weeds are controlled.

Diphenamid is used from seeding or transplanting until 1 month after these operations to control most annual weeds.

Napropamide has proven excellent in controlling many weeds in peppers and pimentoes; it suppresses the growth of nutsedges.

Nitralin is used only on the transplanted crop; application may be from 6 weeks prior to planting until planting time or immediately thereafter. Nitralin should be incorporated 1–1½ inches deep within 2 days after application. Most annual weeds are controlled.

Paraquat may be used broadcast or in bands to kill all vegetation preparatory to planting peppers. In a minimum-tillage program, seeding should disturb the soil as little as possible to prevent bringing new seeds to the surface.

Trifluralin, liquid or granular, is used in preparing the land for transplanting. Application should be at or just before transplanting or at layby. Avoid use on sandy soil. Most annual weeds are controlled.

POTATOES

Ametryne is used in potato growing to kill the vines preparatory to digging; weeds that interfere with harvest are also killed; 10 to 17 days are required.

CDAA in granular form is used immediately after the last cultivation to kill annual grasses; the granules should be brushed from the potato vines by dragging a canvas after the applicator. CDAA plus CDEC is used preemergence immediately after planting to control annual broadleaf and grassy weeds.

Chlorbromuron is applied preemergence, broadcast or on bands, to soil surface after planting to control many annual broadleaf and grassy weeds; avoid use on sandy soils.

Dalapon is used preemergence to the crop to control annual grasses; it is also used 2 to 3 weeks prior to planting to control quackgrass; plowing just before planting improves the control.

DCPA may be used to control annual grasses and some broadleaf weeds. Application should be at planting, or up to 9 weeks thereafter; scale dosage to soil type.

Dichloropropene is used as a fumigant to control quackgrass. It is applied preplanting and time must be allowed for the vapor to dissipate.

Dinoseb amine may be used preemergence just before the plants break through to control broadleaf and grassy weeds; grasses require a high dosage. Dinoseb in the form of the general weed killer is applied 10 to 20 days before harvest to kill the vines. This aids in harvest and reduces spread of late blight.

Diphenamid is used preemergence at planting time or soon after to control a wide spectrum of annual weeds. It can also be used at layby as a directed spray to handle the same array of weeds. Mixed with dinoseb and applied at emergence, it controls an even broader spectrum of weeds.

EPTC may be used preemergence soil-incorporated before planting or at last cultivation to control annual grasses, Johnsongrass seedlings, and a number of broadleaf weeds. It should not be used within 45 days of harvest.

Linuron is used preemergence, applied between planting and crop emergence, to control most annual weeds. It should not be used on sandy soils nor on soils low in organic matter. The residual waiting period is around 4 months.

Metribuzin, monolinuron, and metobromuron have also been found effective.

Paraquat may be applied by air before planting to emerged weeds. It can be sprayed between planting and the time the soil begins to crack at emergence or for preharvest vine and weed killing; avoid this use on potatoes to be used for seed.

Sesone may be used pre- or postemergence and monthly after planting to kill germinating annual weeds. Sesone requires rainfall or sprinkler irrigation.

Trifluralin is applied and incorporated after planting and up to the time the tops are removed. It kills most annual weeds.

PUMPKINS, SQUASH

Chloramben is used preemergence at planting time to kill most common annual weeds.

DCPA is used 4 to 6 weeks after planting when the plants have 4 or 5 true leaves to kill germinating weeds; most common annual weeds are controlled.

Dinoseb is used preemergence from planting time until ground cracking to kill most annual weeds. Postemergence use requires directed spraying and shields to protect the crop plants.

Naptalam has been used for many years to control weeds in cucurbita crops. It is applied preemergence as a spray or in granules. Chlorpropham may be included in the treatment to broaden the spectrum of weeds controlled.

SWEET CORN

Alachlor used preemergence, preplant incorporated kills a wide array of annual grasses and broadleaf weeds. Alachlor can be used with fluid fertilizers.

Ametryne is applied postemergence as a directed spray after corn has attained a height of 12 inches. It kills most annual weeds.

Atrazine may be used in the fall or spring or as a split application in both fall and spring to control quackgrass. Plowing a week or so after application enhances the herbicidal action. Atrazine is used preemergence, prior to planting, to control nutsedge. Shallow cultivation may be used 2 to 3 weeks after application. The spring application may be made before planting, at planting, or soon after weeds emerge. Addition of a bland oil increases the herbicidal action against grasses; a wide array of annual weeds is controlled.

Butylate applied preplant incorporated is effective against annual grasses, Johnsongrass seedlings, shattercane, fall panicum, and nutsedge.

CDEC is used preemergence, after planting or just before the crop plants emerge, to control many annual weeds.

Cyanazine kills a wide array of broadleaf and grassy weeds. It is applied before planting, at planting, or just before the crop emerges. Scale dosage to soil type; do not use on sandy or low-organic soils. Use fall-seeded grains, alfalfa, or other forage or cover crops to follow cyanazine-treated crop.

Dalapon as a directed postemergence spray is used to control annual grasses, especially foxtail. It may be combined with 2,4-D to control a broader spectrum of weeds. When corn is 8–20 inches tall, use leaf lifters as shields.

Dinoseb, as the amine salt, is used preemergence at planting to kill annual weeds and postemergence while corn is in the 2-leaf stage. Do not use when the temperature is over 85°F.

EPTC is used to control Johnsongrass seedlings, wild cane, nut-sedges, and other weeds. It is applied and incorporated immediately after planting; a heavier dosage against nutsedge should be applied 7 to 10 days before planting.

Linuron is applied as a postemergence spray when corn is at least 15 inches tall. Linuron controls a wide array of annual weeds.

Propachlor is used preemergence or very early postemergence to control many annual weeds; it is effective under diverse climatic conditions; it excels on heavy soils; it can be mixed with liquid nitrogen fertilizer.

Simazine, the classical corn herbicide, is used preemergence, applied before, at, or soon after planting, to control most annual weeds. Simazine is low in solubility; it presents a soil-residue problem; label recommendations for succeeding crops should be followed.

2,4-D is used preemergence to control annual weeds as they emerge, postemergence as a directed spray when corn is 8–12 inches tall; it may be combined with dalapon against grasses.

Sweet Potatoes

CDAA is applied over-the-top immediately after setting the plants to control annual grasses.

Chloramben is used at slip-planting time to control most annual weeds.

DCPA will control a wide array of annual weeds when applied preemergence to weeds at transplanting or at layby up to 6 weeks after transplanting time.

Diphenamid is used preemergence at transplanting time or at bedding to control a wide variety of annual grasses and broadleaf weeds.

EPTC is used preplant incorporated at planting or within 2 days after planting of slips; it should be applied prior to irrigation.

TOMATOES

Bensulide is applied preemergence incorporated preplanting to control a long list of annual weeds; broadleaf weeds are controlled in semiarid, irrigated areas. Rainfall or irrigation is essential. The soil residue waiting period is 18 months.

CDAA is used within 2 days of transplanting to control annual grasses.

CDEC is applied after seeding or transplanting to control many annual weeds preemergence. CDAA may be mixed with CDEC to control both broadleaf weeds and grasses.

Chloramben, applied broadcast before weeds emerge after transplanting or preplant incorporated in seeded tomatoes, controls a wide array of annual weeds. At layby, chloramben granules may be applied over the crop to give uniform ground cover and protection against late-germinating weeds.

DCPA is applied 4 to 6 weeks postplant, or on direct-seeded plants 4–6 inches in height; established weeds are not controlled. DCPA acts on a wide array of annual weeds.

Diphenamid may be applied from 1 week prior to seeding to 1 month after seeding or transplanting. (Fig. 15–1.D). The treatment should be sprinkler irrigated or incorporated. Scale dosage to soil type; most annual weeds are controlled. Trifluralin may be added to diphenamid to control a very wide spectrum of annual weeds.

Metribuzin is used preemergence or postemergence on tomatoes. Injury may be minimized by avoiding application during or immediately after cloudy weather.

Nitralin is recommended on only transplanted tomatoes. It is applied anytime from 6 weeks prior until planting or immediately after planting. It should be incorporated 1–1½ inches deep in the surface soil; irrigation is not required, it is not susceptible to leaching; many annual weeeds are controlled.

Paraquat is used to kill existing vegetation on the land preparatory to seedbed working; soils should contain clay.

Pebulate is used preplant incorporated, before or just after seeding, and before transplanting. Incorporation by power-driven equipment or by discing and cross-discing should follow immediately after application; most annual weeds are controlled.

Trifluralin, fluid or granular, is used preemergence incorporated at blocking or thinning time in direct-seeded tomatoes, and before transplanting. Trifluralin may be applied to growing plants by directed spray between rows and under plants; incorporate immediately. Most annual broadleaf and grassy weeds are controlled.

WATERMELONS

Bensulide applied preemergence, preplant incorporated is used to control both annual grasses and broadleaf weeds. Irrigation may be used instead of mechanical incorporation.

DCPA is applied to control many broadleaf and grassy weeds by application preplant or when the crop plants have 4–5 true leaves.

Paraquat may be applied by ground rig or by air to kill all existing weeds prior to planting melons. In a minimum-tillage program, seeding should avoid disturbing the soil as much as possible to prevent the germination of newly exposed seeds.

Trifluralin should be applied to melons when plants have 3–4 true leaves; incorporate at once; the spray should be directed between rows and under the plants. Scale dosage to soil type. Many annual weeds are controlled.

REFERENCES

Romanowski, R. R. 1970. Weed control in vegetable crops. *F.A.O. Internatl. Conf. on Weed Control.* Davis, Calif., p. 184–197.

16

Tree and Vine Crops, Ornamentals

DECIDUOUS TREE FRUITS AND NUTS

Chemical weed control in tree, vine, and ornamental crops is gaining in popularity as growers find that it reduces the costs of producing a crop, that it is beneficial to the plants because it eliminates the pruning of shallow feeder roots so often caused by heavy tillage equipment, and that it eliminates alternate host plants of orchard-tree diseases. Lange (1970) has reviewed the weed-control methods, the losses and costs due to weeds, and the benefits of weed control in deciduous fruit and nut crops. Much of his information stems from personal experience as Extension Weed Control Specialist at the University of California.

One herbicide has emerged as useful in all tree crops; this is paraquat, which is used as a spray to kill all annual broadleaf weeds and grasses; cheeseweed and knotweed are not controlled; top growth of perennial weeds is scorched but regrowth occurs. In using paraquat care must be taken to avoid allowing the spray to contact green stems, foliage, or fruit. Do not spray under windy conditions; use shields to protect young trees and do not allow access to animals.

Another innovation in perennial-weed control in orchards and vineyards is the application of nitroaniline herbicides by means of subsurface soil application. Most of the experimental work with this method has involved use of trifluralin; at a rate of 2 quarts per acre applied by a sprayblade, bindweed and other perennial weeds have been held in check for a whole growing season. In such a program the area is disced thoroughly to destroy all weeds and grass. For all soil

299

textures, 2 quarts of trifluralin in 40 to 80 gallons of water are applied so as to thoroughly cover the bare soil beneath the blade operated at a 4 to 6 inch depth. If the soil develops cracks upon drying, shallow tillage should be carried out to prevent bindweed shoots from emerging. This method has been used successfully in vineyards and in the following tree crops: almond, pecan, walnut, nectarine, peach, apricot, orange, lemon, grapefruit, tangerine, and tangelo.

A report from Idaho (Warner, 1973) states that subsurface layering of trifluralin with a moldboard plow proved successful, giving as high as 97 percent control in preliminary experiments where a standard plowshare was used at a depth of 9 inches.

Various aromatic oils (weed oils) are also used to suppress growth of annual weeds in orchards and vineyards. The earliest nontillage programs used weed oil to hold weeds down.

Dinitro contact sprays (dinosam, dinoseb) have also been used both as fortifiers to increase toxicity of oils and in emulsions to kill common, annual weeds and to suppress perennials. Care must be taken to avoid contacting green stems, foliage, and fruit. And dinitrophenols are toxic if they are allowed to contact skin or are ingested; care should be taken to keep these chemicals off the skin, out of eyes, and outside the body; they are poisonous.

ALMONDS

Dalapon is used to control annual and perennial grasses. Avoid spraying tree trunks, foliage, and fruits. Repeat application when new foliage develops on grass. Injury can result if rainfall or irrigation immediately follows application.

Napropamide provides excellent grass control. Nitralin controls a wide array of common weeds. These two herbicides should be applied preemergence to the weeds.

Trifluralin is used preplant incorporated in land being planted to almonds. Annual grasses and many broadleaf weeds are controlled.

Simazine may be used in trees 3 years old or older. There are restrictions as to soil type, irrigation methods, and varieties; the Mission (Texas) varieties are sensitive.

APPLES

AMS is used to kill poison ivy and poison oak in apple orchards. The spray should be applied when these pests are in full leaf and the spray should be kept off foliage and fruit.

Chlorthiamid has proven effective in controlling weeds in Golden Delicious and Cox's Orange Pippin in Europe.

Dalapon is used as a directed spray on grass foliage in a circle of radius 3 to 4 feet from the tree trunks; dalapon leached into roots of trees may cause injury. Annual and perennial grasses are controlled.

Dichlobenil is applied preemergence in orchards to control a large number of common, annual weeds. It may be used in bands over the tree rows or broadcast. Dichlobenil applied by sprayblade has controlled field bindweed for a whole season.

2,4-D is used as a directed spray on the orchard floor to control a wide array of broadleaf weeds, including some perennials. Drift onto trunks, limbs, leaves, or fruit should be avoided.

Diphenamid may be applied at any convenient time preemergence to weeds to control a wide variety of annual weeds. The soil should be bare at the time of application.

Diuron may be used in the spring to control many annual weeds. Rainfall or irrigation is needed to activate this chemical. Dwarf varieties of apples should not be treated with diuron.

MSMA is used on nonbearing apples up to one year before bearing to control Johnsongrass, Dallisgrass, nutsedge, cocklebur, ragweed, sandbur, puncturevine, and many annual weeds.

Nitralin is useful both in nonbearing and bearing trees.

Simazine is used preemergence in established apple plantings to control most annual weeds; it should be applied to bare soil; fruit and foliage should not be sprayed.

Terbacil may be applied in spring before weed seeds germinate to control quackgrass, nutsedge, horsenettle, hoary cress, sheepsorrel, and many annual weeds.

APRICOTS

Dalapon may be used to control annual and perennial grasses. The chemical should not be applied to a circle 3 to 4 feet in diameter under each tree.

MSMA is used to control Johnsongrass, Dallisgrass, nutsedge, cocklebur, ragweed, sandbur, and puncturevine in apricots; avoid the trunks of young trees, foliage, and fruit. Regrowth of weeds should be resprayed but not over 3 applications should be made in one year.

Napropamide and nitralin are effective in apricots.

Trifluralin may be applied preplant incorporated in new orchards. It may also be used around bearing trees; annual weeds are controlled.

CHERRIES

In cherry orchards dalapon may be used to control annual and perennial grasses by postemergence spray. Avoid applying to a circle 6 to 8 feet in diameter under each tree. Treatment may be repeated.

Dichlobenil is used in cherries to control annual broadleaf and grassy weeds and certain perennials; it should be applied to bare soil preemergence to weeds; avoid contacting foliage or fruit.

MSMA is applied on certain perennial grasses and a few broadleaf annuals; it may be used again if regrowth appears but should not be used over 3 times in any one year.

Simazine is used preemergence to weeds on established cherries to control most annual broadleaf weeds and grasses; application should be prior to blossoming of the trees.

FILBERTS

Dichlobenil applied preemergence to the bare soil in spring or used in the late fall or early winter on established plants will control most annual weeds and certain perennial weeds.

Simazine used preemergence in the spring or after harvest in the fall will control most annual grasses and broadleaf weeds; split applications in fall and spring keep dosage to a minimum and avoid building up residue in the soil.

NECTARINES

Napropamide preemergence incorporated is useful in nectarines.

Trifluralin may be used as a preemergence incorporated herbicide to control most annual weeds in young or in bearing trees; use directed spray on the latter.

PEACHES

Dalapon is used in peaches to control annual and perennial grasses. It should not be sprayed under bearing trees.

Dichlobenil is used preemergence incorporated to weeds to control annual and certain perennial weeds; in young trees it may be applied 4 weeks after planting; applied by sprayblade, it inhibits growth of field bindweed for one season.

Dinoseb is used as a contact spray to kill annual weeds; care should be taken to avoid trunks of young trees and all foliage or fruit.

Diphenamid may be applied at any time of year to control annual weeds. It should be applied to bare soil. Avoid application within 90 days of harvest. Do not use on peaches on sandy soil.

MSMA is used to control perennial grasses in peaches; if weeds resprout, treatment may be repeated. Do not use in bearing orchard.

Napropamide and nitralin are useful herbicides in peaches.

Simazine is used preemergence to weeds at any time of year to control most annual broadleaf weeds and grasses. Use only on trees established one year or more; restricted to the area east of the Mississippi.

Terbacil will control quackgrass, yellow nutsedge, horsenettle, sheepsorrel, and many annual weeds. Use only on trees established for 3 years. Scale dosage to soil textural grade.

Trifluralin is used preplant or as a directed spray around established trees; it must be incorporated; controls most annual weeds.

Lord and Vlach (1973), in a 6-year study on herbicides, mulching, mowing, and cultivation, found that a combination of paraquat plus simazine was equal in producing growth and yield of trees to cultivation or hay mulch. Where grasses were controlled only by mowing, the trees were lower in nitrogen, had less growth, and produced less fruit.

PEARS

AMS is used to control poison oak and poison ivy in pears; treatment should be made on foliage in full leaf; avoid contacting foliage and fruit; a surfactant aids coverage.

Dalapon may be used as a directed spray on Johnsongrass, Bermudagrass, and other perennial and annual grasses; avoid treating the soil directly under the trees; do not spray within 30 days of harvest.

Dichlobenil is used in pears to control annual weeds and certain perennials. It should be applied preemergence to the weeds on bare soil in established trees; 4 weeks after planting new trees. Avoid foliage and fruit.

2,4-D amine is used to control a number of perennial weeds in orchards. It is applied to vigorous weed growth on the orchard floor; avoid drift onto foliage and fruit of trees.

Dinoseb may be used as a contact spray in the spring before blossoming to control annual grasses and broadleaf weeds. Contact of trunks or foliage should be avoided.

Diuron is applied in spring preemergence to weeds to control most annual weeds and grasses. Half of the dosage may be put on postharvest in the fall, the other half in the spring; avoid contact of foliage or fruit.

MSMA is used as a directed spray to control vigorous perennial grasses and certain broadleaf weeds; respraying may be required if weeds resprout. Avoid trunks, foliage, and fruits of trees.

Nitralin is effective in both nonbearing and bearing trees.

Simazine is used to control annual weeds around established trees prior to weed emergence and blossoming of trees or in late fall after harvest. Avoid contacting foliage or fruit; use only once per year.

PECAN

Dichlobenil is used preemergence on clean, cultivated soil and incorporated shallowly to control annual weeds. It may be used in new orchards 4 weeks after planting or on bearing trees. Applied in fall or early winter to the soil surface for leaching in by rainfall, dichlobenil controls Canada thistle, catsear, orchardgrass, Russian knapweed, and other annual and perennial weeds.

Nitralin applied preemergence incorporated is effective against most weeds.

Trifluralin is used preemergence incorporated in new and established orchards; apply as a directed spray in the latter; most annual weeds are controlled.

PLUMS, PRUNES

Dalapon is used to control annual and perennial grasses in plum and prune orchards. The chemical should be applied when weeds have made vigorous growth; avoid applying under trees; treatment may be repeated.

Dichlobenil is applied preemergence to weeds on clean, cultivated soil to control annual grasses and broadleaf weeds; certain perennials are susceptible. New orchards may be treated when trees have been in for 4 weeks; do not apply within 1 month of harvest.

Dinoseb is used as a contact spray to control annual weeds in early spring, prior to bloom, or during winter dormancy; avoid spraying foliage and trunks.

MSMA will control certain perennial grasses and broadleaf weeds if applied during vigorous growth. Avoid application to stems, bark, leaves, or fruit. Do not use in year of harvest.

Napropamide and nitralin are new herbicides useful in trees.

Simazine may be used to control annual weeds and seedling grasses in established orchards. Application should be prior to weed emergence in the spring or in the fall after harvest. French prunes are sensitive to simazine except at low rates.

Trifluralin is used preplant incorporated in new orchards and as a directed spray around established trees to control annual grasses and many broadleaf weeds.

WALNUTS

Dichlobenil is used in walnuts to control most annual weeds when applied preemergence on clean soil in spring. Incorporation, mechanical or by rainfall, is required. This herbicide may be used in new orchards 4 weeks after planting; it should not be applied within 30 days before harvest; it controls most annual weeds. When a heavy dosage is applied in late fall or early winter, certain perennial weeds are controlled.

Diuron applied during the winter dormancy controls most common weeds through the summer growing season.

Nitralin is useful on nonbearing trees only.

Simazine applied preemergence to weeds in established orchards will control most annual weeds. Only one treatment should be made per year; avoid foliage and nuts.

Trifluralin applied incorporated before planting new orchards or as a directed spray to soil around established trees will control most annual weeds.

CITRUS FRUITS, AVOCADOS, DATES, FIGS, MANGOES, OLIVES

CITRUS NURSERIES

The growing of young trees for planting orchards is an important business, and weed competition with young trees can seriously slow their development to marketable size. Weed oil, dinoseb as a contact spray, and paraquat can all be used in preparing land for planting tree seeds or cuttings. Preemergence herbicides can be used that will protect the young emerging seedlings from competition. And weed sprays, both selective and nonselective directed, can be used to keep the nursery clean. It is essential that weed seeds, rhizomes, or roots not be carried with nursery stock to new fields; this is particularly true of plants that are sold in cans. Bermudagrass, nutsedge, and oxalis are perennial weeds that are often disseminated in this way.

Dichlobenil is used, applied broadcast and incorporated by rainfall or light, overhead irrigation, to activate the chemical. Citrus seeds should be planted below this chemical blanket. Dichlobenil should not be used in a newly planted orchard until one year after planting. Many weeds are controlled. Dinoseb may be used as a directed spray to control weeds in the nursery; care should be taken to avoid contacting the tree seedlings with this spray as it will injure them seriously. Most annual weeds are controlled.

Diphenamid may be used but care must be taken to avoid contacting the trees either above ground or the roots. It is useful for spraying the middles to kill a wide variety of annual weeds.

EPTC may be used preemergence incorporated in well-established citrus nurseries to kill a great number of annual and perennial weeds. Nutsedges may be killed by repeated treatments.

LEMONS

Bromacil is used preemergence in lemon orchards to control most annual weeds and some perennials, for example, Johnsongrass, Bermudagrass, pangola grass, and nutsedge. Applied to the soil surface, it should be washed into the topsoil layer by rainfall or sprinkler irrigation.

Dichlobenil is popular in Europe for use against annual weeds in orchards. It is applied preemergence incorporated to bare soil in the spring; a second treatment may follow after 90 days. It may be used in new orchards one year after planting. Dichlobenil handles most annual weeds, also a number of shallow-rooted perennials; it is applied by sprayblade to suppress field bindweed.

Dinoseb is a contact-spray material used to control annual weeds in lemons. Care must be taken to keep dinoseb spray off the trees, trunks, limbs, leaves, and fruit. Most annual weeds are controlled.

Diuron may be used at anytime of year where activation by rainfall or sprinkler irrigation is possible. This material should not be applied directly to the trees; it may be used on young orchards one year after planting. It controls most annual weeds.

Krovar I, a proprietary mixture of bromacil and diuron, has proven effective for controlling many annual weeds in citrus.

Monuron is like diuron except that, being more water soluble, it should not be used on very sandy soils. It kills the same array of weeds.

MSMA is used as directed spray to control perennial grasses and some broadleaf weeds; avoid contacting the trees; do not use over 3 times in one year.

Simazine is used preemergence to weeds in established orchards to control most annual weeds; avoid spraying trees; do not use on sandy soils.

Terbacil is applied preemergence to control many annual weeds in orchards established for 2 years or more; avoid contacting trees; most annual weeds and some perennial grasses are controlled.

Trifluralin is used preemergence incorporated to kill annual weeds and seedlings of perennials. It is applied by directed spray avoiding the trees.

LIMES

Dichlobenil is used preemergence incorporated to bare soil in spring; it controls most annual weeds and some shallow-rooted perennials.

Dinoseb is used as a contact spray to control all weed growth in orchards; useful in nontillage; care should be taken to avoid contacting trees.

Diphenamid is used, applied at any time of year, to control most annual weeds, preemergence. It is put on by directed spray to avoid the trees; it controls a wide variety of weeds.

Krovar I is useful for weed control in limes.

Monuron is used to control most annual weeds in citrus. Applied preemergence to the weeds it should be incorporated by rainfall or irrigation; it is preferred on medium to heavy soils; diuron is better on sandy soils.

MSMA is used by directed spray to control perennial grasses; it should be applied to vigorous growing weeds; application may be repeated if weeds resprout; no more than 3 applications should be made in one year.

ORANGES, GRAPEFRUIT

Bromacil is used in citrus to control annual weeds. It may be applied at any time of year, preferably before or at time of weed emergence. It should be used only in orchards 4 years or more of age; dosage should be scaled to soil type. Bromacil controls most annual weeds and such perennials as Johnsongrass, Bermudagrass, pangola grass, and nutsedge.

Dalapon is used postemergence by directed spray to control all grasses, particularly the perennials; the chemical should not contact trees nor should it be applied under trees.

Dichlobenil may be used preemergence to weeds, applied to bare soil in the spring and incorporated. It controls a wide array of annual and shallow-rooted perennial weeds. It may be used in new orchards one year after planting.

Dinoseb is used as a contact herbicide to control all weed growth in orchards, application being made to the orchard floor avoiding the trees.

Diuron may be used preemergence incorporated at any time of year where rainfall or sprinkler irrigation may wash the chemical into the soil. Dosage should be scaled to soil type; monuron is preferred on heavy soils, diuron on light to medium grades; the orchard should be one year old from planting; most annual weeds are controlled.

Krovar I is effective in orange and grapefruit orchards.

MSMA is used as a directed spray to control perennial grasses in nonbearing trees; if weeds resprout the treatment may be repeated but not more than twice in one year.

Nitralin is used in nonbearing citrus plantings.

Simazine may be applied at any time of year with rainfall or sprinkler irrigation to activate the chemical. Apply as a directed spray avoiding the trees; trees should be one year from planting. Most annual weeds and seedlings of perennials are controlled.

Terbacil may be used in orchards 2 or more years from planting to control weeds preemergence by directed spray. Annual weeds and such perennials as Bermudagrass, torpedograss, and Johnsongrass are controlled.

Trifluralin is used preemergence, incorporated on land to be planted to orchard, and to trees established 2 or more years. In applying, avoid contacting the trees and injuring them with incorporation equipment. Most annual grasses and many broadleaf weeds are controlled.

TANGERINES

Dichlobenil is used to control annual weeds. It should be applied preemergence to weeds on bare soil in the spring; a second application may follow after 90 days. This chemical controls a wide array of annual weeds and some shallow-rooted perennials.

Dinoseb is used as a contact herbicide to kill all weed growth in orchards; it is commonly used in nontilled groves.

Monuron has been used for years to control annual weed growth by preemergence treatment; it is preferred on heavy soils; diuron is better on light soils.

MSMA applied as a directed spray will control certain perennial grasses as well as annual weeds. Application should be directed, avoiding the trees. The treatment may be repeated if weeds resprout; not more than 3 applications should be made in any one year.

VINE, BUSH, AND SMALL FRUITS

CANEBERRIES, BLACKBERRIES, BOYSENBERRIES, LOGANBERRIES, RASPBERRIES

Weed oils, dinitro contact sprays, and paraquat are used in these crops to control annual-weed growth in the middles and beneath the bushes by directed spraying; care must be taken to avoid contacting the crop plants at any time that foliage and fruit are on them.

Chlorpropham is applied preemergence during the dormant season and avoiding the plants, to control winter annual grasses and some broadleaf weeds; chickweed is controlled by fall application.

Dichlobenil is used preemergence on bare soil between the bushes in early spring to control annual weeds and some shallow-rooted perennials; shallow incorporation improves the control. At heavier dosage dichlobenil may be used in late fall or early winter to control many perennial as well as annual weeds; incorporation is not necessary if rainfall or snow are present.

Diphenamid may be used after planting vines and preemergence to the weeds in nonbearing blackberries and raspberries. It kills a wide variety of annual weeds.

Simazine is used in late fall after harvest or in early spring before weeds emerge to control most annual weeds. A heavy dosage may be used to control quackgrass but care must be taken to avoid treating the crop plants.

GRAPES

As with caneberries, oils, dinitro contact sprays, and paraquat may be used on grapes to destroy annual-weed growth; care must be taken to avoid application to the vines.

Dalapon is used directed as spot treatments to control Bermudagrass at 4–6 inches height and Johnsongrass when 12–18 inches tall. Avoid application to trunks or foliage of vines.

Dichlobenil is used in early spring, preemergence to weeds in bare soil with shallow incorporation, to control annual weeds and some shallow-rooted perennials. At higher dosage applied in late fall or early winter, it may be used to control Canada thistle, artemesia, fescue, orchardgrass, quackgrass, and Russian knapweed. Incorporation is not required; use only on established vines one or more years after planting.

2,4-D must be used with great care in and around grapes; some varieties are extremely susceptible to this growth regulator. By careful spraying of low-volatile forms at low pressure in high volume with flooding nozzles, field bindweed has been controlled with no injury to grapes; application should be made in summer after length growth and fruit set is past. Wax bars containing 2,4-D have been used with success in some vineyards.

Diuron is used in late fall or early winter preemergence to control annual weeds. Application is to middles between the vine rows, and only in vineyards 3 or more years from planting.

EPTC may be applied after cultivation in irrigation water to control annual weeds and perennial weed seedlings; it should not be applied within 40 days of harvest.

MSMA may be used as a directed spray on nonbearing vines to control perennial grasses and some broadleaf weeds; the spray should not contact the grape plants. If weeds resprout a repeat application may be made but not over 3 applications should be made in one year.

Napropamide and nitralin are effective herbicides in vineyards.

Simazine is widely used to control annual weeds in grapes. It may be applied in late fall following harvest until spring, prior to weed emergence; the vines should be established at least 3 years from planting.

Trifluralin, liquid or granular, may be used preemergence incorporated in grapes to control annual weeds; do not apply within 60 days of harvest. This chemical may also be used preemergence in spring in preparing land for planting grapes, and by sprayblade in summer to control field bindweed.

SMALL FRUITS

Blueberries, Cranberries, Currants, Gooseberries, Strawberries

Again, weed oils, dinitro contact sprays, and paraquat may be used in preparing land for planting and for weed control in existing plantings, but extreme care must be taken to avoid contacting the crop plants; even spray drift is hazardous in lush, growing crop plants.

Chloroxuron is used postemergence in the spring and fall on established strawberrry beds or in newly established plantings; application may follow renovation in fall with a repeat treatment in the spring; avoid application within 60 days of harvest.

Chlorpropham is used in the fall to control chickweed after emergence in berry crops. It will control many annual weeds in blueberries applied in fall or spring on bare soil; also on cranberry plants while dormant.

Dalapon may be used from early June to mid-July to control grasses, sedges, and rushes in cranberry fields; mainly for ditches and shores; application may be made again after harvest.

DCPA is used on newly planted or established strawberry beds to control annual weeds; repeat application may be made in late summer or fall. Treatment should not be made after first bloom and at low dosage on sandy soil.

Dichlobenil is used preemergence to weeds applied in spring to bare soil in blueberries. On cranberry beds dichlobenil may be used on the dormant crop in spring or in late fall after harvest. Both annual and perennial weeds are controlled.

2,4-D may be used on raspberries and brambles by preemergence application in early spring. Spraying must be directed to avoid contacting the vines. On strawberries it may be used postplanting or postharvest.

Diphenamid is used on strawberries after transplanting, on established plants during dormancy or after harvest following renovation. It controls a wide variety of annual grasses and broadleaf weeds.

Norflurazon is proving effective in cranberries.

Sesone may be used on tolerant varieties of strawberries, applied to established plantings before bloom or after harvest following cultivation.

Simazine may be used against most annual weeds in cranberries by applying preemergence to weeds in fall after harvest or in spring before growth starts. On cranberries simazine is applied in spring before growth starts and preemergence to weeds to control annual weeds. At double normal dosage, applied in fall or split and applied in fall and spring simazine is used to control quackgrass.

ORNAMENTALS, TURF, FLOWERS

ORNAMENTALS

On ornamental plants in nurseries, shelterbelts, highway-landscape plantings, forest-tree plantings, and Christmas-tree farms, chemical weed control is becoming standard practice. The current question is, not if herbicides should be used, but what herbicide? where? in what species or variety? under what conditions? against which weeds? The following pages list the chemicals being used, the time of application, and the weeds against which they are used. The crop species and varieties constitute such a number that it is impossible here to consider each one.

Atrazine is used broadcast or on bands in fall, winter, or early spring to control most annual weeds preemergence in Christmas trees and some ornamentals. Rainfall or sprinkler irrigation provides for leaching the chemical into the topsoil layer where weed seeds germinate. See label for tolerant species.

Amizine, a mixture of simazine and amitrole, is used on highway verges and in many other places to control growing weeds and maintain a weed-free condition throughout the year. This material should not be applied so as to contact crop or ornamental plants; it causes chlorosis of leaves and may result in serious injury.

Bensulide is used as a soil-applied preemergence herbicide to control crabgrass, annual bluegrass, and other annual grasses in well-established shrubs, bushes, turf grasses, and dichondra.

Cacodylic acid is used postemergence for general weed control. It is quickly inactivated in the soil but it leaves a permanent soil residue of arsenic. Care must be taken to avoid desirable foliage.

Chloramben will provide up to 8 weeks control of most annual weeds and grasses under established ornamentals; it is useful in parks, cemetaries, herbaria, and other places where annual-weed growth is unsightly or interferes with other useful plants.

Chlorpropham, both liquid and granular, may be used to eliminate annual grasses in nurseries, beneath coniferous plants, and in seedbeds before or at planting time.

Dazomet is a soil fumigant used preplanting to kill germinating weed seeds, insects, diseases, and nematodes in planting soils. It should be watered into the soil; allow 2 weeks after treatment before planting or more time if soil temperature is below 60°F.

DCPA, WP or granular, is applied preemergence to bare soil in early spring to control annual grasses and broadleaf weeds. It is also an excellent preemergence herbicide to control annual grasses and some broadleaf weeds in turf grasses.

Dibutalin, a new dinitroaniline herbicide, is effective against many weeds in ornamentals and flower crops.

Dichlobenil is used preemergence to annual weeds or after cultivation in spring or fall to control a number of annual and shallow-rooted perennial weeds. At heavier dosage dichlobenil will control perennial weeds, including Canada thistle, quackgrass, Russian knap-

weed, and nutsedge; it can be used around some established ornamentals or on land on which containers of nursery stock are held to
keep them weed free.

Dinoseb may be used as a contact spray in spring, directed to avoid
crop plants; low-pressure, hooded boom or shielded nozzles are preferred; all weed growth may be killed.

Diphenamid is used in spring or fall preemergence to weeds in
established ornamental trees, woody shrubs, flowers, and iceplant and
other ground covers along highways. Rainfall or overhead irrigation
helps incorporate the chemical. It controls a wide variety of annual
grasses and broadleaf weeds.

EPTC is used pre- and postplanting to control annual weeds in
cropping situations; incorporation is essential. There is no residue
problem.

Metham is used preplanting as a soil fumigant to control both
annual and perennial weeds, including nutsedge and Bermudagrass.
No soil cover is needed but the herbicide should be incorporated or
watered in.

Methyl bromide is a volatile soil fumigant that is used preplant
under a gas-tight cover to kill seeds of weeds, nematodes, and soil
disease organisms; it is also effective against perennial weeds; being
extremely poisonous it must be handled with care.

Naptalam is used as a herbicide to control annual weeds in established woody plants by directed spray, avoiding the crop.

Nitralin has proved effective in ornamentals and flowers.

Paraquat is used to control growing weeds; it is applied by directed
spraying or shielding valuable plants. It should not be sprayed under
windy conditions, nor allowed to drift; if all vegetation is not killed a
repeat treatment may be necessary; used widely in nontillage programs.

PCP is used like dinoseb as a contact spray to kill annual weeds.
Low pressure and hooded nozzles are necessary to avoid drift damage.

Sesone is used preemergence to weeds as a directed spray in established plants to control annual weeds in tree rows, especially
conifers.

Simazine is applied preemergence to weeds in fall or spring to
control annual weeds. It can be used only in tolerant species of ornamentals, but finds use on walkways, fence lines, and around buildings
and equipment in parks, school grounds, Christmas trees, and nurseries. (Figs. 16–1 AB, 16–2 AB)

Trifluralin, liquid and granular, is used in ornamentals preplant
soil-incorporated when setting out new liners and in established ornamentals for long-range weed control. It can be applied overtop and
incorporated on established plants.

FIGURE 16-1.   A. Weed control in amaryllis seedlings with simazine at a rate of 2 pounds per acre. These young plants are developing free from weed competition. B. Dutch iris nursery. Simzine at 2 pounds per acre is maintaining a weed-free condition. Two untreated beds at left center.

Vorlex is used preplanting by injection into moist, well-prepared soil; a plastic cover holds vapors in and gives complete control of weeds, insects, nematodes, and disease organisms.

TURF

Turf culture, involving home lawns, parks, public gardens, ceme-taries, and golf courses, is a multimillion dollar business, occupying hundreds of thousands of acres of land and using many thousands of professional and amateur workers. Chemical weed control has lightened the labor of these many people by eliminating the tedious

FIGURE 16-2.   A. Thuja trees in containers in a nursery. Simazine was applied to the area before the containers were moved in. B. Douglas fir nursery. Again, simazine at 2 pounds per acre is maintaining a weed-free ground surface.

hand labor so long associated with turf care. Selective herbicides to control dandelions, chickweeds, crabgrass, annual bluegrass, nutsedge, oxalis, and many other turf weeds make relatively easy the mainten-ance of clean, vigorous turf. (Elmore and McHenry, 1971 a, b.)

AMA, a mixture of amine methane-arsonates, is a selective crab-grass herbicide used in turf.

Atrazine is used preemergence and early postemergence to control annual weeds in St. Augustine grass, centipede grass, and Zoysiagrass grown for sod production. It is also used to control weeds on edges, alleys, and any noncrop areas around turf nurseries or turf in parks, cemetaries, and golf courses.

Bandane serves as a preemergence herbicide to control crabgrass in turf. It may be used at seeding time or in established turf.

Benefin is a preemergence, annual-grass herbicide used on established turf; it should be applied before germination of the weedy grass seed.

Bensulide is a preemergence herbicide used to control annual grasses and some broadleaf weeds in established turf; reseeding of treated area must be delayed for 4 months after treatment.

Bromoxynil is used in weeding new lawns. It is applied postemergence when the weeds are in the 2–4 leaf stage and less than 2 inches tall and the lawn grass has emerged. Kills mostly broadleaf weeds. Dosage rate may be increased if weeds get above 2 inches.

Cacodylic acid is used for general weed control. It is applied 5 to 10 days before seeding. If all weeds are not killed, a repeat application may be required. This chemical is quickly inactivated in contact with soil.

Calcium arsenate controls not only crabgrass but annual bluegrass and chickweed. It is applied preemergence in March or April or in early fall and it lasts for the total following season. It may be applied with a fertilizer spreader. Control is dependent on the amount of arsenate in the soil in relation to phosphorus.

Dalapon is used in spot treatments to control perennial grasses by directed spray. Its effects last for 3 to 6 weeks in warm, moist soil; it may be used at any time that the target grasses have foliage.

Dazomet is a soil fumigant used in preparing the land for planting turf. It should be applied at least two weeks before planting time and a plastic cover will increase effectiveness; it controls seedling weeds, soil-borne diseases, insects, and nematodes.

DCPA is used preemergence for crabgrass control; it may be applied in fall to control annual bluegrass, in winter or early spring for crabgrass; it controls several other turf weeds, including creeping speedwell.

Dicamba may be applied any time that weeds are actively growing. It controls common and mouseear chickweed, curly dock, dogfennel, clovers, red sorrel, carpetweed, henbit, knotweed, and other broadleaf weeds; also St. Augustinegrass, carpet grass, clovers, and dichondra; bentgrass tolerates dicamba; avoid root zones of shrubs, trees, or flowering plants.

2,4-D is used postemergence on established turf to control dandelions, buckhorn plantain, curly dock, and other easy-to-kill broadleaf weeds. The low-volatile esters are translocated; applied with a wetting agent they may control wild onion, wild garlic, and other more difficult weeds.

Diphenamid may be used on established dichondra lawns. It may be applied preplant or preemergence; prior to weed-seed germination it will control a wide variety of annual grasses and broadleaf weeds.

DSMA is used postemergence to control crabgrass, other annual grasses, chickweed, Dallisgrass, and other weeds of turf.

Endothall turf herbicide is used to control a variety of broadleaf weeds and grasses including annual bluegrass. It should be applied under temperature and moisture conditions favorable to turf growth. St. Augustine, Bermuda, and some other grasses may be browned during hot, dry weather.

Mecoprop is used as a postemergence spray to control creeping broadleaf weeds, such as red and white clovers, chickweed, knotweed, and ground ivy in turf; plantain and dandelion are also controlled.

Metham is used preplant on a well-prepared seedbed to control all weed seedlings, disease organisms, insects, and nematodes preparatory to planting turf.

MSMA applied postemergence to weeds is used to control annual grasses in established turf. Dallis grass and kikuyugrass are also controlled. Two or 3 applications at 10–14 day intervals are required; avoid using on St. Augustine or centipede grasses.

Paraquat is used to kill all weed growth on land being prepared to plant to turf; it may be applied up to the day of seeding.

Pronamide (Kerb) is used pre- or postemergence to control annual bluegrass in Bermudagrass turf. Apply while the weed is emerging up to the 2-leaf stage.

Siduron is applied immediately following seeding of turf to kill annual grasses such as crabgrass, foxtail, and barnyardgrass; rainfall or sprinkler irrigation is required; treatment may be repeated one month after the first application.

Silvex may be applied postemergence while weeds are small to control chickweed, henbit, knotweed, burclover, pennywort, white clover, and other weeds in established turf. Not effective under drought conditions; warm, sunny weather preferred. Injury may occur on stoloniferous grasses.

Simazine is used preemergence to control most annual broadleaf weeds and grasses in preparing beds for sod production. Used only on St. Augustine, centipede, and Zoysia grasses.

Terbutol (Azak) is used preemergence in established turf to control crabgrass; it should be applied prior to crabgrass germination; overseeding should be delayed for 6 months.

Vorlex is a soil fumigant used preplanting on a moist, well-prepared seedbed to control annual and perennial weeds and grasses, disease organisms, insects, and nematodes.

FLOWER CROPS

Alachlor is an effective herbicide in gladiolus.

Bensulide may be used postplanting to control annual grasses and some broadleaf weeds around bulbs.

Chloramben will provide up to 8 weeks control of most annual weeds and grasses under established flowering herbs and bushes; directed spray is preferred.

DCPA is used preemergence to weeds immediately after lining out stock to control a wide array of annual grasses and broadleaf weeds. The labels on the containers should be observed with respect to the flowers cleared for use.

Dinoseb may be applied preemergence to control all annual weeds in gladiolus, daffodils, tulips, and other bulbs; should not be applied after shoots emerge from the bulbs.

Diphenamid, WP or granular, is used preemergence to control a wide variety of annual grasses and broadleaf weeds in roses, asters, chrysanthemums, dahlias, marigolds, petunias, phlox, salvia, shasta daisies, snapdragons, stocks, sweet williams, and zinnias; use on established plants.

DNOC (Sinox) may be used preemergence to control most weeds in gladiolus.

EPTC is applied immediately after planting and incorporated to control many annual weeds. It should not be used around bulbs prior to flowering.

Nitralin, applied at any time from 6 weeks preplant until immediately after planting, will control many annual weeds in flower crops. It should be incorporated 1–1½ inches deep in the surface soil.

Nitrofen, applied preemergence immediately after planting or postemergence while the crop is from cotyledon to the 4th leaf stage, will kill most common weeds in stock; the soil surface should be moist at the time of application. It is also useful in transplanted carnations and chrysanthemums.

Trifluralin may be applied preplant when setting out gladioli corms, or over-the-top to roses and other established flower crops; incorporate where possible or increase dosage for surface application. Most annual weeds are controlled.

CONCLUSIONS

In closing this chapter it must be reiterated that these comments are all general and subject to error in many specific cases. In using herbicides on these many crops, one should read the labels on the containers for specific directions concerning dosage rates, times of application, names of weeds controlled, and specific tolerances and sensitivities of crops and weeds. Information from county agents, industry servicemen, commercial applicators, and experienced growers is useful in making decisions on weed-control operations. Short cuts, bargains, and fly-by-night operators are usually costly in the long run; they may actually prove to be tragic.

REFERENCES

Elmore, C. L., and W. B. McHenry. 1971a. Weed control in large turf areas. In *Turfgrass Pests Manual* 41. Calif. Agr. Expt. Sta. Extension Service. Berkeley: University of California.

_____ and _____. 1971b. Guide to turfgrass pest control. Calif. Agr. Expt. Sta. Extension Service. To be used in conjunction with Manual 41.

Lange, A. H. 1970. Weed control methods, losses and costs due to weeds, and benefits of weed control in deciduous fruit and nut crops. *F.A.O. Internatl. Conf. on Weed Control.* Davis, Calif., p. 143–162.

Lord, W. J., and E. Vlach. 1973. Responses of peach trees to herbicides, mulch, mowing, and cultivation. *Weed Sci.* 21:227–229.

Warner, C. L. 1973. Subsurface layering of trifluralin with a moldboard plow for field bindweed control. Western Society of Weed Science 1973 Annual Meetings. Proceedings Vol. 26, pp. 27–29.

17

Weed Control in Forest and Range

One of the greatest weed problems of the world is that of controlling woody plant species. Such plants may be weeds in the forest, they may occupy valuable range land, and they may invade good agricultural land.

Control of woody plants is an activity that has occupied man since prehistoric times, and it is one in which, because of ignorance, man has wasted untold effort in futile, backbreaking labor. Much of this labor can now be avoided if the modern knowledge of plant ecology is put to use.

Through the ages plants have distributed themselves according to their needs for moisture, nutrients, light, protection, etc., and so we find vegetation localized into forests, woodlands or savannah, brushland, grassland, and desert. The most prominent factor determining this distribution is precipitation; the forests occupy the regions of highest moisture, the deserts the lowest.

In spite of propaganda to the contrary, it is now well recognized that, in general, forests develop and grow in regions of high precipitation; trees have no way of attracting or producing rainfall. Because forests and high precipitation go together, forest soils in general are leached soils, usually quite low in inherent fertility, and so are suited only to the growth of trees except where abundant fertilizers are available. While many recently glaciated, recent alluvial, and delta soils are inherently fertile, primary soils of ancient origin are low in fertility, particularly where subject to heavy precipitation. If our forefathers had known this, much agonizing toil could have been avoided in the settling of America. While the cutting of a farm from a forest may be an attractive ideal, particularly for a person of puritan-ical ideas, practically it is a futile process, as millions of acres of abandoned New England and lake states farms attest.

Although newly cutover forest land may appear to be highly fertile, as soon as the accumulated organic matter is gone, the inherent low fertility, resulting from long, continued leaching, will become evi-dent; and as crops decline, weeds take over, and the land is headed back to the forest. Over three hundred years of experience have taught us

FIGURE 17-1.   Oaks overtopping this stand of red pine have been sprayed with a heavy-ester formulation of 2,4,5–T. After one or two applications the pines are released and become dominant; broad leaf species gradually disappear. (Photograph by John L. Arend, Lake States Forest Experimental Station. Print supplied by the Dow Chemical Co.)

that forest lands should be kept in forest. This principle is now taking form in the programs of tree farming being instituted in many areas of the world. In tree farming, weedy trees are being recognized as such and are being subjected to chemical control. (Fig. 17–1; Theisen, 1967).

Klingman (1970) reviews the current trends in control of brush and herbaceous weeds on range lands. He describes mechanical, chem-ical, and management systems in the control of brush and concludes that herbicides are essential tools for management of forage and graz-ing lands.

Methods of Controlling Woody Species

Brush and other woody species are controlled by several methods: (1) cutting, (2) burning, (3) bulldozing, (4) "bushwhackers," rollers, mowers, discs, etc., (5) chemicals, (6) insects (in biological control), and (7) managed grazing.

The conversion of brushland to pasture often involves more than just brush control. In addition to killing the existing stand of brush species, a pasture-seed mixture usually must be seeded, fertilizer may be required, the new crop needs to be protected and encouraged until a good ground cover is established, and, finally, grazing must be man-

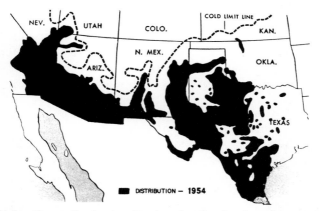

FIGURE 17-2. Generalized map showing the distribution of mesquite in the Southwest. The northern limit of mesquite appears to follow closely the average annual minimum temperature isotherm of –5°F. (From Texas Agr. Expt. Sta. Bul. 935, 1959.)

aged so that good forage species are maintained without reversion to brush or weedy herbs. The control of brush seedlings is an important aspect of this program. Fertilizers are sometimes applied to increase pasture plant competition. In many places, development of irrigation results in vastly improved pasture.

GRAZING

Many small- to medium-sized ranges have been successfully cleared of brush by intensive grazing, usually with goats. It often pays to supplement this grazing by cutting the larger trees and brush; chemical methods might also be employed. Where a profit can be made by sale of the grazing animals or their products, intensive grazing is an excellent method of brush clearing. However, where there is no sale for the animals, the method becomes costly, as it is necessary to provide fences and water and sometimes supplementary feed and even shelter.

Many millions of acres of land in the world are covered with brush. Much, because of topography and soil character, has a brush climax; much has been changed from range land to brush by overgrazing, uncontrolled burning, and other disturbances. (Fig. 17–2; Fisher et al., 1959).

In many areas, it is desirable to convert brushlands to usable range; this applies not only to lands previously bearing forage species but also to naturally occurring brushlands. The advantages of grass cover over brush are: (1) greater production of forage, (2) greater conservation of water, (3) less erosion of the soil, and (4) better control of wild fires.

Many people now object to the burning or the chemical control of brush. Few seem to realize that the chaparral and mesquite of the Southwest, and brush in most of our mountains have evolved in the presence of periodic wild fires, set by lightning, and are adapted to such an environment. Burning, chemical spraying, and controlled grazing are usually effective in converting such lands into useful, productive range.

In the final analysis grazing is a selective process; animals choose the more palatable species, and overgrazing or grazing at the wrong time shifts the plant population in the direction of a weedy cover. In grazing annual species, seed production must be assured; in grazing perennial species, storage of root reserves is essential.

Love (1961) gives an excellent analysis of range management practices. He describes experimental work from many areas where range research is being conducted. He discusses ideal management practices for a number of forage species, for example, crested wheatgrass, red brome, soft chess, and Idaho fescue. And he describes rest-rotation as a system designed to satisfy the growth requirements of the key species on the range. Love also emphasizes the need for knowledge of the forage plants on the part of the range manager. Only as the operator knows the various factors that function to improve or to deplete his range may he use the tools of fire, fertilizers, seeding, mechanical and chemical clearing, biological control, and sound grazing management to maintain and improve his forage supplies.

BURNING

Controlled burning (Fig. 17–3) may be the cheapest and most practical method of eliminating brush. However, it has certain limitations. It must be done under a well-organized program with adequate men and equipment and with prearranged firebreaks. Where such provisions are not made, fires may escape and cause untold damage.

Many brush situations are ideal for burning; others do not lend themselves to this method. If the brush is thin or growing in scattered

FIGURE 17-3. Controlled burning is a primary tool in the reclamation of brushlands. Top, after the fire. Bottom, reseeded area the following spring. (From Calif. Agr. Expt. Sta. Cir. 371)

patches, a burn may leave many areas untouched. On the other hand, if the brush is dense, burning may destroy the seeds of forage species; in this event, unless the area is seeded after the burn, serious erosion and reinfestation with brush may follow. Many brush species sprout from

stumps after a burn, and some measures must be taken to control the
resprouts or reinfestation may result in a denser stand than that
originally present. Where forage grasses and herbs are present in sufficient quantities, a reburn two or three years after the major burn may
handle the situation. Wright (1974) describes the many advantages of
prescribed burning and cites many examples.

Chemicals are also promising for controlling resprouts and brush
seedlings that follow a burn. In spite of these various drawbacks,
burning may be the most practical means for controlling brush in
many areas.

BULLDOZING

Brush clearing by bulldozing has become very popular in the
West, and thousands of acres are cleared this way each year. The
method is useful only on a relatively smooth land; it is rather slow and
hence restricted to limited areas. After bulldozing, there remains the
problem of burning the piled brush, reseeding the burned areas, and
controlling resprouts and brush seedlings. Under semiarid conditions
only a few species, such as live oak, resprout from roots and crowns left
in the soil; many species are completely eliminated by uprooting or by
cutting below ground level. In regions of summer rainfall, more species
tend to resprout after bulldozing; hence this method is less successful.
On small ranges where the soil is rich, the method is popular; it rapidly
and completely eliminates the existing stand and brings the land into
full production soon after clearing is completed. The method is not
applicable to rough, steep, or rocky land and is too slow to be practical
over large holdings.

SPECIAL HEAVY EQUIPMENT

Heavy weighted rollers, special discs, mowers, and equipment
such as the "bushwhacker," which pulverize brush by an action like
that of a hammer mill, are used to control brush. These tools may even
pulverize the woody material and spread it over, or work it into, the
soil. This enables the forage species to develop and to compete for
sunlight, water, and nutrients. In natural grasslands, if grazing is
managed so that the herbaceous species survive and crowd out the
brush seedlings, these methods are effective. In some situations burning in the second or third year may eliminate brush seedlings, and in
others chemicals may be used. The point to be emphasized here is that
these mechanical methods are limited to handling the existing stand of
brush and must be followed by other management and control practices if complete control of brush is to be effected. As methods in a
control program, they are excellent; as single operations, they usually

fail and may even result in thicker stands of brush than those originally present.

The mowing of moderate-sized woody species is practiced in the
Southwest. There are types of mowers that will cut not only herbaceous weeds but woody shoots of willows and salt cedars up to 2 in. in
diameter.

Grelen (1959) describes methods of mechanical preparation of pine-
planting sites in Florida sand-hill soils. A heavy, tandem, double-

FIGURE 17-4. Weighted roller for destroying brush. To do a good job, the
knives must be sharp. (Photograph by the Marden Mfg. Co. Auburndale,
Florida.)

drum brush chopper (Fig. 17-4) has proved to be the best tool for
preparing planting sites. This machine eliminates scrub oak and wire-
grass competition and leaves the topsoil in place. Heavy bulldozing
often disturbs the surface, promoting rill erosion and loss of organic
matter. Scalpers and rakes of various sorts are used; each must be tried
and tested with respect to the effects on the particular soil involved.

Chemical Methods

Although chemicals such as sodium arsenite and sodium chlorate were used for many years for controlling woody plant species
(Melander et al., 1954), other more phytotoxic and more convenient
materials are now available.

Chemicals are now being used for the control of many species including oaks, maple, mesquite, eucalyptus, gorse, manzanita, *Ce-anothus*, willow, sagebrush, coyote brush, rabbit brush, and salt cedar. Chemical treatment of woody plants may be made in the following ways: (1) *foliage sprays* to full-grown plants, to sprouts, or to seedlings, (2) *dormant sprays* to full-grown plants, (3) *basal spray* on intact bark, (4) *spray* or *liquid application* to basal cuts or frill-ringed stems, either standing plants or stumps (Coulter, 1954), and (5) soil application using granules.

Many different chemicals have been used to kill woody plants, but the principle toxic materials now employed include: (1) formulations of 2,4-D or 2,4,5-T, 2-(2,4-DP), and silvex, (2) amitrole (amino triazole) and amitrole-T, (3) Ammate (ammonium sulfamate), (4) glyphosate, (5) karbutylate (Tandex), (6) bromacil, (7) picloram, and (8) cacodylic acid.

In the treatment of woody plants with chemicals, the following factors influence the effectiveness of control: (1) species tolerance; (2) habit of growth, whether sclerophyllous (pertaining to plants with thick, leathery leaves), or nonsclerophyllous, evergreen or deciduous; (3) age and vigor of growth as reflected in the degree of cuticle development and succulence; (4) environmental factors, such as rainfall, temperature, soil moisture, or shade, as they indirectly affect plant succulence; and (5) formulation, dosage, and coverage of chemicals applied. (Mohan, 1972).

Spray treatments on trees, brush, or seedling growth may be made by aircraft, ground rig, or knapsack sprayer. Patchy brush and seedling growth may be sprayed by ground rig or knapsack sprayer. Basal and stump treatments are usually made by knapsack equipment. Many woody species are susceptible to one or more of these formulations. Where these various species occur in relatively pure stands, the particular chemical to which they are susceptible should be used; where mixed stands occur, one of the mixed "brush killers" containing both 2,4-D and 2,4,5-T should be used. As a matter of fact, the majority of woody species are sensitive to both 2,4-D and 2,4,5-T. However, there is little evidence of complementary action; i.e., each chemical in the mixture should be applied at the approximate concentration required to kill the species treated when a high degree of specificity exists.

In the formulation of these chemicals, an oil, usually diesel oil, may be necessary as a carrier. In foliage sprays on nonsclerophyllous plants or on young sclerophyllous types, water or an emulsion of 1 to 2 percent diesel oil in water is adequate. Here, care must be taken to avoid a rapid kill of leaves and thus prevent translocation of the chemical. For foliage sprays on sclerophyllous vegetation, the low-volatile esters, i.e., butoxyethanol, isooctyl, or propylene glycol butyl ether esters of the phenoxy compounds in oil emulsion or diesel oil, are used. If applied by airplane, 1 to 5 gal of oil or oil emulsion per acre as the carrier and penetrant usually proves satisfactory. For treatment of dormant plants, the esters should be applied in straight diesel oil.

AMMONIUM SULFAMATE (AMMATE)

When Ammate is used as a foliage spray on seedling and low brush, add 1 lb to each gal of water and apply as a coarse spray. A wetting agent is desirable if the foliage is waxy. When used on stumps and in cut bark and frill rings, apply a solution of 4 lb per gal of water or use the pure salt (Fig. 17–5). In general, the complete frill when Am-

FIGURE 17-5. Treating stumps with Ammate. Cutting or frilling the bark aids in penetration of the chemical. (Photograph by United Forest Service.)

mate is used results in much better control. Ammate is also useful for controlling poison ivy and poison oak.

CHLOROPHENOXY HERBICIDES

The introduction of the chlorophenoxy weed killers has presented undreamed-of opportunities in the control of woody plants. Application by airplane of 1 or 2 lb of the active chemical dissolved in 5 to 10 gal of oil or water has been effective on certain brushy species, and this method makes practical the reclamation of thousands of acres of range that have been lost to agriculture through mismanagement, weed introduction, and other processes. Already many thousands of acres of sagebrush have been successfully treated in the central, south central, and southwestern states (McIlvain and Savage, 1949). Continued research (Alley, 1956; Hyder et al., 1958a, 1958b) is proving sagebrush

control to be economical, and other range weeds are being handled
when factors governing the physiology of the plants are observed.
Moisture supply as determining vegetative vigor is probably the most
important factor (Hyder et al., 1958a; Mohan, 1972).

Studies by Sonder and Alley (1961) show that soil-moisture retention is improved by sagebrush control on areas having 100 percent

FIGURE 17-6. Sprayer for basal treatment of trees. An oil solution of 2,4–D or
2,4,5–T is used and the basal portion should be thoroughly wet to the ground
line and even below. (Photograph courtesy of Dow Chemical Co.)

control of this woody species. Where drifting is common, no differences
in snow-holding capacity of plots could be found, but where drifting
did not occur, plots having a high degree of sagebrush control retained
snow longer in the spring. This led to more uniform melting and hence
greater moisture retention by the soil.

Ester formulations of 2,4-D have proved most effective on big
sagebrush (Alley, 1956; Hyder et al., 1958a) and on green rabbit brush
and gray rabbit brush (Hyder et al., 1958b; Mohan, 1972). Weldon et al.
(1958) have found that 2 lb of 2,4-D per acre will give around 75 percent

control of sagebrush seedlings and that, with 75 percent control of mature sagebrush, range land will remain relatively free of seedlings for four years or more.

For basal and stump treatments of trees, the esters in straight oil are usually best. Small stems require much less material per inch of diameter than large stems. It is important that the base of trunk or stem be wet thoroughly down to the ground line in order to reduce sprouting (Fig. 17–6). Basal treatments when the bark has a high

FIGURE 17-7. Chemical control of trees. Left, making the cuts at the base of the trunk; center, applying the 2,4–D by means of a pressure oil can; right, treating a tree with a Reuel Little Tree Injector.

moisture content or its surface is wet are frequently less satisfactory than when the bark is dry. Penetrants may improve results (Melander et al., 1954).

Where cuts and frill rings are used, the undiluted formulation of the amine salt of 2,4-D (3 to 4 lb per gal) is adequate on many woody species. The water-soluble amines are superior to the esters when placed in cuts or frills. (Fig. 17–7; Leonard, 1957).

The cut-surface or frill-ring treatment of trees introduces the water-soluble salt of 2,4-D, 2,4,5-T, picloram, or glyphosate, directly into the open xylem tissues for absorption and translocation along the hydrostatic gradients set up by supplying liquid to the tissues. Leonard et al. (1965a, b) have studied the application of this method to a number of woody species. Since Leonard's early work (1957) this method has been used on thousands of acres of forest, woodland, and range to eradicate weedy trees (Peevy, 1973; Sterrett, 1972). Turner (1973) has confirmed the logic in using the water-soluble amine salt solution in this practice.

The hormone-type chemicals are best applied as sprays to forest lands during the period from the time the leaves are fully expanded until they start to harden off in midsummer. Sprays with 2,4,5-T are commonly required; they are less injurious to conifers than 2,4-D and may be effective even after the leaves start turning color in the autumn (Coulter, 1954). Treatments on cut stumps or through cut or frill-ringed bark seem most successful when made during summer, fall, and winter. Early spring is apparently the poorest time to make such treatments; basal applications in oil carrier follow the same rule but seem less subject to season.

Dosage rates vary widely. Some of the inherently tolerant species respond to high dosage where increasing dosage on susceptible species may not increase the effects of the treatment. Sagebrush has succumbed to 1 lb of 2,4-D per acre in water, oil, or emulsion. Some species respond to 2- to 4-lb dosage rates; a few seem to require even more chemical.

Aircraft spraying with 2,4-D, 2,4,5-T, and mixed formulations is becoming common in many forest regions (Offord and Voss, 1951; Arend and Coulter, 1955; Gysel, 1957). Alder, willow, oak, maple, aspen, and other relatively worthless species may be suppressed by such means and the stands opened up for more vigorous growth of conifers. Thinning, cut-surface chemical treatment, brush spraying, burning, and many other practices are being introduced in tree-farm management to provide optimum conditions for tree-crop growth. Roe (1959) has devised methods for accurate use of chemical sprays on small plot areas in the forest. These methods are very useful in screening and evaluating new herbicides. Peevy and Burns (1959), in Louisiana, have reported satisfactory control of blackjack oak, post oak, black oak, and sweetgum from aerial application of the butoxy-ethanol ester of 2,4,5-T at 2 lb per acre in 5 gal of solution. Gibbs (1960), in Texas, used diesel-oil solutions of the isooctyl ester of 2,4,5-T to treat sweetgum and oak trees by tree injection. Using 40 lb acid equivalent to 100 gal of diesel oil, Gibbs obtained 100 percent control of treated trees; with 20 lb, about 67 percent were killed.

Peevy (1961) studied the relations between volume, dosage, and extent of coverage in basal spraying of blackjack oak in Louisiana. Best results were obtained by using 64 ml per in. of trunk diameter of a solution containing 8 lb acid equivalent of the PGBE ester of 2,4,5-T in

100 gal of diesel oil applied in 8-, 12-, and 16-in. bands as basal sprays in February. (Fig. 17–6). In situations where volatility of the chlorophenoxy compound is a hazard, oil-soluble amine formulations and invert-emulsion formulations of heavy esters are being used. These include formulations of 2,4-D, 2,4,5-T, and mixtures of these compounds. For controlling coniferous species cacodylic acid and its salts, and the diethylene glycol ester of TCA have been introduced where mixed stands are to be treated. The TCA may be combined with 2,4-D or 2,4,5-T. Special formulations of all these materials designed for mist-blower and low-volume aerial application are available (Kirch, 1961). Krygier and Ruth (1961) have found that heavy-ester formulations of silvex and 2,4,5-T may be useful in suppressing salmonberry (*Rubus spectabilis*) in seedling stands of western hemlock and Sitka spruce. Peevy (1973) reports that bromacil is more effective than picloram in killing post oak and blackjack oak. While bromacil was best for controlling overstory species such as post and blackjack oak, picloram excelled in handling the most numerous understory plants, such as American beautyberry, huckleberry, and sassafras.

A recent report from New Zealand (Anon., 1971) states that a blend of picloram and 2,4,5-T has proved effective in eliminating gorse, broom, sweetbrier, and blackberry; other species controlled are tutsan, boxthorn, tutu, and oriental clematis.

One further development in forest-pest control is the selective elimination of mistletoe in eucalyptus with 2,4-D. Treatment involves making a series of shallow holes through the bark into the sapwood and filling these with a 10 percent solution of the amine salt of 2,4-D. This can be prepared from the 4-lb per gal formulation by mixing 1 part formulation with 4 parts water. The holes should be spaced so as to provide one hole per inch diameter of the trunk at a level of around 4 ft. This method has proved very effective in Australia. Research on control of dwarf mistletoe on coniferous trees in the United States is in progress.

Very often, after trees have been cut down, sprouts grow from below the soil line or along the sides of the stumps, and the final destruction of the stumps may involve considerable labor. Particularly is this true where many trees have been cut, as in the clearing of a hedgerow or firebreak. Sprouting stumps may be readily killed. Organic arsenicals, sodium chlorate, 2,4-D, 2,4,5-T, picloram, glyphosate, and combinations may be used as toxicants.

In using diesel oil as a carrier for herbicides to kill stumps, a number of important facts must be noted. The oil and chemicals do not translocate extensively in plant tissues; consequently, the tissue responsible for the production of sprouts must be thoroughly treated. The formulation should be applied as a fine spray; the entire surface of the stump should be thoroughly wet; to bring about complete killing, it is best to go over each stump thoroughly to assure absorption of a toxic dose. Water-soluble chemicals are effective in preventing sprouting of freshly cut stumps.

Concentrated amine solution of 2,4-D placed in cuts through the bark at the soil line is effective. Space the cuts 4 in. apart.

Efforts to control and eradicate undesirable brush on the range lands and in the forests, particularly of the western United States, have attained tremendous proportions. Numerous investigations are under way at many stations, both state and federal. A variety of methods, mechanical and chemical, have been demonstrated as economical. As stated, formulations of the heavy esters of the chlorophenoxyacetic and chlorophenoxypropionic acids and of amitrole have come to the fore as relatively cheap and effective materials to control such woody species. As the result of research and field experience, definite recommendations are issued for the control of various woody species growing under certain environmental conditions. But considerable variation occurs in the effectiveness of different formulations on a given species. In New Zealand (Upritchard, 1969) mixtures of 2,4,5-T and picloram have proved superior to either chemical alone. Similar results have been obtained in Texas (Hoffman et al., 1972).

Leonard (1956) and Leonard and Crafts (1956) have described methods that have proved effective for controlling brushy species in California. Under the semiarid conditions of western range lands, the heavy-ester forms of the phenoxy compounds have shown greater effectiveness than salts or light esters; some diesel oil in the foliage sprays improves results; diesel oil alone as carrier is best in basal sprays.

Worley, Bramble, and Byrnes (1957) describe trials with basal treatments on bear oak (*Quercus ilicifolia*) in Pennsylvania. They used the butoxyethanol ester of 2,4,5-T at a concentration of 12 lb acid equivalent per 100 gal with kerosene as the carrier. They stressed the need for covering the root collars of the plants, and they obtained their best results by early winter treatments. Volumes sufficient to cover the basal stems and root collars were required, and at least three years were needed to obtain an accurate measure of the permanent kill of their trees.

In basal treatments on intact bark, the ester forms seem best, and they are usually applied with diesel oil as the carrier; the low-volatile esters of either 2,4-D or 2,4,5-T are particularly effective on very resistant woody species. The minimum effective concentration appears to be two percent (acid-equivalent basis); the trunk should be wet from 6 to 12 in. above the ground line with enough liquid to wet the bark down into the ground. For cut-bark and frill-ring treatments, water may be used as a carrier. The amine salt formulation alone is most satisfactory. The main purpose for using the ester in oil is for putting out basal treatments with one mix for a variety of stem diameters; it is often necessary to cut into the larger stems to produce an effect. The amine, alone or in water, applied to cut surfaces, is more effective than the esters in oil, probably because it is more readily translocated. Two percent of the esters in the oil is satisfactory. With the amines, the concentration will vary with the method of application, and it may be easiest to use small quantities of undiluted amine formulation in cuts (Leonard, 1957).

FIGURE 17-8.   A power right-of-way maintained by spraying periodically with herbicides. (Photograph courtesy of John D. Farmer Jr., Virginia Electric and Power Co.)

Spraying for control of seedlings and resprouts on stumps of burned or bulldozed brush follows practically the same rules as spraying grown brush. Seedlings are more susceptible when young; as they mature, the leaves acquire a heavy cuticle and become impermeable to the chemicals. Seedlings and resprouts of the harder brush species should receive ester forms in oil carrier because the salts in water fail to penetrate in these plants. Kay, Leonard, and Street (1961) found that daubing stumps of madrone and tanoak with a 4 lb per gal formulation of the amine salt of 2,4-D proved to be the most effective method for killing them. Madrone was successfully treated in February, April, and October; tanoak, in February and October; July treatment was poor with both species. Fig. 17–8 shows a power right-of-way maintained by spraying periodically with herbicides.

In the early work on tree killing, the light aliphatic esters of 2,4-D and 2,4,5-T were applied by airplane. These produced rapid browning of the foliage but little permanent effect on the woody parts of the trees. Introduction of the low-volatile esters resulted in more extensive injury, but from a single application there was seldom complete killing. Within the past decade repeated sprays have been applied, and often almost complete killing results after a second treatment; a third spray usually completes the kill (Leonard and Carlson, 1959, 1960). This is extremely encouraging because it proves that airplane application of herbicides may be useful in tree and brush control over the millions of acres of woodland and scrub that cover large areas of the earth's surface. No other method is rapid enough to cope with the tremendous areas involved. And airplane application will pay whenever the economics of livestock or forest-products production reaches a level where two or three applications of a herbicide can be compensated by the increased production that results. Such applications have been made at a price around $5 per acre (Arend and Coulter, 1955); they cost more today.

Introduction of the propionic analogues of 2,4-D, 2,4,5-T, and silvex is another advance in woody-plant control. These compounds have broadened the spectrum to cover many species of oak, cherry, maple, and other difficult woody plants that the acetic compounds would not control. Amitrole and amitrole-T are additional useful compounds.

Picloram as described in Chapter 12 is an extremely effective woody-plant herbicide. It is used in quantities in the control of woody plants along rights-of-way, on roadsides, firebreaks, and tank farms, and wherever woody plants present a problem.

Ivens (1971) reports on the use of picloram and 2,4-D for killing brush species in Kenya. Treatment in May during the latter part of the rainy season gave the best results. Even where the kill was less than 100 percent, Ivens points out that many of the resprouting trees had been killed to ground level; the resprouts growing in the grass were subject to grazing and caused little interference with the use of the forage by cattle.

In forest nurseries, desmetryne or pyrazone have been combined with amitrole to give more complete weed control. In transplanted trees, atrazine, lenacil, linuron, propachlor and simazine have all proved useful. Where grasses predominate, combinations of amitrole plus simazine and dalapon plus simazine are effective in humid climates.

In the use of chemicals to prevent resprouting of stumps, Leonard and Murphy (1965) found that rainfall moistening a chemically-treated stump increases the movement of the herbicide (2,4-D, 2,4,5-T) into the stump. Ivens (1972) in controlled experiments found this same effect when he applied picloram salt (Tordon 22K) and 2,4,5-T amine to cut stem pieces of *Populus gelrica* Ait. More downward movement of the herbicide into the cuttings occurred when they were sealed at the base with wax or left in the air to dry than when the stems stood in 25 mm of water.

In the clearing of land, in the maintenance of firebreaks, and often in ordinary gardening, it is necessary to kill trees or to prevent resprouting of stumps. Considerable research has been conducted during the last few years that is designed to standardize stump-killing procedure and to utilize chemicals in an improvement of methods.

It has long been recognized that, if the bark of an isolated tree is severed by girdling through the cambium layer, the tree will eventually die through starvation of its roots, and the continued destruction of resprouts around the stumps, whether done mechanically, chemically, or by the browsing of sheep or goats, will starve the roots and kill the stumps, providing there are no root grafts with neighboring trees.

DICAMBA

This herbicide may be used at any time by injection into frill rings or by tree injector (Figs. 16–6, 7, 8) to kill a large number of tree species, including red alder, white ash, aspen, basswood, beech, birch, dogwood, sweetgum, hickory, red and sugar maples, blackjack oak, post oak, persimmon, white pine, shortleaf pine, and others.

Bromacil and karbutilate granules are effective in controlling weedy trees and brush in drainage ditches, railroad rights-of-way, and industrial sites; rainfall or sprinkling is necessary to wash the chemical into the root zone. These chemicals are general, soil-borne herbicides; they usually kill all plant species on the treated area. Their great advantage is their convenience. They may be transported into inaccessible areas by pack mules or dropped from a helicopter.

With the greatly increasing demands on our forests for lumber, fiber, humus, turpentine, and organic chemical materials, it is evident that tree weeding will increase in importance through the years. To date, formulations of 2,4-D, 2,4,5-T, and mixtures of the two have proved most useful in controlling weedy trees. In addition, 2-(2,4-DP), silvex, dicamba, picloram karbutilate, glyphosate, tebuthiuron, and amitrole are finding special uses; other chemicals will undoubtedly be added to this list. One will find, in many publications and reports, tables listing species "susceptible" and "resistant" to different formulations. These tables apply only on a regional basis, or they may be quite general. Because they are voluminous, they cannot be reproduced in a book of this sort. The following references, listed at the end of the chapter, will be found useful to those who are interested in control of woody plants: Anon., 1959; Burt, 1957; Cornelius and Talbot 1955; Fischer et al., 1959; Klingman and Wilcox, 1960; Leonard et al. 1965c; Leonard and Harvey, 1956; Melander, 1949, 1950; Melander et al., 1954; Mohan, 1972; Offord et al., 1962; Rudolph and Watt, 1956; Sampson and Shultz, 1957; Theisen, 1967; Wright, 1974; Young et al., 1948, 1950.

REFERENCES

Alley, H. P. 1956. Chemical control of big sagebrush and its effect upon production and utilization of native grass species. *Weeds* 4(2):164–173.

Anon. 1959. Brush control practices for right-of-way maintenance. *U.S. Dept. Agr. REA Bul. Electric* 131–17, Telephone 441–2. April.

Anon., 1971. Facts from farmer use and trials of Tordon brush killer 520. *Service*, Spring-Summer 1971. p. 10–13.

Arend, J. L., and L. L. Coulter. 1955. Aerial applications of herbicides. A promising method for releasing conifers. *Down to Earth* 11(1):18–20.

Burt, E. O. 1957. Review of literature on brush control. *U.S.A.F. Air Res. and Devlpmt. Command Tech. Note 1*. 34 pp. July.

Cornelius D. R. and M. W. Talbot. 1955. Rangeland improvement through seeding and weed control on east slope Sierra Nevada and on southern Cascade Mountains. *U.S. Dept. Agr. Agr. Handb.* 88.

Coulter, L. L. 1954. Some aspects of right-of-way brush control with 2,4,5-T and 2,4-D. *Weeds* 3(1):21–27.

Fisher C. E., C. H. Meadors, R. Behrens, E. D. Robinson, P. T. Marion, and H. L. Morton. 1959. Control of mesquite on grazing lands. *Tex. Agr. Expt. Bul.* 935. 24 pp. August.

Gibbs, C. B. 1960. Iso-octyl ester of 2,4,5-T in hardwood control. *Weeds* 8(3):462–463.

Grelen, H. E. 1959. Mechanical preparation of pine planting sites in Florida sand hills. *Weeds* 7(2):184–188.

Gysel, L. W. 1957. Effects of different methods of releasing pine on wildlife food and cover. *Down to Earth* 13(2):2–3.

Hoffman, G. O., M. E. Merkle, and R. H. Haas. 1972. Controlling mesquite with TORDON 225 mixture herbicide in the Texas blackland prairie. *Down to Earth* 24:(4):16–19.

Hyder, D. N., W. R. Furtick, and F. A. Sneva. 1958a. Differences among butyl, ehtyl and isopropylester formulations of 2,4-D, 2,4,5-T, and MCPA in the control of big sagebrush. *Weeds* 6(2):194–197.

————, F. A. Sneva, D. D. Chilcote, and W. R. Furtick. 1958b. Chemical control of rabbitbrush with emphasis upon simultaneous control of big sagebrush. *Weeds* 6(3):289–297.

Ivens G. W. 1971. Seasonal differences in kill of two Kenya bush species after foliar herbicide treatment. *Weed Res.* 11:150–158.

————. 1972. Movement of herbicide applied to cut ends of *Populus gelrica* stems. *Weed Res.* 12:279–283.

Kay, B. L., O. A. Leonard, and J. E. Street. 1961. Control of madrone and tanoak stump sprouting. *Weeds* 9(3):369–373.

Kirch, J. H. 1961. Woody plant control. Amchem. Experimental materials for the 1961 season. Feb. 24. pp. 7–10. (Mimeographed report.)

Klingman, D. L. 1970. Brush and weed control on forage and grazing lands. *F.A.O. Internatl. Conf. on Weed Control.* Davis, Calif., p. 401–424.

Klingman, G. C., and M. Wilcox. 1960. Part 1. Railroad weed control, North Carolina State College. Part 2. Chemical control of vegetation. 1959 AAR Report reprinted from *Amer. Ry. Engin. Assoc. Bul.* 556. February.

Krygier, J. T., and R. H. Ruth. 1961. Effect of herbicides on Salmonberry and on Sitka spruce and western hemlock seedlings. *Weeds* 9(3):416–422.

Leonard, O. A. 1956. Studies of factors affecting the control of chamise (*Adenostoma fasciculatum*) with herbicides. *Weeds* 4(3):241–254.

————. 1957. Effect of phenoxy herbicide concentrates applied to cuts of sprouting tree species. *Weeds* 5(4):291–303.

———— and C. E. Carlson. 1959. Aircraft spraying of blue oak. *Calif. Agr.* 13(12):3.

———— and ————. 1960. Kill of blue oak and poison oak by aircraft spraying with phenoxy herbicides. *Weeds* 8(4):625–630.

———— and A. S. Crafts. 1956. Translocation of herbicides: III. Uptake and distribution of radioactive 2,4-D by brush species. *Hilgardia* 26(6):366–415.

———— and W. A. Harvey. 1956. Chemical control of woody plants in California. *Calif. Agr. Expt. Sta. Bul.* 755.

———— and A. H. Murphy. 1965a. Relationship between herbicide movement and stump sprouting. *Weeds* 13:26–30.

————, R. C. Glenn and D. E. Bayer. 1965b. Studies on the cut surface method 1. Translocation in blue oak and madrone. *Weeds* 13:346–351.

————, C. E. Carlson, and D. E. Bayer. 1965c. Studies on the cut surface 2. Control of blue oak and madrone. *Weeds* 13:352–356.

Love, R. M. 1961. Forage. In *Range, Pastures, and Their Improvement,* eds. Hughes, Metcalf, and Heath. Department of Publications, State University of Iowa, Iowa City

McIlvain, E. H., and D. A. Savage. 1949. Spraying 2,4-D by airplane on sand sagebrush and other plants of the Southern Great Plains. *Jour. Range Mgmt.* 2:43–52.

Melander, L. W. 1949. Resumé of 1949 progress made in research of woody plants. *No. Cent. Weed Control Conf., 6th Ann. Meeting Res. Rpt.* pp. 137–177.

_____. 1950. Control of woody plants. *No. Cent. Weed Control Conf., 7th Ann. Meeting Res. Rpt. Sum.* pp. 227–270.

_____, E. A. Lungren, and W. M. Watson. 1954. Killing native barberry with hormone-type herbicides. *Weeds* 3(2):123–130.

Mohan, J. M. 1972. 14 years of rabbitbrush control in Central Oregon. *Jour. Range Mgmt.* 26:448–451.

Offord, H. R., and C. M. Voss. 1951. Fogging Ribes, white pine, and brush with 2,4-D by helicopter. *Weeds* 1(1):61–69.

_____, V. D. Moss, W. V. Benedict, H. E. Swanson, and A. London. 1962. Improvements in the control of ribes by chemical and mechanical methods. *U.S. Dept. Agr. Cir.* 906:1–72.

Peevy, F. A. 1961. Control of blackjack oak by basal spraying with 2,4,5-T. *Weeds* 9(1):50–53.

_____. 1973. Bromacil and picloram under Southern upland hardwoods. *Weeds Sci.* 21:54–56.

_____ and P. Y. Burns. 1959. Effectiveness of aerial application of herbicides for hardwood control in Louisiana. *Weeds* 7(2): 178–183.

Roe, E. I. 1959. Determining minimum amounts of herbicide needed for aerial brush control. *Weeds* 7(2):178–183.

Rudolph, P. O., and R. F. Watt. 1956. Chemical control of brush and trees in the Lake States. *Lake States Forest Expt. Sta. Station Paper* 41. October, 57 pp.

Sampson, A. W., and A. M. Schultz. 1957. Control of brush and undesirable trees. *Unasylva.* 49 pp.

Sonder, L. W., and H. P. Alley. 1961. Soil-moisture retention and snow-holding capacity as affected by the chemical control of big sagebrush (*Artemisia tridentata* Nutt.) *Weeds* 9(1):27–35.

Sterrett, J. P. 1972. Injection of red maple and hickory with picloram, 2,4-D, and 2,4,5-T. *Down to Earth* 27(2):18–21.

Theisen, P. A. 1967. Chemical weeding and release of conifers in southwestern Oregon. In *Herbicides and Vegetation Management. A Symposium of the School of Forestry.* Corvallis: Oregon State University, Sept. 7, 1967, pp. 152–160.

Turner, J. D. 1973. Laboratory experiments on "cut bark" treatments with herbicides using cutting of *Populus euroamericana.* '1–78'. *Weed Res.* 13:91–100.

Upritchard, E. A. 1969. Formulations of picloram with 2,4,5-T for brushweed control. *New Zealand Weed and Pest Control Conf. Proc.* p. 180–186. 1969.

Weldon, L. W., D. W. Bohmont, and H. P. Alley. 1958. Reestablishment of sagebrush following chemical control. *Weeds* 6(3):298–303.

Worley, D. P., W. C. Bramble, and W. R. Byrnes. 1957. Investigations of the use of 2,4,5-T esters as a basal spray in the control of Bear Oak. *Weeds* 5(2):121–132.

Wright, H. A. 1974. Range burning. *Jour. Range Mgmt.* 27:5–11.

Young, V. A., F. R. Anderwald, and W. C. MCully. 1948. Brush problems on Texas ranges. *Tex. Agr. Expt. Sta. Misc. Pub.* 21. 19 pp.

———, C. E. Fisher, R. A. Darrow, W. C. McCully, and D. W. Young, 1950. Recent developments in the chemical control of brush on Texas ranges. *Tex. Agr. Expt. Sta. Bul.* 721. 18 pp.

18

Weed Control
in Irrigation and Drainage Ditches,
Lakes, and Streams

The growth and spread of weeds in and along irrigation ditches, drains, lakes, and streams comprise one of our most serious weed problems (Anon., 1949; Blackburn and Sutton, 1970; Shaw and Timmons, 1949; Timmons, 1960; Timmons, 1970a,b). These weeds are of three types: (1) ditchbank weeds, (2) emersed and submerged aquatic weeds attached to the banks or bottom, and (3) free-floating aquatics.

DITCHBANK WEEDS

Most common weeds thrive on ditchbanks, where they find the soil surface well drained and, at the same time, well supplied with subsoil moisture. Wilkinson (1961) has shown that the growth of water-stargrass, a common aquatic weed, may be closely correlated with light intensity. In a study of growth with light intensity over a period from April to October, growth was highly dependent upon the intensity of light. Figure 18–1 shows an irrigation ditch in the spring before the irrigating season had started. In addition to hindering the flow of water, weeds ripen millions of seeds that float out onto the land and provide a constant source of infestation. This figure also shows a lined ditch during the irrigation season. The banks have been sterilized to provide for free flow of the water and elimination of weeds and weed seeds.

In some irrigated regions it has become common practice to plow ditches during the winter. This practice has two drawbacks: (1) it is

340

expensive and requires time and special equipment; (2) in many regions, it results in erosion (Fig. 18–2). The colloidal fractions of the soil are eventually washed away, and the ditch becomes wide and inefficient. Relocation of the ditch utilizes valuable new land and leaves in the place of the old ditch a strip of leached, sandy, infertile soil.

FIGURE 18-1.   Top, an unlined irrigation ditch in the spring before cleaning; bottom, a cement-lined ditch with sterilized strips along the banks. Weed-free and clean, this ditch delivers a maximum volume of clean water.

Irrigation engineers recommend concrete lining as an answer to the ditch-weed problem. Often, difficulties are encountered even after lining has been installed. Tall weeds line the ditches and eventually fall in, gathering silt and stopping flow of the water.

Even in cases where the banks of a canal have been periodically disced to control weeds, trailing weeds grow along the edge of the lining and drop seeds into the water. Bermudagrass and puncturevine growing along the concrete lining of irrigation ditches may trail for many feet. Gathering silt, these weeds build up a berm that must be removed each winter by hand labor. Figure 18-1, bottom shows what can be accomplished by soil sterilization in the way of weed control. Such a ditch is pleasing to the eye, carries water with maximum efficiency, and does not spread weeds onto fertile acres.

FIGURE 18-2. An irrigation ditch plowed to remove weed growth. This practice leads to undesirable erosion.

The gradual spread of watergrass and similar weeds throughout irrigated lands is forcing a change in ditch-weed-control methods. Concrete lining and ditchbank sterilization are gaining in popularity, and complete weed control will eventually be practiced in most irrigated regions.

Planting banks with pasture grasses and clovers is a promising method, according to experiences on Federal Reclamation Projects (Anon., 1949). Sod grasses stabilize the banks, keep out weeds, and at the same time furnish pasturage for livestock. On northern projects, brome grass and crested wheatgrass are planted on the drier portions of the banks, and strawberry clover is planted on the moist strip at the water's edge. Search is being made for grasses suitable for use on ditchbanks in the Southwest. Many of these ditches are now infested with Bermudagrass and Johnsongrass. Although they exclude other plants and stabilize the banks, they are considered weeds in cultivated fields and, with heavy pasturing, Johnsongrass tends to be weakened.

Burning and chemicals (Chapter 6) are coming into use to control noxious perennials, willows, and poison hemlock, both on Bureau of Reclamation projects and in irrigation districts (Fig. 18–3).

AQUATIC WEEDS

Although ditchbank weeds are difficult to control, emersed and submerged aquatic weeds constitute an even more difficult problem because part or all of the weed is under water. Aquatic weeds are of three types: submerged, emersed, and surface.

SUBMERGED AQUATICS

These weeds are normally attached to the bottom of a ditch and grow entirely beneath the surface of the water. They cause the most trouble from the standpoint of reduced water flow in irrigation ditches. The most common submerged aquatics are sago pondweed (also called horsetail moss), stonewort, water milfoil, cabomba, and waterweed (*Elodea*).

EMERSED AQUATICS

These are rooted below the surface, but the plants rise above the water line. They have a wide distribution and do much damage. Besides hindering the flow of water, they encourage mosquito propagation, thus adding to the mosquito-control problem. The most common emersed aquatics are tule, cattail, bur reed, sedge, rush, arrowhead, burhead, and water plantain.

SURFACE AQUATICS

Some of these float freely on the water, while others are attached to the sides or bottom of the ditch and float only in a fixed area. The following are a few examples: yellow waterweed, water hyacinth, water lettuce, broad-leaved pondweeds, parrot feather, and pennywort.

CONTROL OF ALGAE

Algae frequently constitute a growth that may interfere with the flow of water in irrigation canals and drainage ditches. Copper com-

FIGURE 18-3.   Selective spraying of canal banks to eliminate noxious weeds. Top, fixed-wing plane; center, helicopter; bottom, a narrow strip has been sterilized to prevent weed seeds from falling into the water.

pounds, chiefly copper sulfate (blue vitriol), have been used effectively to destroy such growth. The practice is to place several pounds in a gunny sack and to suspend it in the water; the sacks should be placed 200 to 300 ft apart. Rosin amine D acetate (RADA) is also an effective algicide. Experience shows that the composition of the water in-

FIGURE 18-4. Dredge used to clean cattails and tules from irrigation and drainage ditches. (Photograph courtesy of Bureau of Reclamation, U.S. Department of the Interior.)

fluences the effectiveness of both copper sulfate and RADA. It is believed that the presence of certain salts, probably chlorides and sulfates, in the water causes the precipitation of the algicides and thus reduces their effectiveness. Aqualin kills algae as well as the higher plants that grow in water.

METHODS OF CONTROL

Aquatic weeds submit to several control methods.

DREDGING

This is probably the commonest way of cleaning weeds from drains and ditches. A dragline dredge may be equipped with a bucket or with a weed fork or other special tools. While the bucket dredge (Fig. 18–4) will do a fairly thorough job of removing most of the weeds, it will also take out a lot of mud in the process. The weed fork will drag out plant growth but leave most of the mud behind. Usually, the more effectively the weeds are removed, the more likely the mud will be removed along with them.

Until recently, dredging was the only available method for many ditch-cleaning jobs, but it has many drawbacks:

1. It can be used only in open ditches.
2. The ditch must be accessible from at least one side.
3. It usually enlarges the ditch and may change its carrying capacity.
4. It may deepen the ditch so that water stands in the bottom and encourages the growth of cattails and tules.
5. It usually leaves a bank or ridge of "spoil" (mud and weed

growth) that must be spread if the underlying land is to be used.

6. It is a slow process.
7. It is expensive.

The cost depends upon the volume and type of weed growth and upon the size of the ditch. Weed forking of a particular ditch may cost $100 per mile. Ridding the same ditch of cattails or tules might require draglining at a cost varying from $10 to as high as $1000 or more per mile. In some situations, a single dredging may last several years; in others, dredging may have to be done once a year or more often to maintain full water capacity. Furthermore, because of the cost, dredging is usually delayed until the weeds are fairly thick, so that the ditch functions for a long period at reduced capacity. Ditches must, therefore, be built oversized to ensure sufficient water delivery—an expensive and inefficient practice. About the only advantage to dredging is that it removes all types of weeds equally effectively.

DRYING

This is a simple, inexpensive, and very satisfactory method for use on submerged aquatics. In districts where water can be withdrawn and the ditch bottoms drained, the tops of underwater weeds will dry up after several days' exposure to sun and air. If clumps of weeds clog the ditch bottom, a plow may be used to open a furrow so that the water will drain away.

The principal drawbacks to this method are that it is ineffective against emersed weeds and some of the floating species, and it requires interrupting the use of the ditch, often during critical dry periods in summer.

HAND CLEANING

This is used in many regions, often being carried on in winter when farm hands are not otherwise occupied. The men cut and remove the accumulated weed growth with heavy knives and hooks. Cattails and tules that are dense and dry are burned. Willows are often slashed and burned along with other dead vegetation that occupies the banks.

BURNING

This is a method of weed control that works for both aquatic weeds and the dry-land species that infest the banks above the water line.

Among the many weeds constituting a problem in the Imperial Valley in California are the tules, cattails, and willows that grow in the water, and the cottonwoods, bamboos, arrowweeds, wild asparagus, and hosts of annual weeds that grow on the ditchbank. Experience in this district has proven that the best results are obtained by first searing the green vegetation followed by complete burning in 10 to 12 days. In searing, a hot flame is passed over the vegetation at such a rate that the plants wilt but are are not charred. Searing kills many plant cells which, in drying, release toxic substances that injure all tissues above ground. These tissues dry rapidly and after about 10 days burn freely from their own heat. The burner is used only to kindle the dry material and to burn the more resistant species. Tules and cattails are eliminated by two years of consistent burning; willows, cotton-woods, and perennial grasses are discouraged but not completely des-troyed. Bamboo requires more drastic treatment.

CHAINING

This is a widely used, relatively inexpensive method. A heavy chain is attached between two teams or tractors on opposite banks of the ditch. As these move, the chain drags over the weeds and breaks them off. Chaining is usually not done until a ditch has become severe-ly clogged, which means that, as with dredging, the ditch operates efficiently for only short intervals after each chaining.

Chaining is most effective for removing submerged aquatics. If all the vegetation is not broken loose the first time, running the chain back in the opposite direction is usually successful. In controlling the cattails, tules, bur reed, arrowhead, burhead, and other emersed species, repeated chainings may be necessary. If chaining is to be really successful, a consistent program must be followed. Old growth must be removed at the beginning of the season, and chaining should then be done whenever new shoots rise a foot above the water level.

There are several disadvantages to the chaining method:

1. In addition to the crew operating the chain, 4 to 20 men are usually required to remove loosened vegetation from the ditch. This may be done with pitchforks or, as in some dis-tricts, with power-operated forks.
2. Chaining will not eradicate weed growth above water, on the ditchbank.
3. In newly or sparsely infested ditches, chaining breaks up sub-merged aquatics which then float downstream, spreading the infestation.
4. Chaining stirs up silt, wears away the ditchbank, and may seriously damage cement or Gunite linings.
5. Cleaning cannot be done near structures, particularly where reverse chaining is necessary.
6. Some water weeds tend to wind around the chain and make it ineffective.
7. Both ditchbanks must be passable.

8. Because of headgates, turnouts, and other structures, a cer-
    tain amount of hand cleaning is required to supplement
    chaining.

In addition to dredges and chains, there are numerous other devices for cleaning ditches, such as special dredgers, discs, revolving
knives, mowing machines, and saw boats. Most of these are useful, but
some may change the depth or shape of the ditch and others may stir
up the sediment which is useful in helping reduce seepage. These
machines may be difficult to maintain mechanically, and generally,
through the years, they only partly relieve the costly, tedious job of
cleaning.

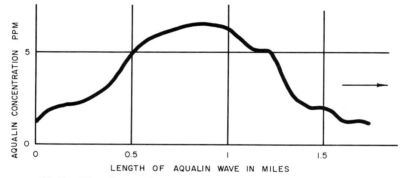

FIGURE 18-5.   The shape of an Aqualin wave, 8 miles below the point of
application. It took this wave 4 hr to pass a given point. The application
involved injection to give 64 ppm for 31 min. The ditch carries 300 cu ft per
sec. (Diagram courtesy of Shell Development Co.)

CHEMICAL TREATMENTS

Many chemicals are now available for use as weed killers; all of
them are effective if applied to the right weeds at the right time. The
operator's problem is one of knowing what materials to use and where,
when, and how to use them intelligently.

ACROLEIN

The compound acrylaldehyde, 2-propenal has been named Aqualin. It is an active chemical that destroys plant cells. It has high
lachrymatory activity (tear gas) in man, and has to be applied only by
licensed operators (Overbeek, Hughes and Blondeau, 1959).

Application is done by pumping the liquid into the water and
allowing it to move as a blanket over and through the aquatic weeds
(Fig. 18-5). Since within practical limits the concentration applied

multiplied by the time of exposure is a constant, the herbicide may be introduced over a time period ranging from 45 min. to 5 hr.

Temperature is important; at 60°F the dosage must be twice that at 80°F so that dosage must be scaled to temperature as well as to plant population. In fast-flowing streams, contact is not so thorough as in slow, so that again dosage must be increased when flow is greater than 25 ft per sec.

Aqualin is used up in its lethal reaction with plant tissue; also a

FIGURE 18-6. Application of Aqualine (acrolein) in an irrigation canal. Top, before treatment; bottom, after treatment. (Photographs courtesy of Shell Development Co.)

certain amount is lost by volatilization. For these reasons the blanket of treated water must be reinforced periodically. However, in contrast with solvent naphtha, Aqualin is effective for distances up to 15 miles from the point of application. Fig. 18-6 shows the effect of Aqualin on aquatic vegetation.

For water temperature above 70°F and water velocity 2.5 ft per sec or less, suggested dosages for Aqualin are 1 to 2 gal per cu ft per sec; for temperatures below 70°F, 2 to 3 gal. Fluorescein may be added to the water to follow its course along the ditch; a quantitative test using potassium permanganate is sensitive to 1 ppm.

Table 18-1 shows the results of the use of Aqualin in irrigation canals. In ponds, reservoirs, or lakes the exposure time is greater so less

Table 18-1. Effect of Aqualin Herbicide and Chaining on the Maximum Water-carrying Capacity of a Large Irrigation Canal. (Data reprinted from Proceedings of the 4th British Weed Control Conference.)

Initial capacity, cfs	Treatment	Capacity cfs	% Increase
311	150 gal Aqualin	552	78
282	Chaining	344	22
344 (after chaining)	100 gal Aqualin	479	48, in addition to the 22% above
253	Chaining	253	No effect
253	280 gal Aqualin	462	83

chemical is required; for temperature above 70°F, 0.5 to 2 gal per acre-foot (1.5 to 6 ppm) are recommended; below 70°F, 1 to 3 gal.

Aqualin has proved to be very low in toxicity to most crop plants; if the concentration in the irrigation water is below 15 ppm, no damage to crops will result from use of the water. Fish are susceptible and may be killed by Aqualin at concentrations of 1 to 5 ppm. In slow moving or still water, fish will swim away from the treated water; in lakes and ponds, if part of the area is treated and then the remainder after 48 hrs, little damage to fish will result.

CONTACT SPRAYS

These may be used on all emersed weed growth above the water line and on common ditchbank weeds. These sprays include diesel, smudge-pot, and other fuel and waste oils and many special commercial products. Fortified-oil emulsions, involving oil carriers, toxic fortifying agents, and emulsion stabilizers, may also be used. A useful formula for a pentachlorophenol concentrate contains ½lb of pentachlorophenol and ½lb of oil-soluble emulsion stabilizer per gal of aromatic oil. This concentrate may be emulsified with water to form a toxic contact spray. Mixtures containing 4 to 20 gal of concentrate per 100 gal of spray are useful. Such commercial products as Dow General weed killer and Sinox General herbicides may be used to formulate fortified-oil-emulsion sprays.

COPPER SULFATE PENTAHYDRATE

This chemical has been used for years to control algae in lakes and streams; it is commonly used in irrigation canals in the Western states. Alkaline waters tend to precipitate it and repeated applications may be required.

COPPER-AMINE COMPLEX

A complex of copper triethanol-amine is used to control filamentous, planktonic, and Chara-type algae in still and moving water; application in cement-lined ditches should be made as soon as the growth becomes visible. There are no restrictions on the use of the treated water; it may be used immediately for swimming, fishing, irrigation, or domestic purposes.

DICHLOBENIL

Granules of dichlobenil may be used in early spring before weeds start growing to control elodea, water milfoil, naiads, coontail, chara, and potamogeton species; it does not harm fish, but treated water should not be used to irrigate crops nor for human consumption. Fish in the water should not be used before 90 days from treatment.

DICHLONE

Dichlone is an algacide used to control bloom producing bluegreen algae only. Normally used as a fungicide, this material should not be applied to potable water.

2,4–D

This hormone-type weed killer is proving valuable for control of water hyacinth (Fig. 18-7), water primrose, pennywort (*Hydrocotyle* sp.), *Sagittaria* and *Alisma* app., and other floating and emersed water weeds. Aldrich and Otto (1959) studied the translocation of 2,4-D in *Potamogeton pectinatus* using ^{14}C-labeled 2,4-D-1-C^{14}. By separating the foliar region of the plant from the end that bore roots, they were able to show that this compound moved from leaves to roots quite freely, but from roots to leaves scarcely at all. This again indicates symplastic movement with the assimilate stream and serves to define the conditions under which one might hope

FIGURE 18-7.   Control of water hyacinth by 2,4–D. Top, a thick growth of the weeds; center, weed dying as a result of spraying; bottom, clear channel after the weeds have sunk and disintegrated. (Photographs courtesy of Boyce Thompson Institute for Plant Research, Inc.)

to control this weed with 2,4-D. This compound is also useful to control water hemlock, milkweed, and other poisonous species often found on ditchbanks and in drains. The ester forms of the chemical are most effective on the waxy leaves of aquatic plants but, because it is highly volatile in this form, 2,4-D should not be used near sensitive crops, such as cotton, tomatoes, black-eyed peas, or sweet potatoes. The amine salts are less volatile, but they too should not be allowed to contaminate water which may be used on susceptible crop plants. Willow, cottonwood, tamarisk, arrowweed, and others are common ditchbank weeds which may be killed by 2,4-D.

Some field experiments indicate fairly satisfactory control of cattail employing a combination of TCA and 2,4-D, to which is added a wetting agent. 2,4,5-T is proving useful to control wild rose, blackberries, poison ivy, and other woody plants on ditchbanks. Amitrole and amitrole-T are effective for controlling cattails and woody ditchbank weeds.

Granular forms of herbicides are coming into extensive use in controlling aquatic weeds. Granular silvex is very effective against submerged water weeds, granular diuron and simazine are being used against many ditchbank weeds, and sodium arsenite, recommended for years, is still proving useful in controlling *Elodea canadensis*.

A method that has proved effective in some regions is the use of 2,4-D esters impregnated on micronized sulfur. A successful formulation includes 12 lb of the ethyl ester of 2,4-D and 6 to 18 lb of sulfur per acre treated. These are mixed in 200 gal of water with an adequate surfactant and sprayed onto the surface of the lake or pond. The sulfur acts as a carrier to hold the 2,4-D which goes to the bottom on the sulfur and is slowly released for absorption by the weeds. Micronized 2,4-D acid has also proved useful for water-weed control, principally in static water.

DIQUAT

This contact herbicide has proved effective in the control of certain aquatic weeds. It should be applied before the weed growth reaches the surface of the water. It is effective against bladderwort, coontail, elodea, naiad, water milfoil, and pondweeds. Spirogyra, pithophora, and some other algae are susceptible. Applied with surfactant to cattails, it kills the top growth. Combined with copper sulfate and triethanolamine, it kills a wide variety of submerged weeds, including hydrilla which tolerates diquat alone; many algae are controlled.

ENDOTHALL

The herbicide endothall (Chapter 12) has been found to be effective in the control of aquatic weeds, including algae, without harming fish or wildlife. For this purpose it is offered as either a liquid or a granular formulation. The liquid may be sprayed on the surface for control of emersed aquatic weeds or injected beneath the surface for submerged weeds. It is active at concentrations of a few parts per million in the water.

Experiments have shown that concentrations up to 100 ppm will not harm trout, salmon, or bass, and the herbicide has no tendency to accumulate in fish.

In the granular form, endothall may be simply sprinkled uniformly over the surface of a lake or reservoir with satisfactory results. Periodic treatments may be made on resprouting species. Endothall is somewhat irritating to the eyes and skin, and one should follow instructions on the label in handling this chemical.

Bassweed, bur reed, coontail, milfoil, a number of pondweeds, and waterstargrass are controlled by endothall. If silvex is included in the treatment, the above weeds plus fanwort, lotus, water cress, water weed, arrowhead, spike rush, water lily, water hyacinth, and water primrose are controlled.

FENAC

Industrial fenac is used on aquatic weeds in exposed soil to bring them under control. The water should be drawn down wherever possible. Fenac pellets applied from a boat have controlled emersed aquatic weeds on the bottom of shallow lakes.

Karbutilate, a new, selective, soil-borne herbicide combining the properties of urea and carbamate toxicants, is proving effective for controlling many annual and some perennial ditchbank weeds.

SILVEX ESTERS

Applied in spring or early summer, silvex esters will control such emersed aquatics as alligator weed, arrowhead, pickerelweed, and water lily. Reapply when regrowth reaches a height of 4–8 inches. In lakes treat only a portion at one time. The potassium salt of silvex is also used to control aquatic weeds.

SOLVENT NAPHTHA

This material gives effective control of submerged aquatics at very reasonable costs (Shaw and Timmons, 1949); (Fig. 18–8). Solvent naphtha is obtained from either coal tar or petroleum and is used commercially as a paint thinner. Chemically, it is benzene substituted with aliphatic groups.

To keep naphtha in a stable emulsion for use as a weed killer, an oil-soluble stabilizer must be used with it. Mahogany soap at 5 percent by volume is recommended for this purpose. It should be thoroughly dissolved in the naphtha before application. Since the term "mahogany soap" is applied broadly to petroleum sodium sulfonates of different types, the product should be bought under a trade name, such as Oronite wetting agent, Ortho emulsifier, oil-soluble Santomerse or Span, or any similar standard stabilizer. The oil companies have tested various mixtures containing both naphtha and a stabilizer, some of which are available for aquatic-weed control. Experience shows that temperature affects the stability of emulsions of solvents in ditch water. The U.S. Bureau of Reclamation recommends using 10 percent emulsifier for waters below 70°F, 7.5 percent for waters between 60 and 70°F, and 5 percent for waters above 70°F.

FIGURE 18-8. Chemical being applied in an irrigation ditch. The white blanket should be maintained for from 30 to 60 min. (From Calif. Agr. Ext. Serv. Cir. 158.)

In early experiments with naphthas on aquatic weeds in ditches, the recommended treatment was a concentration of 185ppmv for 1 hr. This is equal to 5 gal of chemical per cubic foot per second of flow applied during 1 hr. This amount was sufficient for the control of many weed species, but much higher concentrations were required to control sago pondweed. Treatments at 600 to 700 ppm killed *Elodea* and *Chara* spp. but gave only about 50 percent injury on mature sago pondweed. Treatment at 1,400 ppm killed sago pondweed if the blanket was reinforced each mile at a rate equal to 500 ppm. This required about 160 gal for the first mile and 53 gal for each additional mile.

Use the following formula for finding the concentration of the chemical, applied in parts per million of any chemical used:

$$\frac{\text{gal chemical} \times \text{wt of chemical per gal} \times 1{,}000{,}000}{\text{cu ft per sec flow} \times 62.4 \times 60 \times \text{min applied}} = \text{ppm}$$

A publication of the Bureau of Reclamation (Anon., 1949) recommends application at the rate of 300 ppm for 30 min. Because water temperature, weed species, and other factors are involved in these treatments, it is suggested that preliminary trials be run before extensive treatments are made with solvent naphtha.

Naphthas suitable for use as aquatic-weed killers are lighter than water and must be thoroughly mixed to ensure good distribution in the ditch water. If the emulsion breaks, the naphtha floats to the top and evaporates.

Since naphthas vary in their chemical make-up, they also vary in toxicity. Because of this, any naphtha to be used for aquatic-weed control should be tested in a small area before being used in quantity.

Although concentrations ranging from 600 to 1,400 ppm may be required, treatment with naphtha is relatively inexpensive when compared with dredging or hand cleaning. The price range is 18 to 40 cents per gallon, with an average of 30 cents for petroleum products. Commercial products combining naphtha and an emulsifier are available at a somewhat higher price.

Caution: Naphthas are highly inflammable. Never use them near an open flame. Even the gas which remains after the drums are emptied will explode if ignited. Naphtha fumes are reported to be toxic to waterfowl.

In purchasing solvent naphtha the following specifications should be used:

Flash point, °F, not less than	80
ASTM D-86, distillation °F:	
Starting point.	278
Not more than 10 percent at	286
Not less than 90 percent at	395
End point not higher than	420
ASTM D-875, aromatics, percent,	
not less than	85

TRICHLOROACETIC ACID (TCA)

The sodium and ammonium salts of TCA are very toxic to grasses and less toxic to some broad-leaved weeds. TCA is being used to kill Johnsongrass, Bermudagrass, and quackgrass. It is most effective as a spray when it is washed into the soil by rains after being applied to the tops of weed growth. It is a valuable addition to our list of herbicides as it does not sterilize the soil for a long period. It may be used to control phragmites, Johnsongrass, and other weeds of ditch and drainage systems.

A number of herbicides not ordinarily associated with aquatic-weed control may be used to get rid of ditchbank weeds. The translocated herbicides amitrole, amitrole-T, glyphosate, picloram, and 2,3,6-TBA are all excellent materials for controlling perennial weeds; they can be used in a number of aquatic situations.

Caution should be used to select only biodegradeable herbicides for use in aquatic-weed situations. These are characterized by short-time effects only; they quickly disappear and leave the environment unaffected.

REFERENCES

Aldrich, F. D., and N. E. Otto. 1959. The translocation of 2,4-D-1-C^{14} in *Potamogeton pectinatus*, a submerged aquatic plant. *Weeds* 7(3):295–299.

Anon. 1949. Control of weeds on irrigation systems. U.S. Bureau of Reclamation. U.S. Printing Office, Washington, 25, D.C.

Blackburn, R. D., and Sutton, D. L., 1970. The use of herbicides in ponds, lakes, and streams. *F.A.O. Internatl. Conf. on Weed Control*. Davis, Calif., pp. 374–386.

Overbeek, J., W. J. Hughes, and R. Blondeau. 1959. Acrolein for the control of water weeds and disease-carrying water snails. *Science* 129:335–336.

Shaw, J. B., and F. L. Timmons. 1949. Controlling submerged water weeds on irrigation systems with aromatic solvents. *Bur. Reclam., Lab. Rpt.* CH-97, Denver, Colo. April.

Timmons, F. L. 1960. Weed control in western irrigation and drainage systems. U.S. Dept. Agr. and U.S. Dept. Int., Joint Rpt. A.R.S. 34–14, September. 22pp.

———. 1970a. Control of aquatic weeds. *F.A.O. Internatl. Conf. on Weed Control*. Davis, Calif., pp. 357–373.

———. 1970b. Benefits and consequences of using herbicides in irrigation systems. *F.A.O. Internatl. Conf. on Weed Control*. Davis, Calif., pp. 387–400.

Wilkinson, R. E. 1961. Effects of reduced sunlight on water stargrass (*Heteranthera dubia*). Weeds 9(3):457–462.

19

Weed Control on Nonagricultural Areas

While hoeing weeds has always been a tedious operation in field crops, it becomes almost unbearable on gravelled or paved surfaces, such as walkways, roadsides, industrial areas, and public parks. Since the introduction of herbicides, chemical soil sterilization has changed all this. In addition to relieving workers of this tiresome task, chemical soil sterilization provides fire prevention, it gives improved access, and it lends more esthetic appeal.

Figure 19–1 shows a ditchbank chemically treated to rid it of weed growth. In addition to making the bank accessible to the irrigator, the chemical treatment eliminates weed seeds from the water and gives this whole roadside situation a pleasing appearance.

Figure 19–2 shows soil sterilization in the stack area of a lumber yard. This treatment reduces fire hazard, makes convenient access to the stacks, and, again, gives a clean, neat appearance.

Whereas arsenic, boron compounds, and sodium chlorate were the principal chemicals available a few years ago, introduction of many new sterilants, particularly karbutilate, the substituted ureas, uracils, and symmetrical triazines, has changed the situation. These newer compounds, active at dosages between 10 and 100 lb per acre, make possible extensive treatment of large areas. Convenient retreatment results in economic maintenance of plant-free areas wherever they are desired. Figure 19–3 illustrates an industrial area that has been treated with soil sterilants.

The railroads are large users of herbicides. The American Railway

Engineering Association has conducted many tests on the use of herbicides and soil sterilants. Klingman and Wilcox (1960) illustrate many examples of excellent weed control on railway ballast and give detailed descriptions of many plots involving all the well-known herbicides used singly and in various combinations. They quote prices on the materials used. This publication is an extremely valuable compilation of plot tests in seven regions representative of the climatic situations throughout the United States. It should be useful to anyone

FIGURE 19-1   Plants growing under modern conditions of agriculture. Trees for shade, alfalfa for forage, and water for irrigation. The ditch has been sprayed to keep it free of weeds.

who is interested in vegetation control on noncropped areas. Figure 19–4 shows a railroad spray train.

ROADSIDES

Weeds usually grow in profusion along roads and highways. Such weeds are objectionable for many reasons: (1) They are a ready source of seed that may infect adjoining cultivated land. (2) They harbor insect and fungus pests that may spread to neighboring crop plants. (3) When dry, they become a fire hazard to adjacent grainfields, hayfields, and woodlands. (4) They present an unsightly appearance. (5) They may cause hay fever. (6) They may impair vision on curves and at

FIGURE 19-2. Weed control on the stack areas of a lumber yard reduces fire hazard, makes stacking and removal of lumber more convenient, and improves the appearance of the yard. (Photograph by Peter Van den Bosch. Reproduced from Calif. Agr. Ext. Serv. Cir. 446.)

FIGURE 19-3. Railway switch that has been treated with monuron to eliminate weeds.

intersections. (7) They may hide guard rails, markers, and culvert-head walls. (8) They may cause drifting snow and soil to pile up.

A great variety of weeds infest roadsides. As a rule, among the weeds of roadsides in any area, may be found those that occur on adjoining agricultural lands. They include a mixture of annuals, biennials, and perennials including woody species, which makes the planning of control operations difficult.

The weed problems of roadsides can be greatly minimized if fences

FIGURE 19-4. A modern railroad spray rig. This rig is adapted to operate on rails or on the highway. (Photograph courtesy of Washburn Agricultural Service.)

are removed. Fences are largely a tradition; they afford little protection from marauders, either livestock or humans. Throughout many parts of the United States, fences along roadsides no longer serve a useful purpose. Except in the strictly livestock-farming areas and even to some extent in these, livestock are seldom driven along roadways; they are transported by trucks. In view of this change in mode of moving livestock, a fence can serve only to keep out pedestrians and motorists, and experience shows that these seldom cause trouble. In the principal fruit and vegetable sections, every year sees the removal of many miles of roadside fences. Following their removal, the strip between the property line and the roadway is leveled; this makes possible mowing or treatment with herbicides. No longer need these miles of fence lines be infested with weeds.

Moreover, on individual farms, there is a growing tendency to remove permanent fences between fields. By so doing, the farmer adds materially to his arable land and eliminates the weed-infested strips bordering the fences. Now that quickly installed, portable fences are available, these are replacing the permanent types.

The principal methods that have been employed to control weeds on roadsides in the United States are as follows: mowing, burning, discing, blading, hand pulling, hoeing, seeding to grasses and legumes, and chemical treatment.

Mowing leaves much to be desired as a control procedure on roadsides; it usually does not eliminate the weeds, it leaves inflammable rubbish, and it allows weeds to mature seeds.

Burning is useful only where weeds have grown to maturity so that they will carry fire; consequently, seeds are usually matured and are not destroyed.

It should be emphasized here that burning weeds along highways is particularly objectionable for several reasons: (1) the danger of setting fire to adjoining grainfields or woodlands, (2) the scorching of shrubbery and trees, and (3) the hazard to traffic from blinding by smoke.

Where oil or other herbicides are used to kill roadside weeds, burning of the dead vegetation is necessary because the treated areas present a greater fire hazard than untreated areas. If herbicides are applied at the proper time, i.e., when the weeds are small, the fire hazard is negligible.

Discing is used to control weeds on shoulders of county and private roads in agricultural regions. It is cheap and effective, but unless done carefully it leads to erosion; it prepares an excellent seedbed for the succeeding year's weed crop.

Blading has the same disadvantages as discing but to a lesser degree, namely, disturbance of the shoulder, loosening of the soil, and mixing of soil and weed seeds. If blading is employed, it should be done before weeds mature seeds; otherwise it will spread the seeds.

Hand pulling, hoeing, and spudding are used to remove weeds about bridgeheads, culverts, trees, and other obstructions on rights-of-way. In many states, the weeds in such situations are treated with herbicides; such treatment appears to be superior to mechanical methods. Especially promising is chemical sterilization.

Chemical Methods

Herbicides are coming into more general use in the control of roadside weeds. The chemicals mentioned in Chapters 10–12 are being applied singly and in various combinations to meet the needs of complete vegetation control. Figure 19–5 shows a roadside sprayer.

Seeding with grasses or low, spreading legumes may be desirable where summer rains are frequent enough to maintain a green, living cover. In grasses such as blue grass, Manhattan ryegrass, or Bermuda grass, 2,4-D may be used to eliminate undesirable weeds. In clover or trefoil the preemergence herbicides recommended for growing these as crops may be used. Occasional mowing may be necessary and MH may be used to inhibit excess growth.

One problem with chemicals for roadside-weed control is injury to shade trees along the right-of-way and on adjacent property. Borate-chlorate soil sterilants may cause chlorosis, and substituted urea herbicides may cause die-back. Care must be exercised in using soil-borne chemicals in areas occupied by roots of valuable trees.

FIGURE 19-5.   Essig compressed-air sprayer mounted on a jeep for roadside and fenceline weed control.

Some tree species are resistant to the ureas, some tolerate the triazines; in using these materials on roadsides one should consult the literature put out by the manufacturers before making the application.

A standard practice for controlling weeds and maintaining weed-free fire strips on state and intercontinental highways is to treat in fall or winter with a long-lasting soil sterilant such as simazine, diuron, or bromacil (Hyvar). Winter precipitation dissolves these materials and washes them into the topsoil where they control weed seedlings soon after germination. All three of these materials will affect perennials, both herbaceous and woody, if the dosage is increased sufficiently.

Where there is green vegetation on the roadsides at the time of using these soil sterilants, amino triazole, glyphosate, or picloram may be added to the spray liquid where perennial weeds are involved. Diquat may be used for knocking down annuals.

Asulam is being used postemergence to control such perennials as johnsongrass, bracken, and poison ivy on roadsides and rights-of-way; tansy ragwort is also susceptible.

Atrazine or monuron may be substituted for simazine or diuron in semiarid to arid regions; being somewhat more soluble, these will move into the topsoil with less precipitation.

The dinitro general-contact sprays may be used to rapidly kill annual weeds in noncrop areas; dinoseb or DNOC is used in this way.

Dicamba alone or in combination with chlorophenoxy herbicides is used to control unwanted woody plants on noncrop lands; a wide variety of species is controlled.

The above-named herbicides are all available in granular form and may be spread by hand or, preferably, by mechanical spreader. Amitrole should be applied as a spray for absorption and translocation to roots.

Fenac is effective for controlling perennial broadleaf weeds as well as many annual weeds on roadsides; it is particularly effective against puncturevine.

Glyphosate is effective against many perennial weeds.

2,3,6-TBA is another translocated herbicide useful for controlling perennial weeds on railroad, utility, and pipeline rights-of-way.

MSMA plus diuron is preferred for controlling Johnsongrass, Dallisgrass, dandelions, bluelettuce, plantain, and chickweed.

Prometone, alone or mixed with contact materials, is used where penetration into the soil is a problem; it is over 20 times as water soluble as atrazine, 150 times as simazine.

Karbutilate is effective in controlling many woody shrubs and trees in forest and woodland roadsides; it is available in liquid or granular forms.

Tebuthiuron is proving effective for total weed control, having long residual action and good stability.

IRRIGATION DITCHBANKS

The chemicals named above are all useful on irrigation-ditchweed control (Fig. 19–1). The special problems of irrigation and drainage ditches involve mainly unlined ones and the principal factors are the very abrupt shifts in soil moisture from saturated to air dry. Within this range certain weeds thrive and cause serious problems; notably knotgrass (*Paspalum distichum*), puncturevine, barnyardgrass, Dallisgrass, Bermudagrass, Johnsongrass, Kikuyugrass, and others. These weeds grow alone or just above the waterlinne and either trail out over or into the water or, growing erect, bend over and drop their seeds into the water.

Weed oils, dinoseb contact sprays, or paraquat may be used as contact materials to kill these weeds in their seedling stages or to knock down more mature growth; translocated materials like MSMA, dalapon, picloram, or glyphosate are used on the perennials.

INDUSTRIAL SITES

Soil sterilization to maintain bare soil is a requirement in many areas; examples are firebreaks in forest, range, or wildlands, oil storage-tank farms, pipelines, ammunition dumps, around poles and bill-boards, railroad rights-of-way, particularly switches (Fig. 19–3), and industrial sites, such as parking areas, electrical equipment, shops and warehouses, factories, etc. As described, the triazine, urea, and uracil herbicides are standard materials for use on such areas; the particular chemical chosen depends upon soil type, annual precipitation, weed species, exposure, and special requirements related to the unique problem involved. Perennial weeds demand herbicides that translocate either via the phloem from foliar sprays or via the xylem following uptake from the soil by roots. Most of the chemicals described in Chapters 10, 11, and 12, which relate to industrial site weed control are soil-borne, and their water solubility and fixation properties must be considered in the choice of chemical; persistance is a prime require-ment of these materials, and low solubility and strong soil retention against leaching are preferred attributes. Once again, the user of these herbicides should read carefully and consider seriously all in-structions on the containers; in this way a serious lawsuit may be avoided.

POWER LINES

Electrical power lines constitute a unique problem in weed control; in order to prevent soil erosion and to maintain cover for game and birds, it is often necessary to control trees and brush and, at the same time, to maintain a cover of grass, herbs, or very low shrubs (Fig. 17–8). This often requires conversion from forest or brush land to the low-growing cover without at anytime baring the soil by complete sterilization.

The original conversion is usually accomplished when the power lines are installed, but preventing the return of the vegetation to the original woody plant cover may require heroic effort on the part of the company environmentalist. 2,4-D, 2,4,5-T, and silvex-LV esters are the common herbicides used for such woody plant control; picloram and glyphosate are more recent additions to the available materials. The chlorophenoxy compounds and picloraam have the happy propensity of controlling broadleaf species while favoring grasses. For this reason they are ideal in that they can be flown on by helicopter, knocking back the brush while conserving the grass cover. Drift, a serious problem in the early days of powerline right-of-way brush control, may now be held under control by use of invert emulsion formulations, or inclusion of several drift-preventing materials that are available.

AIRFIELDS

Weed control around airfields, an old problem, has become an even greater one as the fields have had to be enlarged for jet aircraft. Although weed control is seldom needed on the actual flight strips because they are generally paved with concrete, the access lanes may be paved with gravel or a thin layer of macadam, and weed encroachment around the edges of these can constitute a real problem. Here picloram, 2,3,6-TBA, and glyphosate are indicated; all three are absorbed both by leaves and roots; applied to foliage they kill the tops of the plants; subsequently washed onto the soil they may continue to act through root uptake.

Where only annual weeds are present, paraquat is probably the preferred material; oils make the area look messy and dinoseb colors it yellow.

Once the approach lanes and other roadways, landing lights, and other structures or equipment have been treated and top growth of weeds eliminated, periodic application of triazine, urea, or uracil soil sterilants should maintain the weed-free condition. In addition to the above herbicides there are many materials adapted to maintaining a weed-free condition; these involve borates, chlorates, borate-chlorate mixtures, and many combinations of these with 2,4-D, 2,4,5-T, 2,3,6-TBA, TCA, DSMA, MSMA, amitrole, ammate, glyphosate, triazines, ureas, uracils, dicamba, picloram, etc. In addition to these, individual users often make up their own mixtures. The problem here is that many of these soil-borne materials may harm trees or shrubs whose roots extend under the treated areas. One should always observe any precautions printed on the labels concerning specific sensitivities of ornamental or native plants to the chemical being used.

VACANT-LOT WEEDS

One problem that is becoming acute with the great interest in subdivision of the land and urban living is the control of weeds on vacant lots in the city (Dudley, 1961).

Weeds in cities are undesirable for three important reasons: (1) when dry, they are a fire hazard, (2) a large number of them may cause hay fever, and (3) they detract from the beauty of the city.

Weeds on vacant lots and in out-of-the-way places are usually neglected and permitted to develop into unsightly and dangerous growths. The control of weeds in lawns, parking lots, golf courses, or in home gardens is also important (Fig. 19–6).

Most cities have ordinances that provide for the mowing or cutting of weeds on vacant lots or other unoccupied areas, but they are commonly ignored or ineffectually enforced. As a rule, the weeds become tall and mature seed before sufficient pressure is brought to bear on the owner to destroy them. Apparently no one is aroused until the

FIGURE 19-6.   Control of crabgrass in the home lawn by means of a selective herbicide. Left, treated area; right, untreated area. (Photograph by courtesy of the Dow Chemical Company.)

damage is done. If any headway is to be made in decreasing the weed population of our cities, the very simple and obvious principle of preventing seeding of weeds must be observed. It is true that in spring and early summer, the vacant lot with its fresh, green growth is a pleasing sight, but soon it is parched and dry and throughout the greater part of the season is not an altogether attractive place. It is, of course, impracticable even to attempt to keep many unused areas absolutely devoid of vegetation, but they should be prevented from growing up to tall weeds. If the simple expedient of several timely mowings, discings, or plowings during the season is resorted to, the more undesirable weed growth will be prevented from seeding. The prevention of seeding of weeds in cities is an administrative matter and is not so scientifically complex as to require the services of a specialist in weed control.

Most weeds are easily and cheaply destroyed when in their seedling stages. Generally speaking, weed control should be practiced in spring and early summer rather than in late summer and fall. The best time to operate is when the weeds are but a few inches high. The cost then will be the least and the results more effective. Also, when weeds are young, any one of the nonpoisonous and noncorrosive contact sprays already described may be employed. These chemicals kill top growth but do not sterilize the soil. Among these are diesel oil and other weed oils which are readily available in any community, being obtainable through most oil stations. Oil is best applied as a fine spray, which ensures a thorough covering of the vegetation with a minimum of material. Equipment of either the hand sprayer or power type for the application of oil in this manner is now available.

The application of oils close to wooden buildings and billboards should be avoided; or the burning over of oil-treated areas should be carefully supervised. In some cities, this is done by the fire department. The burning of weeds near or under ornamental trees and shrubs should be avoided, since too often irreparable damage is done by this practice.

Nontoxic soil sterilants such as chlorates, borax, bromacil, diuron, and simazine are finding increasing use in the sterilization of areas where no vegetative growth is wanted. Reference is made chiefly to unpaved driveways and alleys and the areas about billboards and poles. It is inadvisable to use arsenicals in cities because of the danger to children and pets. As a rule, extensive use of 2,4-D in cities is inadvisable because of damage to ornamentals, unless it is done under the supervision of responsible parties. This does not mean that it should not be used to control weeds in home gardens, if this is done with care.

An obvious problem in vacant-lot weed control is that one never knows when the lot will sell and some one will build a house and landscape the yard. Many times when this is done where a long-lasting sterilant has been used, lawns and shrubs may suffer or even die. For this reason, in treating vacant lots one should choose a chemical that will volatilize or break down in the soil within the season of application. Asulam, benefin, bensulide, benzomarc, butylate, chloropropham, chlorthiamid, cycloate, dazomet, diallate, dicamba, dichlobenil, diquat, DSMA, erbon, fenac, glyphosate, MAMA, metham, methazole, molinate, MSMA, nitrofen, pebulate, pronamide, propachlor, napropamide (Devrinol), sesone, swep, terbutol, triallate, tricamba, and vernolate are among the herbicides that have the necessary qualities for this use. For those who are not familiar with using herbicides under these rather exacting conditions, it is recommended that they not only read the labels carefully, but also consult with municipal agencies responsible for cleaning vacant lots to find the materials best fitted to

FIGURE 19-7. Control of ragweed in New York City by 2,4–D. The knapsack sprayer is convenient for treating isolated patches. (Photograph by courtesy of the Dow Chemical Company.)

the special conditions of the locality. It is best to plan on one or more treatments annually to provide the necessary control. Appendix Table 3 gives data on the persistence of a number of herbicides in soils under California conditions.

RAGWEED CONTROL

Ragweed can cause such severe hay fever that allergic people have to migrate to ragweed-free localities at the time the pollen is flying.

The Department of Health, New York City, Bureau of Sanitatary

Engineering, Weed Control Unit, has economically and effectively controlled ragweed since 1946 by spraying all infested areas within the city with a solution of 0.1 percent 2,4-D (Fig. 19–7). Treatments are made during June and July or at such time as to prevent pollination. The plants slowly die, and no seeds are produced. The effectiveness of the ragweed program is attested by a report of the National Pollen Survey Committee of the American Academy of Allergy, which found the 1946 ragweed count in New York the lowest since 1937.

DSMA, 2,4-D amine, dicamba, and other herbicides are useful in controlling ragweed.

REFERENCES

Dudley, E. 1961. Urban weed control: A progress report. *13th Calif. Weed Control Conf. Proc.* January, pp. 27–34.

Klingman, G. C., and M. Wilcox. 1960. Part 1. Railroad weed control, North Carolina State College. Part 2. Chemical control of vegetation. 1959 AAR Report reprinted from *Amer. Ry. Engin. Assoc. Bul.* 556. February.

20

Equipment For Applying Herbicides

Herbicides are applied to weeds via the foliage or via the roots. Foliage applications are made by spraying, by dusting, or by using wax bars containing the herbicide. Root applications may be made by applying sprays, dusts, or pellets to the soil, followed by incorporation by rainfall or cultivation, by injection or mechanical mixing with the soil, or by sprayblade application whereby a thin layer of herbicide is laid down on the flat soil surface and covered by a layer of friable soil. Volatile herbicides or fumigants require sealing of the soil surface by sheet plastic, by a shallow irrigation, or by rolling. Recommendations on application methods, soil sealing, and other important aspects of herbicide use are given on the containers.

The prime requirements of any machine or tool for applying pest-control materials are: (1) that it dispense material at a uniform, controllable rate, (2) that it distribute the material uniformly over the area being treated, and (3) that it be easily calibrated to apply a predetermined dosage. Any applicator meeting these requirements will do a satisfactory job if kept in good repair and if placed in the hands of a conscientious operator. In the use of herbicides, the application may be as important as the chemical or its formulation.

The three major types of sprayers used for weed control are hand-operated knapsacks, power-driven ground machines, and aircraft. Choice between these depends upon the area to be treated, the equipment, and the man-power available.

Knapsack Sprayers

Of the hand-operated types of sprayer, the knapsack with a capacity of 3 or 4 gal is the most useful for spraying small, scattered weed

371

patches or areas inaccessible to power equipment (Fig. 20-1). Paint sprayers, hose proportioners, and small, insecticide atomizers are generally restricted in usefulness to the home garden; bucket and barrel sprayers require two persons and are less maneuverable than knapsack sprayers.

The hydropneumatic knapsack sprayer uses either compressed air or some other gas under pressure to force liquid out of the tank. The compressed-air sprayer with a built-in pump is very common and simple to maintain but has the disadvantage of having to be pumped up at intervals to maintain a fairly uniform pressure.

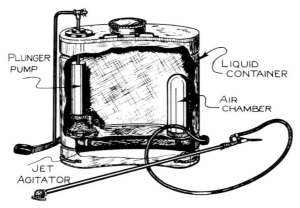

FIGURE 20-1. Cutaway drawing of a knapsack sprayer, showing the pump, the agitator, and the air chamber. These sprayers are used in great numbers in row crops such as sugar cane; also on small farms and around home gardens for applying all types of pesticides. (From Calif. Agr. Expt. Serv. Cir. 389.)

Kits are available for converting compressed-air sprayers by using small cylinders of carbon dioxide as the pressure source; or the entire sprayer, including tank, may be purchased as a unit. Such carbon dioxide sprayers include an automatic regulating value which maintains a constant pressure on the solution tank and a safety valve to ensure against overpressure from improper adjustment.

Constant-pressure knapsack sprayers, which the operator can pump continuously while he is spraying, use either a plunger pump or a diaphragm pump to force the liquid into the hose, with a small air chamber to minimize surging (Fig. 20-1).

Although knapsack sprayers are intended primarily for small areas or for spot treatment on larger areas, there are instances where the cost of application for broadcast spraying of large fields is comparable to that of using power sprayers. In irrigated cane plantations in the tropics, the lines or rows of cane may be in the bottom of the irrigation furrows, with ridges in the middle. Power equipment running on the ridges tends to break them down, so that it is difficult to control the water. Furthermore, some plantations use concrete, U-section, surface flumes for distributing water to the furrows, and it would be necessary to move the flumes to permit entry of power equipment into each section of a field. The ridges between lines are not disturbed by men carrying knapsack sprayers. The men can easily step over the flumes;

FIGURE 20-2. A boom attached to two knapsack sprayers, used to apply pesticides where even coverage is essential. (Photograph by courtesy of Compania Shell de Venezuela.)

by using specially designed hand booms, a man sprays the middle between two rows as fast as he can walk and, with a well-organized mixing and refilling station and a well-trained crew, labor efficiency on the order of 15 acres per manday is achieved.

Adaptation of modern herbicides to use in countries where land holdings are small may require use of small sprayers. Figure 20-2 shows the use of a two-man, hand-boom sprayer. Knapsack sprayers of various types are in use in many crops, for example, sugar cane, rice, small grains, coffee, sisal, and flax, and in row crops, orchards, and vineyards. Though less efficient than power sprayers, these inexpensive sprayers make possible the use of powerful herbicides which greatly reduce labor requirements for growing these crops.

Small-plot sprayers for accurate application of experimental materials have been designed by many research workers. These have proven invaluable in the testing of thousands of compounds in the search for new and better herbicides.

As greater numbers of chemicals become available for testing, greater precision is necessary, decontamination in shifting from one compound to another becomes of increasing importance, and general convenience lends usefulness to spray applicators. McLane, Dean, and Minarik (1954) describe a machine that combines these advantages and still may be constructed at a nominal cost. By varying air flow, the particle size of the spray droplets is subject to accurate control. And being completely portable, the machine is useful at a distance from a power source. It is powered by a storage battery and a small, electric motor.

Small Power Sprayers

There are many uses for small power sprayers, which are available in many forms. They are used in home gardens, in parks, on small farms, and in experimental work. For most herbicide application such a small sprayer consists of the standard parts: a tank; a pump; essential plumbing, including pipes, strainers, pressure regulator, boom, nozzles, etc.; and a power supply, usually a small gasoline engine.

A special type of small power sprayer is the logarithmic dosage sprayer used in experiments. The idea of a logarithmic delivery of a spray solution was introduced by Pfeiffer et al. in 1955. This was a sprayer large enough to handle an 8-ft boom, and it was mounted on a Land Rover for field experimentation. A number of these were manufactured by Fisons Pest Control Limited of Felixstowe, Suffolk, England, and they found use in many parts of the world.

Soon after the initial appearance of the logarithmic sprayer, a number of smaller models were constructed, varying from wheel-mounted rigs for field-plot work to track-mounted models for use in small-field and greenhouse experimentation. Examples are the machines of Day (1958), Leasure and Falkenstein (1958) (Fig. 20–3), Friesen (1958), Wensley (1958), Leasure (1959), and Yates and Ashton (1960).

The logarithmic dosage sprayer has distinct advantages in field testing of herbicides. It delivers the chemical at a logarithmically decreasing rate; that is, if one starts with a 1 percent solution, after a certain number of feet the concentration will be ½ percent; after the same number of feet, ¼ percent, and so on until a dilution is reached that is no longer useful. On a single species one can readily ascertain the minimum lethal dose of a chemical, the maximum tolerated dose, and the maximum dose that produces no symptoms. On mixed vegetation, as in a pasture, one can read off the minimum lethal dose for each species and hence determine the selectivity of chemicals. The logarithmic method permits the rapid evaluation of many herbicides with a minimum of time and labor. Fisons Pest Control Limited make the Chesterford Logarithmic Sprayer in a larger size mountable on a jeep or Land Rover. These machines are being used the world around for herbicide evaluation.

FIGURE 20-3. Small logarithmic sprayer used in applying herbicides in experimental work. (Photograph by courtesy of the Dow Chemical Company.)

Power Sprayers

The most common type of power equipment for dispersing herbicidal liquids is that which uses a hydraulic pump; this may be of the plunger, rotary, or centrifugal type. The liquid is forced through nozzles which break it up into droplets and direct the droplets at the surface to be covered.

Low pressures, in the range of 20 to 125 psi, are commonly used in weed spraying. This permits the use of simple, low-cost gear and centrifugal pumps in place of the plunger pumps required to give adequately high pressure for spraying orchard pests.

Aerosol generators of the thermal type have been generally unsatisfactory for herbicide application; the aerosol-sized droplets are ineffective except with growth regulators, and with them the hazard from uncontrolled drift is too great.

Mist sprayers or spray dusters, in which a large volume of air from a blower is used to disperse a relatively small volume of liquid introduced into the air stream by atomizing nozzles, are subject to some of the same objections as the aerosol generator. The droplets are generally somewhat larger, but they are blown out horizontally and so the width of swath and uniformity of distribution are affected by air

FIGURE 20-4. A large field sprayer used to spray grain fields, alfalfa, and other field crops for the control of weeds. (Photograph courtesy of Washburn Agricultural Service.)

currents. They have been used occasionally in weed control on ranges, for selective spraying of wheat fields where drift hazard to other crops is negligible, and for spraying brush along roads in wild, forested areas. For most open-field spraying, however the conventional boom sprayer will cover as wide a swath, can be adjusted to as low a gallonage per acre, and will cover more uniformly and with less disturbance of the pattern by wind.

GENERAL TYPES OF FIELD SPRAYERS

The hydraulic-pump weed sprayer ranges in size from the small utility sprayer, with a capacity of 2 to 4 gpm capable of handling a hose line or a short boom, up to self-propelled field sprayers that spray a 60-to 70-ft swath (Fig. 20–4).

The estate-type utility sprayer has a plunger pump and can therefore provide sufficient pressure for orchard or cattle spraying but, by adjusting the pressure regulator, lower pressures for weed spraying are provided.

Field sprayers may be truck-mounted, tractor-mounted, self-propelled, or trailer-mounted. Trailer mounting, usually on a single-axle, pneumatic-tired trailer, is most popular for spraying broadcast or close-drilled crops, since this does not interfere with normal use of the tractor for other purposes. Mounting on a wheeled cultivating tractor and driving the pump from the power take-off is popular for spraying

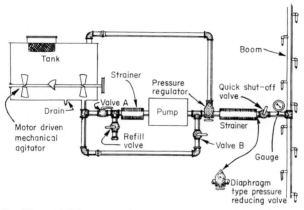

FIGURE 20-5. Essential features of a power spray rig for weed control. (From Akesson and Harvey, Calif. Agr. Expt. Sta. Cir. 389.)

row crops, as the unit has a short turning radius and the nozzles can be precisely adjusted in relation to the rows.

Choosing a Field Sprayer

In choosing or designing a field sprayer, one should consider the various essential elements of a power sprayer, i.e., boom, pump, power unit, and tank, and their size or capacity in relation to one another and to the acreage to be sprayed and the gallonage applied (Fig. 20–5).

BOOM

The necessity for covering a given acreage in a given time when traveling at a given speed sets the length of boom. However, lengths above 50 ft are seldom practicable, and additional units should be provided rather than trying to exceed that length. The relation of length of boom to the factors mentioned is given by the formula:

$$\frac{\text{sq ft per acre} \times \text{number of acres}}{\text{working hours} \times \text{mph} \times \text{ft per mile}} = \text{boom length}$$

Akesson and Harvey (1948) give an example and derive a rough rule based on it.

For example, 250 acres to be covered, at 5 miles per hour, in 3 eight-hour days (assume 30 percent loss of time to be used in filling tank and for turns, leaving 17 actual working hours),

$$\frac{43{,}560 \times 250}{17 \times 5 \times 5{,}280} = 24.26 \text{ ft boom length}$$

With the same example, we may use a rough rule for finding boom length for general-volume spraying:

At 5 mph, for 3 working days, allow 1 foot of boom for each 10 acres to be sprayed. For the 250 acres, this gives a boom length of 25 feet.

In practice, booms for spraying broadcast or close-drilled crops range from 16 to 50 ft in length. For calibrating and checking over-all field dosages, it is convenient to have the length some multiple of 100 in. (8 ¼ ft or ½ rod) as that width swath equals 1 acre per mile.

The length of row-crop booms is some multiple of the row spacing and, for precision underspraying of weeds in the row, should be the same as the number of drills on the planter.

Booms should be sectioned and hinged to reduce width when moving between fields or on the highway. Means should also be provided for adjustment of height to suit varying weed and crop conditions. Outrigger wheels on a jointed boom help to keep a long boom parallel to the ground.

PUMP

When the length of the boom has been decided upon, the size of the pump is determined by that figure, by the gallonage per acre, and by the speed of the machine. The formula for determining the required discharge in gallons per minute (gpm) is:

$$\frac{\text{boom length} \times \text{ft per mile} \times \text{mph} \times \text{gpa}}{\text{sq ft per acre} \times 60} = \text{gpm}$$

Using the same figures for boom length and for speed—25 ft and 5 mph—as in the example on determining boom length, and assuming 100 gpa, the example becomes:

$$\frac{25 \times 5{,}280 \times 5 \times 100}{43{,}560 \times 60} = 25.25 \text{ gpm}$$

From this calculation, we can draw the rough rule that 1 gpm is discharged per foot of boom when applying 100 gpa at 5 mph. At lower speeds, a lower discharge is required to maintain the same gallonage per acre, so that at 4, 3, 2, and 1 mph, the respective requirements are 4/5, 3/5, 2/5, and 1/5 gpm per ft of boom.

The required discharge per foot of boom is also proportional to the gallonage per acre, so that at 75, 50, 20, and 10 gpa, the respective requirements are 75/100 or 3/4, 50/100 or 1/2, 20/100 or 1/5, and 10/100 or 1/10 gpm per ft of boom.

By equally simple mental arithmetic, we can calculate the required discharge for any combination of miles per hour and gallons per acre. Thus, 25 gpa at 2½ mph gives 25/100 × 2.5/5 or 1/4 × 1/2 = 1/8 gpm per ft of boom.

Returning to our original example where a 25-ft boom was chosen, and assuming that the 250 acres in question are planted to peas which we wish to spray with a dinitrophenol selective at 80 gpa, we can now determine the size of pump required. This will require 0.8 gpm per ft of boom, or 0.8 × 25 = 20 gpm. Because accurate pressure regulation cannot be maintained when the capacity of the pump is only equal to the discharge of the boom and because some allowance should be made for lowered efficiency of pumps as they wear, it would be wise to choose a pump having a capacity somewhat greater than 20 gpm, say 25 gpm. If hydraulic agitation is used in the tank, even greater capacity is necessary, probably up to 40 gpm in this case.

As mentioned previously, most low-pressure sprayers are equipped with either a rotary or a centrifugal pump rather than a reciprocating pump. Rotary pumps are of three general types: gear, roller, and flexible impeller. These are all positive-displacement pumps, with discharge proportional to the speed of rotation. The clearances in gear pumps, both internal- and external-flow types, are rather close, and the pumps lose efficiency rather quickly if gritty solids are pumped. Flexible impeller pumps should never be allowed to run dry, and they will not usually develop over 50 psi pressure. Roller pumps, especially those having plastic-coated rollers and a hardened metal case, should wear well, and their design automatically adjusts for some of the increased clearances due to wear.

Centrifugal pumps are not positive-displacement pumps. Instead, they develop pressure from high liquid velocity imparted by the rapidly rotating impeller. As clearances are relatively high, suspended solids are not injurious except in the regenerative turbine type where the fine blades wear out if the solids are gritty or abrasive. Single-stage centrifugal pumps must be operated at relatively high speeds (3,000 to 3,600 rpm) in order to provide sufficient pressure for spraying. For this

reason, centrifugals are not so well adapted to driving by power ta-
keoffs on tractors as rotary pumps. Centrifugals are therefore powered
independently, often by direct connection to high-speed, air-cooled
engines. Multistage centrifugals develop more pressure than single-
stage pumps when operated at the same speed.

POWER UNIT

If one is buying an assembled sprayer, the manufacturer will have
provided a power unit of appropriate horsepower for the pump; if one is
assembling a sprayer, he will want to determine the power requirements of the pump he has chosen. The pump manufacturer will
usually furnish upon request charts showing horsepower requirements
at various pressures and discharge rates. If such data are unavailable,
the water-horsepower equation may be used to find the approximate
power requirements:

$$\text{hp} = \frac{\text{lb pressure} \times \text{gpm}}{1{,}715 \times \text{efficiency}}$$

The efficiency factor may vary from 20 to 80, depending on the
type and size of the pump. In the absence of exact data, it is better to
use a low figure for efficiency, so that the unit will not be under-
powered.

The performance of pumps is sometimes rated in gallons per
minute at various heads in feet. Feet of head (for water) are converted
to pounds per square inch by dividing by 0.43.

TANK

Having decided on the length of boom, the capacity of pump, and
the size of power unit, the fourth major consideration in choosing or
designing a field sprayer is the size of tank, The choice depends upon
several factors: the length of the boom, the average length of the fields
to be sprayed, the number of gallons applied per acre, and the type of
carriage as determined by ground conditions. Time lost in filling a
small tank is time lost from spraying. Opposed to this is the expense of
providing a track-laying carriage or large balloon tires for supporting
large tanks to prevent miring down in wet ground, compacting the soil,
and leaving deep ruts.

Some system of agitation is desirable in sprayer tanks, even when
completely soluble materials are being used, to ensure homogeneity of
the solution; agitation is a necessity for oil emulsions and heavy
suspensions. Hydraulic agitation suffices for readily soluble or self-
emulsifying materials, but mechanical agitation is required for emulsions containing a high percentage of oil. The mechanical agitator may

consist of a series of paddles on a shaft running horizontally through the tank or of a propeller at one end.

In the hydraulic system of agitation, a pump of considerably higher capacity than required to supply the boom is used, and the excess flow is bypassed from the pressure regulator and forced back into the spray tank through a series of holes in a pipe laid in the bottom of the tank.

FIGURE 20-6. Spray patterns of two nozzle types. The flat-fan type (left) is most popular on weed-control machinery. (From Akesson and Harvey, Calif. Agr. Expt. Sta. Cir. 389.)

Mechanical agitation is more efficient than hydraulic agitation in terms of power requirements and generally gives more uniform dispersion. In the horizontal-shaft and paddle system, the paddles should have a total width equal to one-half the length of the tank, and the blade peripheral speed should be between 300 and 400 ft per min. Thus, in a 250-gal tank 3 ft in diameter and 5 ft long, there should be four blades 8 in. wide and 12 in. long, turning at 95 to 128 rpm. This will require ¼ to ½ hp.

A similar tank using hydraulic agitation would require around 30 gpm at 100 psi, and the power requirement would be 3 to 4 hp.

CHOOSING NOZZLES AND SPACING THEM ON THE BOOM

Nozzles which produce a flat, fan-shaped spray are considered better than cone-spray types, for they give more uniform coverage and greater drive (Fig. 20–6). However, it is difficult to produce flat-fan

FIGURE 20-7. Left, nozzle flooding-type low-pressure designed to deliver coarse droplets of spray liquid without drift. This nozzle works at pressures of 1 psi or less. Right, the spray pattern of the flooding-type nozzle. (Photograph by courtesy of W. E. Yates, University of California, Davis, California.)

nozzles discharging less than 0.03 gpm and so, for very low gallonage rates, say in the range of 2 to 3 gpa, cone nozzles may have to be used.

The delivery rate of a nozzle, usually measured in gallons per minute, is determined by the diameter of the orifice, in thousandths of an inch or in sixty-fourths of an inch, and by the liquid pressure, measured in pounds per square inch. The delivery rates given in tables supplied by nozzle manufacturers are usually based on water as the liquid. Oils, emulsions, and other liquids or suspensions having different viscosity than water will be discharged at a different rate at the same pressure; delivery rates should be measured using the actual formulation which is to be sprayed in the field.

With the development of invert emulsions to reduce spray drift, new nozzles were designed to handle these viscous mixtures. Such equipment has proved useful for spraying in forests, for killing brush and trees in areas of mixed crops, and for controlling field bindweed in vineyards (Yates, 1960). Figure 20-7 from Yates illustrates the droplet sizes produced by special nozzles designed for coarse droplet application. By means of the flooding type flat-fan nozzle it has been possible to apply 2,4-D sprays in vineyards with no injury to the vines.

The delivery rate of the nozzles and their spacing on the boom are important because these two factors, in conjunction with the speed of the machine, establish the gallons per acre applied. It was shown in the section on choosing the spray pump that the application of 100 gpa at 5 mph requires 1 gpm per ft of boom. One could, therefore, choose

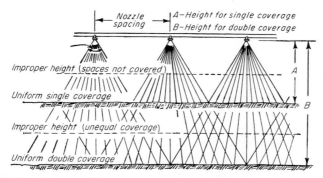

FIGURE 20-8. Two possible arrangements of a boom with respect to height. With nozzles fan-type, either single or double coverage may be obtained. The nozzle patterns should overlap to give a uniform spray volume across the boom. (Diagram by courtesy of N. B. Akesson.)

nozzles that delivered 1 gpm and by spacing them 1 ft apart, apply 100 gpa when driving 5 mph. Or the same number of gallons per acre would be applied by using nozzles delivering 1½ gpm and spaced 1½ ft apart.

The spacing of nozzles in row-crop spraying is set by the row spacing. For some purposes, one nozzle is placed directly over each row, with the boom height adjusted so that the spray fans meet between rows. Where it is desired to avoid hitting the crop foliage with the spray, nozzles are placed to center between rows, with the edges of the spray fans meeting in the row at the base of the crop plants.

For open-field spraying, nozzles are usually best spaced from 12 to 24 in. apart, the exact distance depending on whether single or double coverage is desired (Fig. 20-8) and on how high the boom is to be carried. If carried high, there is more likelihood of wind interfering with the spray pattern and also increasing the drift; if very low, the end of the boom may run into the ground on rough land and the tops of tall weeds may not be covered.

The spacing depends too on the included angle of the spray fan. Nozzles are available in a variety of included angles, but 65 and 80 deg are most commonly used. The angle varies slightly with pressure, but this is not very important within the usual working range.

By using the chart (Fig. 20-9), one can pick the proper nozzle spacing for different angles of fan at given nozzle heights.

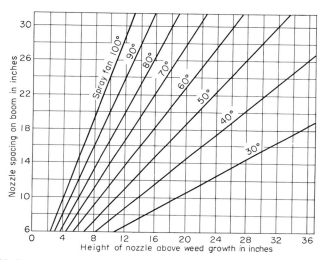

FIGURE 20-9. Relation between nozzle spacing, nozzle height, and spray fan angle for proper coverage. (From Akesson and Harvey, Calif. Agr. Expt. Sta. Cir. 389.)

Once the spacing has been set, there remains only the choosing of orifice tips that deliver the proper number of gallons per minute for the job at hand. The correct figure may be computed by formula or read from charts or tables. The formula is:

$$\frac{\text{gpa} \times \text{nozzle spacing, in.} \times \text{mph} \times \text{ft per mile}}{\text{sq ft per acre} \times \text{min per hr} \times \text{in. per ft}} = \text{gpm}$$

As an example, suppose that a spray is to be applied at 80 gpa, nozzles 16 in. apart, sprayer speed 4 mph.

$$\frac{80 \times 16 \times 4 \times 5{,}280}{43{,}560 \times 60 \times 12} = 0.86 \text{ gpm}$$

Some manufacturers furnish tables from which the proper orifice size and operating pressure can be read directly for any combination of speed and gallons per acre.

CHECKING THE SPRAYER

When the boom is set up with nozzles and the sprayer all ready to go, a test run should be made to see that the gallonage per acre is actually that desired. First, the tractor speed should be fixed by timing it over a measured course and the throttle set at the point giving the desired speed. Table 20-1 gives the feet per minute equivalents for miles per hour in the range of speeds usually employed in spraying.

Table 20-1.   Distance Traveled per Minute at Various Speeds

Speed, mph	Distance traveled, ft/min
1	88
1.5	132
2	176
2.5	220
3	264
3.5	308
4	352
4.5	395
5	440
6	528

If much spraying is to be done, it may be desirable to purchase a tractor speedometer to ensure uniform speed under different conditions of slope and footing.

With the throttle set and the pressure adjusted, start with a full tank of spray and drive 40 or 80 rods (⅛ or ¼ mile) while spraying. Then measure the amount of spray solution required to refill the tank. If 40 rods were driven, the formula for finding the gallons per acre actually applied is:

$$\frac{\text{gal used} \times 66}{\text{Length of boom, ft}} = \text{gpa}$$

If 80 rods were driven, substitute the figure 33 for the figure 66 in the formula.

For example, with a boom covering 24 ft, it required 4 gal to fill the tank after spraying for 40 rods with a setup calculated to apply 10 gpa.

$$\frac{4 \times 66}{24} = 11 \text{ gpa}$$

The operator can decrease pressure slightly or increase speed until he checks out exactly at 10 pga; if he prefers, he can adjust the concentration of chemical so that the per-acre dosage is put into 11 gal instead of 10.

Another method of checking is to use a specially graduated glass jar with fittings to hold it so as to catch the discharge from a single nozzle while driving a given distance. The liquid level is then read directly in gallons per acre from graduations that take nozzle spacing into account. This method assumes that all nozzles are discharging at the same rate. In any case the discharge of all nozzles should be checked from time to time to see that they are reasonably uniform; also it is advisable to check on orifice wear, which results in higher gallonage.

SPRAYER ACCESSORIES

In addition to the major sprayer components —pump, power unit, tank, boom, and nozzles—there are several accessories which provide ease and continuity of operation. These include pressure regulators, control valves, line strainers, nozzle screens, pressure gauges, spring-loaded check valves, and suck-back devices for preventing nozzle drip. A pressure regulator, or relief valve, is essential with positive-displacement pumps to prevent injury to the machine when the boom valves are closed. The regulator also serves to maintain a uniform pressure despite minor variations in engine speed. A regulator is not necessary with centrifugal pumps, because the liquid merely churns in the pump when the discharge valves are closed. The pressure can be adjusted while spraying by changing the engine speed or by using a simple control valve on the bypass line, but a pressure regulator, as with a positive-displacement pump, compensates for changes due to uneven speed.

A pressure gauge, is, of course, necessary for calibrating and checking to insure uniform application. The gauge need not have a maximum reading of over 150 lb. It should be mounted where the operator can see it at all times.

Dirt, sand, and other coarse solids plug nozzles and cause excessive wear on pumps and regulators. Strainers in the tank opening, the suction line, the boom line, and the nozzles will largely eliminate these losses. The tank opening should have a screen of 50 to 80 mesh to keep out large particles and lumps from improperly mixed spray materials. A similar mesh screen should be placed in the suction line to the pump to keep out gritty particles which might injure the pump. A screen with smaller openings, 100 to 150 mesh, should be placed in the pressure line to keep small particles from reaching the nozzles; screens in the nozzles themselves will prevent plugging from rust and scale that may flake off from the piping and boom behind the line strainer.

Spray tanks made of plastic and fiberglass are on the market. Ingredients, such as cosolvents, surfactants, or oils, of some herbicidal sprays may cause such tanks to deteriorate allowing fragments of plastic or glass fibers to accumulate in the tank; these often clog screens and cause delays in spraying.

It is necessary to have a main cutoff valve between the pump and the boom, and it is an advantage to have cutoffs for the individual boom sections so that the swath may be narrowed when finishing out a field. It is convenient to have these valves in one place where the operator can reach them handily. Some manufacturers assemble them into what they call a master control, control manifold, or control block.

Dripping or "drooling" of spray solution from the nozzles, even with the control valve turned off, is not only a nuisance, but if the sprayer has to stop in the field, usually results in killing the crop in that spot. This dripping is from gravity flow of liquid held in the boom. One way to eliminate it is to place spring-loaded check valves, set to open at 5 to 10 psi, between the boom and the nozzles. An additional precaution is the use of a venturi ejector placed in the line ahead of the pressure regulator on a bypass line with a valve. When the bypass valve is closed, spray passes out the side tube of the ejector and on to the boom. When the bypass valve is open, the liquid passes through the venturi and back to the tank, creating a negative pressure in the boom and causing the check valves at the nozzles to close instantly. The boom thus remains full of liquid, ready for resumption of spraying without delay.

Check valves are so lightly spring-loaded, to keep down back pressure, that they have a tendency to stick open if any dirt gets on the seat. The pull of the venturi added to the tension of the spring tends to overcome this defect. At the same time, the venturi alone, without check valves, does little good, for liquid will drop from some nozzles while air is entering through others.

Aircraft Sprayers

The design and operation of aircraft sprayers are subjects to be undertaken only by professional engineers and highly skilled professional pilots. It will suffice to briefly cover the subjects in general.

The components of most aircraft sprayers are similar to those of ground-borne sprayers and include a supply tank, agitator, pump, boom, valves, screens, nozzles, pressure regulator, and pressure gauge. Calibration is similar also, except that the speeds involved are gener-

FIGURE 20-10. Top, spray plane with boom and cutoff valves for application of herbicides; bottom, the Pawnee agricultural monoplane. (Photographs by courtesy of N. B. Akesson.)

ally in the range of 80 to 90 mph with fixed-wing aircraft (Fig. 20–10), instead of the 3 to 5 mph usual with field sprayers. Where necessary, lower speeds may be attained by helicopters. Furthermore, the maximum gallonage that it is economically feasible to apply by aircraft is generally considered to be in the range of 10 to 15 gpa; 5 gpa is a common rate when oil is used as a diluent.

Tank capacity varies generally from around 30 gal for light planes of the Cub type to around 75 gal for Bell and Hiller agricultural helicopters, to 100 or 150 gal for Stearman-type biplanes, and to 90 to 110 gal for the Alouette II helicopter (Grundy and Bennett, 1960).

Pumps are driven by a small, direct-connected propeller, by a V-belt drive from the main engine, or by an electric motor.

Agitation, when provided, is generally hydraulic, utilizing the return flow from a large-capacity centrifugal pump.

Booms, often of streamlined tubing to reduce drag, are usually about the length of the wing span, or enough less to prevent excessive drift at the wing-tip vortices. Nozzles are usually of the eddy-chamber type, which delivers a conical spray, and are tapped in at 8- to 12-in. spacings.

As nozzle drooling can result in serious damage to fields of susceptible crops when ferrying or turning over them, it is common practice to have individual cutoffs on each boom outlet, Putting suction on the boom when the main valve is cut off by means of a venturi device is an additional precaution used by some operators.

In addition to the boom-and-nozzle dispersing system described above, another system involving rotating brushes or spinner plates is used by some commercial operators. Liquid flows by gravity to the distributor heads—two to six in number spaced under the lower wing—where rotating wire brushes or two closely spaced discs driven by propellers throw it out centrifugally at right angles to the line of flight. Shearing action of the slip stream helps to break the liquid into small droplets. This shearing effect also affects droplet size with boom-and-nozzle systems when nozzles are directed perpendicularly.

SPRAY DRIFT FROM AIRCRAFT SPRAYING

In aircraft spraying, the requirement of spreading a relatively few gallons of spray per acre, as contrasted to ground spraying, means that spray droplets must be smaller in order to give the same degree of coverage as measured by the number of droplets per square inch. In some wheat areas, as little as 1 gal of an oil solution of an ester of 2,4-D is sprayed on an acre. The spray is released at a greater height than in ground spraying, and the passage of the plane itself sets up turbulence. All these factors result in an accentuated spray-drift problem when applying herbicides that may be injurious to nearby fields.

It is good practice in calibrating a spray plane to include a determination of the range of droplet size as well as the spread and uniformity of deposit. One should avoid having too many droplets below about 100 microns diameter (approximately 1/250 in.) for, as shown by

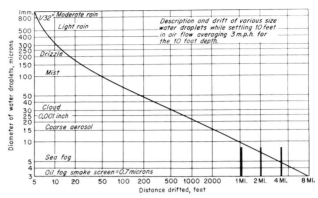

FIGURE 20-11. Chart showing the relation between droplet size and distance of spray droplets drift in a 3-mph wind.

the chart in Figure 20-11, the distance that droplets of given size are carried by air currents while falling a given distance increases rapidly with diameters below the 50- to 100-micron range.

Aircraft spraying should, of course, be done when air is still or nearly so; this not only avoids drift but ensures better deposits. Convectional currents, which usually occur at temperatures above 85°F when the sun is high, prevent sprays from settling and so accentuate drift.

APPLICATION OF INVERT EMULSIONS

A recent advance in the use of chlorophenoxy herbicides is the formulation of invert-type (water-in-oil) emulsions. These are thick and may be applied in such a way that few satellite droplets are formed, hence the drift problem is reduced. Figure 20-12 shows an invert-type emulsion of 2,4-D (top), and the spray boom of a plane with large hose connections and a positive-displacement pump. Figure 20-13 shows a rotary dispenser for invert emulsion attached to the front of a helicopter. This method is being developed for using the phenoxy-type herbicides in regions where sensitive crops are growing.

One company has marketed a device which mixes the invert emulsion at the nozzle, thus avoiding pumping the thick, viscous emulsion. A number of thickening agents made of polysaccharide gum are used. These thickeners increase the viscosity of the spray solution and materially reduce the number of very fine droplets. Another device is the microfoil boom, consisting of many small capillary tubes inserted into a large distributor pipe; the capillaries order the flow of solution into small paralleled streams that break up into uniform-sized drop-

FIGURE 20-12. Top, a drum of emulsion invert-type mixed and ready for application; bottom, a spray boom with positive displacement pump, large hose connections and low-pressure nozzles for applying invert-type emulsions. (Photographs by courtesy of N. B. Akesson.)

lets, relatively free of the satellite fines that drift great distances. An additional method is the inclusion of a foaming agent. When applied through air-inducting nozzles, such spray mixtures issue from the spray boom as a foam. Not particularly effective from the air, this foam-type spray is relatively free of fine droplets when applied by ground rig.

While all of the above methods greatly reduce the production of the small, 50 micron or less, droplets, Brazelton et al. (1973) point out that large-drop producers, whether of the nozzle type or the microfoil, or those resulting from formulation, such as thickeners, particulating agents, or foam still produce some fines. One should not ignore this but, as Brazelton et al. point out, all precautions concerning drift should be observed. Microweather, temperature, humidity, wind velocity, and inversions should be taken into account; proximity to susceptible crops is of paramount importance.

FIGURE 20-13. A rotary invert-emulsion dispenser on the front of a helicopter. This disk rotates, throwing the droplets from the flow-type nozzles where they are driven outward and downward by the air currents from the rotor of the helicopter. (Photograph by courtesy of N. B. Akesson.)

APPLICATORS FOR GRANULAR HERBICIDES

With the rapid increase in popularity of granular formulations of preemergence herbicides, there has been a corresponding interest in machines to apply these materials. Many of these machines are simply chemical applicators designed to deliver the granular materials in an even coating over the soil surface for incorporation by rainfall. These are usually refined fertilizer drills, and they may be limited with respect to the minimum volume which they apply so that diluents or additives must be used to provide sufficient volume. Danielson and Chambers (1957) describe an experimental field distributor for granular herbicides. This machine employs an auger enclosed in a slotted tube as a metering device, and it is designed for application of granulated herbicides based on Attaclay as a carrier in the granules. An applicator for granulated herbicides may be bought in kit form for attaching to a planter. Figure 20–14 shows the applicator in place on a planter.

FIGURE 20-14.   Gandy granular herbicide applicator in place on a planter. (Photograph by courtesy of the Gandy Company, Owatonna, Minn.)

With the mechanization of row-crop agriculture, once a seedbed has been prepared, it is now possible to carry a crop through to harvest with no tillage and with little need for compacting the soil by driving tractors through the crop. Figure 20–15 shows a planter equipped with applicators for insecticides and granular herbicides.

As *soil fumigants* of low volatility such as *Vapam* and *Eptam* have been introduced, soil incorporation has been found essential for efficient use of these materials. For soil incorporation, the soil must be stirred after or during application of the chemical to the surface. Application may be as a spray, as a dry, pulverized chemical, or as granules. The simplest method is simply discing or rototilling after the application of the chemical. Now, many machines are in use that plant and cover the seeds, apply the chemical, and smooth the row. Some designs enable one to plant the seed to a certain depth and to incorporate the herbicide to a lesser depth. This placement tends to increase the selectivity of the chemical on the crop and hence to allow the application of a dosage which might injure the crop if incorporated to the same depth as the seed.

FIGURE 20-15.   Gandy granular herbicide applicators (rear) and insecticide applicators (front) mounted on a planter and ready for operation. (Photograph by courtesy of the Gandy Company, Owatonna, Minn.)

One sugar-beet grower in California has built a machine that shapes the beds, plants the seed, applies fertilizer, sprays on a preemergence herbicide, and smooths the top of the bed all in one operation. While this multiple operation makes for a very complicated machine, it saves time and money.

FUMIGANT INJECTORS

Fumigant injectors of both hand- and power-operated types are available commercially; as with field sprayers, the user may construct a power injector by assembling the component parts. The rapid increase of soil nematodes and soil-inhabiting insects has resulted in the designing of numerous modifications in fumigant injectors to meet special requirements. In general, a fumigant injector can be thought of as an underground sprayer. It has a reservoir tank, a pump, and a metering device for controlling the delivery rate so that an exact dosage is applied. In hand-operated injectors (Fig. 20–16) the metering device is the pump itself. Such pumps are the positive-displacement

FIGURE 20-16. A hand-operated fumigant injector. (Photograph by courtesy of Wheeler, Reynolds, and Stauffer, San Francisco, California.)

type and are calibrated by varying the stroke. In most power injectors, (Fig. 20–17) a continuous stream of fumigant is applied either in the bottom of the plow furrow or behind the shanks of a chisel-cultivator; in these, the rate of delivery is set by the line pressure and by the size of the orifice, just as with spray nozzles. Delivery rate and tractor speed then determine the gallons of fumigant per acre.

Tractor-mounted field sprayers may be converted to fumigant injectors by placing the spray boom with a manifold over the tool bar; by clamping chisel shanks to the tool bar with a delivery tube welded on down the back; and by providing a means of placing a metering orifice in the line between the manifold and the delivery tubes. Some manufacturers provide the necessary parts for the conversion.

Subsurface Applicators

Volatile preplant herbicides present an application problem. If applied to the soil surface for subsequent mixing by discing or roto-tilling, considerable chemical is lost and much is wasted in the dry top soil layer. If injected by means of the standard fumigant injector, the distribution is not right to provide a weed-free band in which the crop

FIGURE 20-17. A fumigant injector power-operated with subsoiler shanks raised. The float and roller smooth and pack the soil to prevent loss of vapor. (Photograph by courtesy of Wheeler, Reynolds, and Stauffer, San Francisco, California.)

grows. Wooten and McWhorter (1961) describe a machine that combines a subsurface knife with one or more spray nozzles so arranged that the soil is lifted by the knife, and the herbicide is sprayed immediately beneath the lifted soil as it settles behind the knife. This puts the chemical in immediate contact with the moist soil; its distribution is such that a weed-free band is provided within which the crop grows. Using Eptam, these workers produced a crop of cotton that required 5.4 hr of hoe labor per acre as contrasted with 17.8 hr where no herbicide was applied.

The subsurface applicator or spray blade, as it is now called, has been adapted for applying preemergence herbicides having a low but effective vapor pressure; two such materials in use are dichlobenil and trifluralin. These materials, applied to the bare soil surface and covered by 4 to 6 inches of pulverized soil, will suppress growth of field bindweed throughout a whole growing season. In use now for several years, this treatment is being adopted by orchardists, vineyardists, and field-crop growers throughout the irrigated Southwest. An excellent report on field bindweed including directions for using trifluralin in its control by the sprayblade method has been put out by the Elanco Products Company (Anon., 1972).

REFERENCES

Anon. 1972. Field bindweed. Getting to the root of the problem. Indianapolis: Elanco, Indiana EA 2094 5-1-72.

Akesson, Norman B. and W. A. Harvey. 1948. Chemical weed-control equipment. *Calif. Agr. Expt. Sta. Cir.* 389:1–43.

Brazelton, R. W., N. B. Akesson, and W. B. Yates. 1973. Safety from drift. *Calif. Weed Conf. 25th Ann. Proc.* Anaheim, Calif., p. 81–90.

Danielson, L. L., and P. R. Chambers. 1957. A field distributor for granular herbicide trials. *Weeds* 5(2):108–111.

Day, B. E. 1958. A simplified logarithmic plot sprayer. *Weeds* 6(4):441–446.

Friesen, G. 1958. The use of a variable dosage sprayer in weed control. *Canad. Jour. Plant Sci.* 38:300–306.

Grundy, W. M., and J. M. Bennett. 1960. Aerial application of herbicides for right-of-way brush control. *Down to Earth* 16(2):6–10.

Leasure, J. K. 1959. A logarithmic-concentration sprayer for small plot use. *Weeds* 7(1):91–97.

Leasure, J. K. and W. J. Falkenstein. 1958. A logarithmic concentration sprayer for small plot use. *Down to Earth* 14(3):2–5.

McLane, S. R., E. W. Dean, and C. E. Minarik. 1954. Precision sprayer for small plots. *Weeds* 3(1):75–79.

Pfeiffer, R., R. T. Brunskill, and G. S. Hartley. 1955. A variable dosage sprayer for agricultural experiments. *Nature* 176:472–473.

Wensley, G. I. 1958. Variable dosage sprayer. *Northeast. Weed Control Conf.* 12:1–7.

Wooten, D. B., and C. G. McWhorter. 1961. A device for surface application of herbicides. *Weeds* 9(1):36–41.

Yates, W. E. 1960. Minimizing spray drift hazards. *Down to Earth* 16(2):15–19.

——— and F. M. Ashton. 1960. Logarithmic dosage sprayer. *Agr. Engin.* 41(7):436–442.

21

Weeds in Our Environment

Ecology is not new but realization of its importance is. Human ecology began to change rapidly with the advent of agriculture. The deleterious effects of man's activities on the environment were greatly intensified with the coming of the industrial revolution. And as population continues to increase and the land area available per person gets to be smaller and smaller, pollution will continue to be a problem.

Much of the current hysteria over pollution arose during the Vietnam war but the causes of pollution have been with us for a long time and correction of pollution will be an expensive process. The use of agricultural chemicals has been caught up in the excitement over pollution. Since the publication of *Silent Spring* in 1962, pesticides have been the target of tremendous activity, some good, but some harmful. The banning of 2,4,5-T for use around the home was not based on evidence for harm to mankind but on animal experiments in which relatively massive doses of 2,4,5-T, containing dioxin as a contaminant, were injected into rats. And the tremendous benefits of 2,4,5-T use in forests and rangelands were overlooked.

All people associated with agriculture recognize the vital role of fertilizers and pesticides in the production of the food required by our present world population. Herbicides in general have not been condemned in the way that insecticides have, but there are recurring attempts to ban the use of all of the phenoxy materials. Just as the banning of DDT is bringing about a resurgence of malaria in India, loss of the phenoxy compounds would soon result in the return of the brassicas and poppies that for centuries held down the yields of cereal crops.

Weeds have been with us since the beginning of agriculture. When man started planting crops and pulling weeds he changed his environment in favor of food-crop production. The only reason for controlling weeds is to change the environment. These changes are necessary to permit the production of food and fiber in amounts needed to feed and clothe our population. They are necessary to insure safety from fire, from the screening effects that obstruct traffic, and from the harmful effects of allergy sources, poison oak, ragweed, etc. And they are essential to the maintenance of the beauty of our mountains, lakes, and shores. Campsites, fishing and swimming areas, and out-of-doors playgrounds should be free of weeds, particularly poison oak and poison ivy.

Vegetation management, including weed control is essential to our health, our nourishment, and our enjoyment of life. These practices alter the botanical environment around us, the composition of the flora and the fauna, the ecology. This is true regardless of the methods we use be they hand pulling, hoeing, plowing, cultivating, burning, or use of chemicals. It is also true of biological control, that is, the use of insects, fungi, or bacteria that selectively destroy weedy plants.

Thus, any successful weed-control practice must change the environment; that is its purpose. Our concern is that it achieves the objective without producing harmful side effects on the soil or on nontarget crop plants. Today our principal concern is with herbicides. Because certain chlorinated hydrocarbon insecticides such as DDT have relatively long persistence in the environment and enter food chains in organisms and biomagnify to high levels, all pesticides have become suspect. Organic herbicides have had little criticism because most of them are low in mammalian toxicity and rapidly biodegradable. The major challenge has been 2,4,5-T as mentioned in Chapter 1.

Environmental contamination by herbicides may be considered under four headings:

1. Entry into the environment
2. Persistence in the environment
3. Residues in the environment
4. Effects on organisms in the environment

1. In order to be effective herbicides must enter the target plants and either kill by contact or move to target sites within the plant. Only when they persist in plant residues or in the soil sufficiently to affect subsequent crops do they become a problem. Many herbicides react with the tissues of the target plant and are detoxified. Some persist in the plant residues and the surrounding soil and so affect subsequent crops. And some move as drifting particles (Fig. 21–1) as vapor or attached to drifting or washing soil. These can do harm and such

FIGURE 21-1. Examples of spray drift from airplanes. Top, rotary-dispenser-type application; bottom, boom with nozzles. Invert emulsions and particulating agents appreciably reduce the fine particles that are shown in these photos. (Photographs by courtesy of N. B. Akesson.)

environmental effects must be avoided. Technologies to handle such situations are being developed.

Drift has been largely eliminated by proper nozzle and boom design, by use of invert-emulsion formulations, use of particulating agents, and change, where possible, to clean, granular products.

Volatility can be avoided by use of heavy esters and salt formulations of the phenoxy compounds. Successful use of certain soil-borne herbicides, such as dichlobenil and trifluralin, which are effective through the vapor phase depends upon a certain low volatility for their effectiveness. They do not present any problems to neighboring or subsequent crops.

In many cases where soil-borne chemicals are used leaching is essential to uptake by living roots which exist only in moist soil. Solubility, rainfall or irrigation, colloidal fixing, and the nature of the chemical all affect the disposition of the herbicide in the soil. Knowledge of these matters is essential to the successful use of such herbicides. So far, no evidence of ground-water contamination from field use of herbicides has been found.

Surface movement of herbicides on soil particles is possible, depending upon such factors as slope of the area, permeability of the soil, state of tilth of the surface, amount and intensity of rainfall, formulation and rate of application, and vegetative cover. A few cases of wind-borne movement of soil carrying 2,4-D have been experienced, and cases of the washing of water-soluble herbicides around sprinkler heads in turf have occurred. No serious wide-scale examples of surface movement of herbicides have been experienced.

2. Appendix Table 3 presents data on the persistence of a number of herbicides in some irrigated California soils. It should be stressed that these values vary greatly with soil type, soil moisture, organic matter, temperature, and the test plant being used in the bioassay.

The length of time a herbicide remains active or persists in soils is important because it relates to the length of time that effective weed control can be expected. Persistence is also important because it affects subsequent crops which may be grown in soils treated earlier. There are six factors which affect herbicide persistence (carry-over) in soil. These are: microorganism decomposition, chemical degradation, adsorption to soil colloids or organic matter, leaching, volatility, and photodecomposition. In addition to these six factors, the dosage rate at which the herbicide is applied will have an effect on activity. However, longevity is not always a reflection of rate since each of the above factors can vary in their influence on herbicide loss from soils.

Probably of greatest influence on herbicide persistence are degradation by soil microorganisms and adsorption. Some herbicides are readily used as energy sources by microorganisms whereas others are used only incidently. Likewise, certain herbicides have greater affinity than others for adsorption to soil colloids and organic matter. Thus, these cases account for the relative independence of persistence to rate of herbicide applied.

In Appendix Table 3, persistence values for each of the herbicides has been determined from research and label information as well as field observations. The values are based on phytotoxicity to a susceptible plant species and reflect only the amount of herbicide residues in soils which may affect subsequent crops. In reality, some herbicide will remain in these soils for long periods and therefore could be detected by sensitive analytical methods.

3.   Residues of herbicides in the environment have been studied in numerous monitoring surveys in the United States. We recognize that treated soils and waters contain herbicides for some period after treatment; this is necessary or we would not kill the weeds. Our concern is with the possibility that appreciable residues may persist for long periods after treatment, or that herbicide residues may occur in untreated or nontarget sites.

Since residues are reported in terms of concentration, that is parts per million (ppm), parts per billion (ppb), or even parts per trillion (ppt), it is important to recognize what these figures actually mean in terms that we can recognize. The amount of soil covering an acre to a depth of 1 foot (one acre foot) weighs about 3½ million pounds. Thus if we apply one pound of chemical per acre and mix it thoroughly throughout the upper foot of soil, the concentration would be 1/3.5 or about 0.29 ppm. If we mix it with only the top 6 inches of soil the concentration would be doubled, about 0.58 ppm.

If we are considering water, we should remember that water weighs 62.4 pounds per cubic foot, or 8.33 pounds per gallon. Thus an acre foot of water, enough to cover an acre one foot deep, weighs 2.7 million pounds and an application of an herbicide at 1 pound per acre foot would result in a concentration of 1/2.7 or about 0.37 ppm. In terms of gallons, 8.33 pounds of herbicide are required to give a concentration of 1 ppm in a million gallons of water.

Some concept of the size of 1 ppb can be obtained by consideration of the population of the whole earth, which is approaching 4 billion people. Thus 4 people represent 1 ppb of all of the people on the earth. Residue concentrations need interpretation in terms of amounts as well as concentrations.

Residues in soils have been monitored for years. A detailed study in six areas over several years revealed only minor amounts of phenoxy herbicides. Out of 264 samples only 4 contained 2,4-D, with an average concentration of 0.032 ppm. None contained 2,4,5-T. In a series of soil samples from grain fields with a known history of 2,4-D use, only 4 samples out of nearly 100 showed 2,4-D and these at fractions of a ppm. In none of these surveys has there been evidence of excessive accumulation of any herbicide in the soil environment.

Likewise there has been no evidence of accumulation in water. A monthly survey of 11 major streams in the western United States in 1967 revealed no residues of 2,4-D, 2,4,5-T, or silvex. A U.S. Geological survey of 20 sites in western streams using refined analytical tech-

FIGURE 21-2. Smoke is used as an indicator of wind direction and velocity. Fine particles of spray as shown in **FIG. 21-1** may hang in the air for many minutes. Finer particles may remain for hours and drift for miles. The still condition shown here is not considered as favorable as a slight breeze away from a sensitive crop.

niques showed only fractional parts per billion of 2,4-D, 2,4,5-T, and silvex in a few out of several hundred samples analysed. Again there is no evidence in any of the studies of accumulation of phenoxy herbicides.

Residue data on herbicides in plants are required for registration. Breakdown curves and total amounts of residues are the basis for the tolerances set. There are pages of such data in every petition for a tolerance. Spot checks by regulatory officials rarely reveal residues in crop plants in excess of established tolerances when the pattern of use has followed label instructions. There is no evidence of excessive herbicide residues in any of our foods.

Residues in animal products are also monitored. In 1969 the consumer and marketing service of the U.S.D.A. analysed 240 samples of red meat fatty tissue from 44 locations across the United States for 2,4-D. Over 96 percent showed no residue, with only 3 samples showing more than 0.10 ppm. None showed as much as 1.0 ppm. There is also no evidence of accumulation in milk, even when 2,4-D was fed directly to lactating cows.

Residues in the air have had only limited study but, as indicated earlier, drift or volatility may result in air contamination for brief

FIGURE 21-3. Plots on the International Rice Research Institution at Laguna, the Philippines. Herbicides are regularly used to eliminate weeds, so that yields of these highly yielding varieties may be compared without interference by competing weeds.

periods (Fig. 21-2). Usually the effects are evidenced on neighboring vegetation; willow and cottonwood trees and certain grape varieties are examples. The symptoms decrease rapidly with distance. A careful study in Washington state revealed a maximum concentration of about 2 ppm of 2,4-D in the air during the spraying season, but considerably less than 1 ppm as an average concentration over a period of days.

4.   Organisms in the environment are affected in several ways. An extensive bibliography on toxic effects of herbicides to a wide variety of organisms was published by the National Agricultural Library in 1968.

There are great numbers of published articles covering specific effects of herbicides on specific organisms.

This book describes the effects of a great number of herbicides on plants. We use herbicides to change the botanical composition of our environment. Selective herbicides are used to kill weeds with a minimum of injury to crop species (Fig. 21–3). Even intensive use of herbicides has produced changes in only limited areas and there are no known instances of the disappearance of any plant species through the use of herbicides.

With the exception of a few herbicides, such as sodium arsenite and the dinitro phenols, which are acutely toxic to animals, the majority of current herbicides may be consumed in large quantities before toxic symptoms appear. Extensive feeding tests are run on all herbicides prior to registration and the hazards, if any, are known. The only animal deaths reported in the last two decades from herbicide use involved sodium arsenite, the use of which is now strictly regulated. This should be contrasted with the many livestock losses from poisonous plants over the same period. Most herbicides are rapidly eliminated from animals in their excreta. At normal recommended rates of application, our currently used herbicides appear to have no direct effects on wild life or farm animals. Residues have not appeared in milk and eggs. There is no evidence of wildlife destruction; to the contrary there are many reports on the beneficial effects of brush and weedy-tree removal on the carrying capacity of ranges and growth of protected forest trees. Changes in plant cover on limited areas have caused population movements to other untreated areas; movement of livestock on the other hand is usually to the treated lands. There has been only limited use of herbicides for improving forage on wildlife areas, a practice that justifies much study.

For man, the only toxic effects reported on the direct ingestion of herbicides have concerned intentional suicide by adults or accidental ingestion by children from carelessness by adults, such as storage of small quantities in soft drink bottles in garages or storerooms. And so, in the final analysis there is no evidence that the use of herbicides today contributes to deterioration of the environment. And the great abundance of clean healthy foods on the shelves of our markets attests the benefits that accrue from the control of our weed pests.[*]

---

[*]Much of the information reported in this chapter has been obtained from Harvey, W. A. 1971. Effects of Weed Control on the Environment. *Calif. Weed Conf. 23rd Annual Meeting, Proceedings*. Sacramento, Calif., Jan. 18–20. pp. 68–73.

Appendix

CONVENIENT MEASURES

1 foot = 12 inches = ⅓ yard
1 yard = 36 inches = 3 feet
1 rod = 16.5 feet = 5.5 yards
1 mile = 5,280 feet = 1,760 yards = 320 rods

1 millimeter (mm) = 0.0394 inch or 1/25 inch
1 centimeter (cm) = 0.3937 inch or 2/5 inch
1 decimeter (dm) = 3.937 inches or approximately 4 inches
1 meter (m) = 3.28 feet or 39⅓ inches
1 kilometer = 1,000 meters or 3,280 feet 10 inches, approximately 0.62 mile

1 inch (in.) = 25.4 millimeters or about 2½ centimeters
1 foot (ft) = 30.5 centimeters or 0.305 meter
1 yard = 0.914 meter
1 rod = 5.03 meters
1 mile = 1.609 kilometers

1 square yard = 9 square feet = 0.8361 square meter
1 square rod = 272¼ square feet or 30.3 square yards or 25.293 square meters
1 acre = 43,560 square feet or 4,840 square yards or 160 square rods or approximately 0.4 hectare
1 hectare = 2.471 acres or 10,000 square meters
1 square mile = 640 acres or 259.0 hectares

1 ounce (oz) = 28.35 grams
1 pound (lb) = 453.6 grams or 0.4536 kilograms
1 ton = 2,000 pounds or 907.2 kilograms
1 gram (g) = 0.035 ounces
1 kilogram = 35.27 ounces or 2.20 pounds
1 fluid ounce (fl oz) = 29.57 cubic centimeters

For *water* or any other substance with specific gravity of 1.0:

1 pint (pt.) = 1.043 pounds or 472.1 grams
1 quart = 2.086 pounds or 944.2 grams
1 gallon (gal) = 8.345 pounds
1 cubic foot (cu ft) = 62.428 pounds or 7.48 gallons

An area 1 mile by 1 rod = 2 acres
1 mile by 8¼ feet = 1 acre
1 mile by 1 foot = approximately ⅛ acre or 20 square rods
8¼ miles by 1 foot = 1 acre
4 rods by 4 rods = 16 square rods or 1/10 acre

1 foot head of water = 0.43 pounds pressure
1 pound per square inch pressure = 2.31 feet water
Hydraulic horse power = gallons per minute × pressure × 0.000584
1 mile per hour = 1.47 feet per second or 88 feet per minute

Application rates based on area:

1 ounce per square foot = 9 ounces per square yard = approximately 17 pounds per square rod or 2,722.5 pounds per acre
1 ounce per square yard = approximately 2 pounds per square rod or 302.5 pounds per acre
1 pound per square rod = approximately ½ ounce per square yard or 160 pounds per acre
1 pound per 100 square feet = 2.72 pounds per square rod or 435.6 pounds per acre
1 pint per square yard = approximately 3¾ gallons per square rod
1 cup per square rod = 10 gallons per acre
1 pint per square rod = 20 gallons per acre
1 quart per square rod = 40 gallons per acre
1 gallon per square rod = 160 gallon per acre

WEIGHT-VOLUME EQUIVALENTS OF WATER*

	1 gallon	1 quart	1 pint
Pounds...............	8.338	2.084	1.042
Ounces...............	133.527	33.381	16.690
Grams	3,782.03	945.507	472.753
Cubic inches	231.0	57.75	28.875
Cubic feet	0.1337	0.0334	0.0167
Fluid ounces	128.0	32.0	16.0
Milliliters.............	3,782.03	945.507	472.753
Liters	3.782	0.945	0.472

*The specific gravity of water = 1.

Appendix Table 1. Listing of Herbicides by Common Name, Trade Name, Chemical Name and Manufacturer

Common Name	Trade Name	Chemical Name	Manufacturer
AC 52993	Prowl	*N*-(ethylpropyl)-2,6-dinitro-3,4-xylidine	Amer. Cyanamid
Acrolein	Aqualin	acrolein, 2-propenal	Shell
Alachlor	Lasso	2-chloro-2′,6′-diethyl-*N*-(methoxymethyl)acetanilide	Monsanto
Allyl alcohol	Allyl alcohol	Propen-0l-3	Shell
AMA	Methar	ammonium methylarsonate	Vineland, Cleary
Ametryne	Evik	2-(ethylamino)-4-(isopropylamino)-6-(methylthio)-s-triazine	Ciba-Geigy
Amitrole	Weedazol	3-amino-s-triazole	Amchem
Amitrole-T	Cytrol	3-amino-s-triazole plus ammonium thiocyanate	Amchem
AMS	Ammate	ammonium sulfamate	duPont, Chipman
Anisuron	—	*N*′-(3,4-dichlorophenyl)-*N*′-(4-methoxybenzoyl)-*N,N*-dimethylurea	
Antor	H22234	*N*-chloroacetyl-*N*-(2,6-diethylphenyl)-glycine ethyl ester	Hercules
Arsenate-calcium	Chip-Cal	tricalcium arsenite	Chipman
Arsenite-sodium	—		
Asulam	Asulox	Methyl sulfanilylcarbamate	May and Baker
Atratone	Gesatamin	2-methoxy-4-ethylamino-6-isopropylamino-s-triazine	Ciba-Geigy
Atrazine	AAtrex	2-chloro-4-(ethylamino)-6-(isopropylamino)-s-triazine	Ciba-Geigy
Azide	Kazide	KN_3, NaN_3	Pittsburg P.G.
Aziprotryn	Mesoranil, Brasoran	2-azido-4-isopropylamino-6-methylmercapto-1,3,5-triazine	Ciba-Geigy
Banair	Banair	2-methoxy-3,6-dichlorobenzene	I. C. I.
Bandane	Bandane, Halts	4,5,6,7,8,8-hexachloro-3a,4,7,7a tetrahydro-4,7-methanoindene isomers	Velsicol

408

Barban	Carbyne	4-chloro-2 butynyl-*m*-chlorocarbanilate	Gulf
Benazolin	Cornox, RD-7693	4-chloro-2-oxo-benzothiazoline-3yl-acetic acid	Boots
Benefin	Balan, Benfluralin	*N*-butyl-*N*-ethyl-α,α,α-trifluoro-2,6-dinitro-*p*-toluidine	
Benoxazole	—	2-(2-chlorobenzylthio)-5-propyl-1,3,4-oxadiazole	Elanco
Bensulide	Betasan, Prefar	*0,0*-diisopropyl phosphorodithioate *S*-ester with *N*-(2-mercaptoethyl) benzenesulfonamide	Takeda
Bentazon	Basagran	3-isopropyl-2,1,3-benzothiadiazinone-(4)-2,2-dioxide	Stauffer
Benthiocarb	Bolero, Saturn	*S*(4-chlorobenzyl)-*N,N*-diethylthiolcarbamate	BASF
Bentranil	Bentranil	2-phenyl-3,1-benzoxazinone-4	Kumiai Chem
Benzadox	Topcide	(benzamidooxyacetic) acid	BASF
Benzazin	BAS 1700 H	2-phenyl-3,1-benzoxazinone-(4)	Gulf
Benzomarc	Benzomarc	*N*-benzoyl-*N*-(3,4-dichlorophenyl)-*N'*,*N'*-dimethylurea	BASF
Benzthiazuron	Gatnon	*N*-(2-benzthiazolyl)-*N'*-methylurea	Pechiney Progil
Bidisin	Bay 5710H	α-chloro-β-(4-chlorophenyl)-methyl propionate	Bayer
Bifenox	Modown-TM	Methyl-5-(2,4-dichlorophenoxy)-2-nitrobenzoate	Bayer
Boron salts	Borax, Borascu	$Na_2 B_4 O_7 . 10 H_2O$	Mobil
Bromacil	Hyvar X	5-bromo-3-*sec*-butyl-6-methyluracil	U. S. Borax
Bromofenoxim	Faneron	3,5-dibromo-4-hydroxybenzaldoxime-*O*-(2'4'-dinitrophenyl)-ether	duPont
Bromoxynil	Brominal, Butril	3,5-dibromo-4-hydroxybenzonitrile	CIBA-Geigy
Brompyrazon	BAS 2430 H	5-amino-4 bromo-2-phenyl-3(2*H*)-pyridazinone	Amchem, Chipman
Butachlor	Machete	2-chloro-2',6'-diethyl-*N*-(butoxymethyl)acetanilide	BASF
Butam	S15544	*N*-benzyl-*N*-isopropyltrimethylacetamide	Monsanto
Butralin	Amex-820	*N*-*sec*-butyl-4-*tert*-butyl-2,6-dinitroaniline	Gulf Oil Corp.
Buturon	Etapur	3-(*p*-chlorophenyl)-1-methyl-1-(1-methyl-2-propynyl) urea	Amchem
			BASF

Appendix Table 1. *(continued)*

Common Name	Trade Name	Chemical Name	Manufacturer
Butylate	Sutan	S-ethyl diisobutylthiocarbamate	Stauffer
Cacodylic acid	Phytar, Erase	Hydroxydimethylarsine oxide	Ansul
Calar	CAMA	Calcium acid methane arsonate	Vineland
Calcium cyanamid	Cyanamid	Calcium cyanamid	Cyanamide
Carbasulam	M & B 9555	Methyl-N-4-[methoxycarbamoyl] benzenesulfonyl-carbamate	May and Baker
Carbetamide	Legurame	D-N-ethylacetamide carbanilate (ester)	Rhodia
CDAA	Randox, Allidochlor	N,N-diallyl-2-chloroacetamide	Monsanto
CDEA	—	2-chloro-N,N-diethylacetamide	Monsanto
CDEC	Vegedex, Sulfallate	2-chloroallyl diethyldithiocarbamate	Monsanto
Chloramben	Amiben, Vegiben	2-amino-2,5-dichlorobenzoic acid	Amchem
Chlorate, sodium	—	Sodium chlorate, $NaClO_3$	Pennsalt, Chipman
Chlorazon	Chlorazon	1-phenyl-4-(α-hydroxy-β',β',β'-trichloroethyl)-amino-5-chloropyridazone-6	BASF
Chlorbromuron	Maloran, Bromex	3-(4-bromo-3-chlorophenyl)-1-methoxy-1-methylurea	CIBA-Geigy
Chlorbufam	BIPC, chlorinate	Butyn-1-yl-3-N-3-chlorophenylcarbamate	BASF
Chlorflurazol	NC 3363	2-trifluoromethyl-4,5-dichlorobenzimidazole	Fisons
Chlorflurenol	Maintain, CF 125	2-chloro-9-hydroxyfluorenecarboxylic acid-9-methyl ester	U. S. Borax
Chlornidine	—	[N,N(2-chloroethyl)-2,6-dinitro-4-methylaniline]	
Chloropicrin	Chloropicrin	Trichloronitromethane	Dow, Monsanto
Chloropon	—	2,2,3-trichloropropionic acid	
Cloroxuron	Tenoran, Norex	3-[p-(p-chlorophenoxy)phenyl]-1,1-dimethylurea	CIBA-Geigy

Chlorpropham	CIPC, Furloe	Isopropyl *m*-chlorocarbanilate	Pittsburg P. G.
Chlorthiamid	Prefix	2,4-dichlorothiobenzamide	Shell
Chlortoluron	Dicuron	*N'*-(3-chloro-4-methylphenyl)*N*,*N*,-dimethyl urea	CIBA-Geigy
Cisanilide	Rowtate	*cis*-2,5-dimethyl-*N*-phenyl-pyrralidine-carboxamide	Diamond Shamrock Corp.
CMA	Calar, Crab-E-Rad	Calcium methanearsonate	
Coppersulfate	Bluestone	Cu SO$_4$	Mountain Copper
Cyanazine	Bladex, SD 15418	2,[4-chloro-6-(ethylamino)-*s*-triazine-2-ylamino]-2-methylpropionitrile	Shell
Cycloate	Ro-Neet	S-ethyl-*N*-ethylthiocyclohexanecarbamate	Stauffer
Cycluron	OMU	3-cyclooctyl-1,1-dimethyl urea	BASF
Cyperquat	S21634	1-methyl-4-phenylpyridium chloride	Gulf Oil Chem.
Cyprazine	Fox-4, Outfox	2-chloro-4-(cyclopropylamino)-6-isopropylamino-triazine	Gulf
Cyprazole	--	*N*-5-(2-chloro-1,1-dimethylethyl)-1,3,4-thiadiazol-2-yl] cyclopropane carboxamide	Gulf
Cypromid	Clobber	3',4'-dichlorocyclopropanecarboxanilide	Gulf
Dalapon	Dowpon, Basfapon	2,2-dichloropropionic acid, sodium salt	Dow
Dazomet	Mylone, DMTT	Tetrahydro-3,5-dimethyl-2*H*-1,3,5-thiadiazine-2-thione	Union Carbide
DBA	DBA	2,2-dichlorobutyrate, sodium salt	Dow
DCPA	Dacthal	Dimethyl tetrachloroterphtalate	Diamond Shamrock
Decazolin	BAS 3490 H	1-(α,α-dimethyl-*β*-acetoxypropionyl)-3-isopropyl-2,4-dioxodecahydroguinazoline	BASF
Delachlor	CP 52223, CP 53619	2-chloro-*N*-(isobutoxymethyl)-2'.6'-acetoxilidide	Monsanto
Desmedipham	EP-475, Bethanol 475	Ethyl-*m*-hydroxycarbanilate carbanilate (ester)	Nor-Am
Desmetryne	Semeron	2-(isopropylamino)-4-(methylamino)-6-(ethylthio)-*s*-triazine	CIBA-Geigy

411

Common Name	Trade Name	Chemical Name	Manufacturer
Dillate	Avadex	S-(2,4-dichloroallyl)diisopropylthiocarbamate	Monsanto
Dicamba	Banvel	3,6-dichloro-o-anisic acid	Velsicol
Dichlobenil	Carsoron	2,6-dichlorobenzonitrile	Thompson Hayward
Dichlone	Phygon	2,3-dichloro-1,4-naphthoquinone	Niagara
Dichlormate	Rowmate, Sirmate	3,4-dichlorobenzyl methylcarbamate	Union Carbide
Dichlorprop	2,4-DP, Weedone	2-(2,4-dichlorophenoxy)propionic acid	Boots, Amchem
Dicryl	Chloranocryl	3',4'-dichloro-2-methylacrylanilide	Niagara
Difenoxuron	Pinoran	N-4-(p-methoxy-phenoxy)-phenyl-N',N'-dimethyl urea	CIBA-Geigy
Difenzoquat	Mataven, Avenge	1,2-dimethyl-3,5-diphenylpyrazolium methylsulfate	Amer. Cyanamid
Dimethazone	--	4,5-dimethoxy-2-phenylpyridazine-3(2H)-one	
Dinitramine	Cobex	$N4,N4$-diethyl-α,α,α-trifluoro-3,5-dinitrotoluene-2,4-diamine	U. S. Borax
Dinophenate	--	2,4-dinitrophenol-2,4-dinitro-6-s-butylphenyl carbonate	
Dinoprop	--	2-isopropyl-3-methyl-4,6-dinitrophenol	
Dinosam	DNAP	2-(1-methylbutyl)-4,6-dinitrophenol	Dow, Niagara
Dinoseb	DNBP Basaniten	2-sec-butyl-4,6-dinitrophenol	Dow, Niagara
Dinoseb-acetate	Aretite	2-sec-butyl-4,6-dinitrophenylacetate	Hoechst
Dinoterb-acetate	MC 1108	2-tert-butyl-4,6-dinitrophenylacetate	Murphy Chem.
Diphenamid	Dymid, Enide	N,N-dimethyl-2,2-diphenylacetamide	Elanco, Upjohn
Diphenatrile	Diphenatrile	Diphenylacetonitrile	Elanco
Dipropalin	--	N,N-di-n-propyl-2,6-dinitro-4-methylaniline	
Dipropetryn	Sancap	2-(ethylamino)-4,6-bis(isopropylamino)-s-triazine	Ciba Geigy
Diquat	Reglone	6,7-dihydrodipyrido[1,2-α:2',1'-c]pyrazinediium ion	ICI, Chipman, S. D.
Diuron	Karmex	3-(3,4-dichlorophenyl)-1,1-dimethyl urea	duPont

Common	Trade	Chemical	Company
DMPA	Zytron	O-(2,4-dichlorophenyl)O'-methyl-N-isopropyl phosphoramidothioate	Elanco
DNOC	Sinox	4,6-dinitro-o-cresol	Dow
DSMA	Ansar 184 Clout	Disodium methanearsonate	Dow / Ansul and others
Endothall	Aquathol, Des-i-cate	7-oxabicyclo[2,2,1]heptane-2,3-dicarboxylic acid	Pennwalt
EPTC	Eptam	S-ethyl dipropylthiocarbamate	Stauffer
Erbon	Baron	2(2,4,5-trichlorophenoxy)ethyl-2,2-dichloropropionate	Dow
Ethalfluralin	El 161	N-ethyl-N-(2-methyl-2-propenyl)-2,6-dinitro-4-trifluoromethyl)benezenamine	Eli Lilly & Co.
Ethiolate	Prefox	S-ethyl diethylthiocarbamate	
Etinofen	--	2-ethoxymethyl-4,6-dinitrophenol	BSI
EXD	Herbisan, sulfasan	O,O-diethyl dithio-bis-thioformate	Roberts, Monsanto
Fenac	Fenac	(2,3,6-trichlorophenyl) acetic acid	Amchem
Fenuron	Dybar	1,1-dimethyl-3-phenyl urea	duPont
Fenuron-TCA	Urab	1,1-dimethyl-3-phenyl urea plus TCA	Allied Chem. Corp.
Fluchloralin	BAS-3921-H, Basalin	N-(2-chloroethyl)-2,6-dinitro-N-propyl-4-trifluoromethyl aniline	BASF
Flumezin	BAS 3480 H	2-methyl-4-(3-trifluoromethylphenyl)-tetrahydro-1,2,4-oxadiazine-3,5-dione	BASF
Fluometuron	Cotoran Lanex	1,1-dimethyl-3-(α,α,α-trifluoro-m-tolyl) urea	CIBA-Geigy
Fluorodifen	Preforan Soyex	P-nitrophenyl α,α,α-trifluoro-2 nitro-p-tolyl ether	CIBA-Geigy
Flurenol	--	9-hydroxylfluorene carbonic acid-(9)	Merck
Fluromidine	Nortron	6-chloro-2-trifluoromethyl-3H-imidazo[4,5-b]pyridine	Fisons
Glyphosate	Roundup	N-(phosphonomethyl) glycine	Monsanto
Glytac	Tritak	Ethleneglycol-bis-(trichloroacetate)	Hooker

Common Name	Trade Name	Chemical Name	Manufacturer
Haloxydine	PP 493	3,5-dichloro-2,6-difluoro-4-hydroxypyridine	Plant Protection
HCA	HCA	1,1,1,3,3,3-hexachloro-2-propanone	General Chem
Hexaflurate	Nopalmate	Potassium hexafluoroarsenate	Pennwalt
Ioxynil	Certol, Actril	4-hydroxy-3,5-diiodobenzonitrile	Amchem
Ipazine		2-chloro-4-(diethylamino)-6-(isopropylamino)-s-triazine	Ciba-Geigy
Isonoruron	BAS-2103 H	*N*-[1 or 2-(3a,4,5,6,7,7a-hexahydro-4,7-methano-indanyl)] *N,N*-dimethyl urea	BASF
Isopropalin	Paarlan	2,6-dinitro-*N,N*-dipropylcumidine	Elanco
Karbutilate	Tandex	*tert*-butylcarbamic acid ester with 3-(*m*-hydroxyphenyl)-1,1-dimethyl urea	
Karsil	NIA-4562	2-methylvaleric-3,4-dichloroanilide	Niagara
KOCN	KOCN	Potassium cyanate	Niagara
			Cyanamide
Lenacil	Venzar	3-cyclohexyl-6-7-dihydroxy-1*H*-cyclopyrimidine-2,4(3*H*,5*H*)-dione	duPont
Linuron	Afalon, Lorox	3-(3,4-dichlorophenyl)-1-methoxy-1 methyl urea	duPont
MAA		Methanearsonic acid	
MAMA	Ansar 157	Monoammonium methane arsonate	Ansul
MCAA		*N*-methyl-a-chloroacetanilide	Ansul
MCPA	Methoxon	[(4-chloro-o-tolyl) oxy]acetic acid	Amchem, Chipman

Common name	Trade name	Chemical name	Manufacturer
MCPB	Cantrol, Thistrol	4-[4-chloro-o-tolyl)oxy]butyric acid	Amchem, Chipman
MCPES	—	2-[(4-chloro-o-toly)oxy]ethyl sodium sulfate	Union Carbide
Mecoprop	MCPP, Mecapex	2-[(4-chloro-o-tolyl)oxy]propionic acid	Chipman, Morton Salt
Medinoterb-acetate	MC-1488	2-tert-butyl-5-methyl-4,6-dinitrophenyl acetate	Murphy Chem.
Methabenzthi-azuron	Tribunil	N-(2-benzothiazoyl)N-methyl-N'-methyl urea	Bayer
Metham	Vapam	Sodium methyldithiocarbamate	Stauffer, duPont
Methazole	Probe	2-(3,4-dichlorophenyl)-4-methyl-1,2,4-oxadiozolidine-3,5-dione	
Methiuron	MH 090	N,N-dimethyl-N'-(3-methylphenyl)thiourea	Velsicol
Methometon	—	2-methoxy-4,6-bis(3-methoxypropylamino-1,3,5-triazine	Uniroyal
Methoprotryn	G36393	2-methylmercapto-4-(3-methoxypropylamino)-6-isopropyl-amino-1,3,5-triazine	Ciba-Geigy
Methylbromide	Profume, Dowfume	Methylbromide	Dow
Metobromuron	Patoran	3-(p-bromophenyl)-1-methoxy-1-methyl urea	Ciba-Geigy
Metoxuron	Dasanex	N-(3-chloro-4-methoxyphenyl)-N',N'-dimethyl urea	Sandoz-Schweiz
Metribuzin	Sencor	4-amino-6-tert-butyl-3-(methylthio)-as-triazine-5(4H)-one	
MH	MH-30	1,2-dihydro-3,6-pyridazinedione	Chemagro
MO 338	CNP	2,4,6-trichlorophenyl-4-nitrophenol ether	Uniroyal
Molinate	Ordram	S-ethylhexahydro-1H-azepine-1-carbothioate	Mitsui Chem. Ind. Ltd.
Monalide	Potablan	α,α-dimethylvalerianic acid-p-chloroanilide	Stauffer
Monolinuron	Aresin	3-(p-chlorophenyl)-1-methoxy-1-methyl urea	Shering
Monoxone	SMA	Monochloroacetic acid	duPont
Monuron	Telvar	3-(p-chlorophenyl)-1,1-dimethyl urea	Plant Protection Ltd.
Monuron-TCA	Urox	3-(p-chlorophenyl)-1,1-dimethylurea mono (trichloroacetate)	duPont
			Allied Chem.

Common Name	Trade Name	Chemical Name	Manufacturer
Morphamquat	Morphoxone	1,1-*bis*-(3,5-dimethylmorpholine-carboxymethyl)-4,4 dipyridilium dichloride	ICI
MSMA	Ansar 170	Monosodium methanearsonate	Ansul
Napropamide	Devrinol	2-(α-naphthoxy)-*N,N,*-diethylpropionamide	Stauffer
Naptalam	Alanap	*N*-1-naphthylphthalamic acid	Uniroyal
Neburon	Kloben	1-butyl-3-(3,4-dichlorophenyl)-1-methylurea	duPont
Nitralin	Planavin	4-(methylsulfonyl)-2,6-dinitro-*N,N*-dipropylaniline	Shell
Nitrofen	Tok-E 25	2,4-dichlorophenyl-*p*-nitrophenyl ether	Rohm & Haas
NOA	—	α-naphthoxy methyl acetate	Schering
NO-Crab	—	Calcium propanearsonate	
Norazine	G 30026	2-chloro-4-isopropylamino-6-methylamino-s-triazine	
Norflurazon	Zorail, San 9789	4-chloro-5(methylamino)-2-(α,α,α,-trifluoro-*m*-tolyl)-3-(2*H*)-pyridazinone	Ciba-Geigy
Nortran	NC8438	2-ethoxy-2,3-dihydro-3,3-dimethyl-5-benzoluranyl methanesulfonate	Sandoz-Wander / Fisons
Orga 3045	TFP	2,2,3,3-tetrafluro propionic acid, sodium salt	Nippon Soda Co.
Oryzalin	Surflan, Ryzelan	3,5-dinitro,*N*⁴,*N*⁴-dipropylsulfanilamide	Elanco
Oxadiazon	Ronstar	2-*tert*-butyl-4-(2,4,-dichloro-5-isopropyloxyphenyl)-Δ²-1,3,4-oxadiazolin-5-one	Rhodia
Oxapyrazon	BAS 3500 H	Dimethylamino ethanol salt of N-[1-phenyl-5-bromo-pyridazone-6-yl(4)]-oxamic acid	BASF

416

Paraquat	Gramoxone	1,1'-dimethyl-4,4'-bipyridinium ion	ICI, SO of Cal.
PBA	Benzak	Chlorinated benzoic acid	Amchem, duPont
PCP	Penta	Pentachlorophenol. Also the sodium salt	Dow, Monsanto
Pebulate	Tillam	S-propyl butylethylthiocarbamate	Stauffer
Pencal	Chip-cal	Calcium arsenate	Rhodia Inc.
Perfluidone	Destun.	1,1,1-trifluoro-4-(phenylsulfonyl)-methane sulfono-O-toluidide	3M Co.
Phenmedipham	Betanal	methyl-*m*-hydroxycarbanilate-*m*-methylcarbanilate	Shering, Nor-Am
Picloram	Tordon Amdon	4-amino-3,5,6-trichloropicolinic acid	Dow
PMA	Agrosan	(aceto) phenylmercury	Linck, Cleary, Scott
Procyazine	CGA-18762	2-[[4,chloro-6-(cyclopropylamino)-*s*-triazine-2-yl]amino]-2-methylpropionitrile	Ciba-Geigy
Profluralin	Tolban	N-(cyclopropylmethyl)-2,6-dinitro-N-propyl-4-trifluoromethyl aniline	Ciba Geigy
Prometone	Pramitol	2,4-*bis*-(isopropylamino)-6-methoxy *s*-triazine	Ciba Geigy
Prometryne	Caparol	2,4-*bis*-(isopropylamino)-6-(methylthio)-*s*-triazine	Ciba Geigy
Pronamide	Kerb	N-(1,1-dimethyl-2-propynyl)3,5-dichlorobenzamide	Rohm and Haas
Propachlor	Ramrod	2-chloro-N-isopropylacetanilide	Monsanto
Propanil	Rogue, Stam-F34	3',4'-dichloropropionanilide	Rohm and Haas, Monsanto
Propazine	Milogard	2-chloro-4,6-*bis*(isopropylamino)-*s*-triazine	Ciba Geigy
Propham	IPC Chem-Hoe	isopropyl carbanilate	Pittsburg P. G.
Proximpham	--	O-(N-phenylcarbamoyl)-propanone oxime	Fahlberg List, DDR
Pyrazon	Pyramin	5-amino-4-chloro-2-phenyl-3(2H)-pyridazinone	BASF, Amchem
Rhizobitoxine		2-amino-4-(2-amino-3-hydroxypropoxy)-*trans*-3-butanoic acid	

417

Appendix Table 1. (continued)

Common Name	Trade Name	Chemical Name	Manufacturer
Sebuthylazine		2-chloro-4-ethylamino-6-*s*-butylamino-1,3,5-triazine	Ciba-Geigy
Sesone	Crag I	2-(2,4-dichlorophenoxy)ethyl sodium sulfate	Amchem
Siduron	Tupersan	1-(2-methylcyclohexyl)-3-phenyl urea	duPont
Silvex	Kuron, Weedone	2-(2,4,5-trichlorophenoxy)propionic acid	Dow, Amchem
Simazine	Princep	2-chloro-4,6-*bis*(ethylamino)-s-triazine	Ciba-Geigy
Simetone	Gesadural	2,4-*bis*(ethylamino)-6-methoxy-s-triazine	Ciba-Geigy
Simetryne	GY-BON	2,4-*bis*(ethylamino)-6-(methylthio)s-triazine	Ciba-Geigy
Solan	Pentanochlor	3'-chloro-2-methyl-*p*-valerotoluidide	Niagara
Sumitol	GS 14254	2-sec-butylamino-4-ethylamino-6-methoxy-s-triazine	Ciba-Geigy
Swep	NIA 2995	methyl 3,4-dichlorocarbanilate	Niagara
TCA	TCA	trichloroacetic acid	Amchem, Chipman
TCBC	Randox	trichlorobenzylchloride	Monsanto
Tebuthiuron	Spike, EL 103	N-(5-*tert*-butyl-1,3,4-thiadiazole-2yl)-N,N'-dimethyl-urea	
Terbacil	Sinbar	3-*tert*-butyl-5-chloro-6-methyl uracil	Elanco
Terbuthylazine		2-chloro-4-ethylamino-6-*t*-butylamino-1,3,5-triazine	duPont
Terbutol	Azak	2,6-di-*tert*-butyl-*p*-tolyl methylcarbamate	Ciba-Geigy
Terbutryn	Igran	2-(*tert*-butylamino)-4-(ethylamino)-6-(methylthio)-s-triazine	Hercules
TH-1568A	ACNQ	2-amino-3-chloro-1,4-naphthoquinone	Ciba-Geigy
Triallate	Avadex BW, Fargo	S-(2,3,3-trichloroallyl)-diisopropyl thiocarbamate	Takeda Chem. Ind.
Tribonate		2,4-dinitrophenyl-[2-(*sec*-butyl)-4,6-dinitrophenyl carbonate]	Monsanto
			Vondelingenplaat

Tricamba	Banvel-T	3,5,6-trichloro-*o*-anisic acid	Velsicol
Triclopyr		[(3,5,6-trichloro-2-pyridinyl)oxy] acetic acid	
Trietazine	Gesafloc	2-chloro-4-(diethylamino)-6-(ethylamino)-*s*-triazine	Ciba-Geigy
Trifluralin	Treflan	α,α,α-trifluoro-2,6-dinitro-*N*,*N*-dipropyl-*p*-toluidine	Elanco
Trimeturon	Bayer 40557	1-(*p*-chlorophenyl)-2,3,3-trimethyl pseudourea	Bayer
Tri-PE	Dimexan	Dimethyl xanthic disulfide	Fab. Chem. P. V.
Tritac	Tritac-EC, Tritac-10G	2,3,6-trichlorobenzyloxypropanol	Hooker
2,3,6-TBA	Trysben, Benzac	2,3,6-trichlorobenzoic acid	Amchem, duPont
2,4-D		(2,4-dichlorophenoxy) acetic acid	Many companies
2,4-DB	Butoxone, Butyrac	4-(2,4-dichlorophenoxy) butyric acid	Amchem, Chipman
2,4-DEB	Sesin	2-(2,4-dichlorophenoxy) ethyl benzoate	Union Carbide
2,4-DEP	Falone	*tris*-2-(2,4-dichlorophenoxy)ethyl phosphite	Uniroyal
2,4-DES	Sesone	sodium 2-(2,4-dichlorophenoxy)ethyl sulfate	Union Carbide
2,4,5-T	2,4,5-T	(2,4,5-trichlorophenoxy)acetic acid	Amchem, Dow, Monsanto
2,4,5-TES	Natrin	sodium 2-(2,4,5-trichlorophenoxy)ethylsulfate	Union Carbide
Vermolate	Vernam	*S*-propyl dipropylthiocarbamate	Stauffer
Vorlex		Methyl isothiocyanate	Morton Salt

Appendix Table 2.

A.   Classification of Herbicides

INORGANIC HERBICIDES

Acids

Arsenic acid	Arsenic trioxide
Arsenious acid	Sulfuric acid

Salts

Ammonium sulfamate	Potassium cyanate
Ammonium sulfate	Sodium arsenate
Ammonium thiocyanate	Sodium arsenite
Boron salts	Sodium azide
Calcium cyanamid	Sodium chlorate
Copper nitrate	Sodium chloride
Copper sulfate	Sodium dichromate
Hexafluorate	Sodium pentaborate
Iron sulfate	Tribonate, Tri-PE
Potassium azide	Tricalcium arsenate
Potassium chloride	

ORGANIC HERBICIDES

Oils

Diesel oil	Stoddard solvent
Polycyclic aromatic oils	Stove oil
Paraffin additives	Xylene-type aromatic oils

ORGANIC HERBICIDAL COMPOUNDS

1.   Aliphatics

Acrolein	DBA
Allyl alcohol	Glytac
Benzadox	HCA
Bidisin	Methylbromide
Chlorfenprop-methyl	Monoxone
Chloropicrin	Orga 3045
Chloropon	TCA
Dalapon	Tridex

2.   Amides

Alachlor	Diphenamid
Butachlor	Karsil
Butam	MCAA
Carbetamide	Monalide

CDAA   Napromide
CDEA   Naptalam
Chlorthiamid   Oryzalin
Cyprazole   Perfluidone
Cypromid   Profluralin
Delachlor   Pronamide
Dicryl   Propachlor
Dinitramine   Propanil
                             Solan

3. Arsenicals
    AMA   Hexaflurate
    Arsenate calcium   MAA
    Arsenate sodium   MAMA
    Cacodylic acid   MSMA
    Calar   No-Crab
    CMA   Pencal
    DSMA

4. Benzoics
    Bifenox   PBA
    Chloramben   Tricamba
    Dicamba   2,3,6–TBA

5. Carbamates
    Asulam   Ethiolate
    Barban   Karbutilate
    Carbasulam   Phenmedipham
    Chlorbufam   Propham
    Chlorpropham   Proximpham
    Cycloate   Swep
    Desmedipham   Terbutol
    Dichlormate

6. Dipyridiliums
    Cyperquat   Morphamquat
    Difenquat   Paraquat
    Diquat   Triclopyr

7. Nitriles
    Bromoxynil   Diphenatrile
    Cyanazine   Ioxynil
    Dichlobenil   Procyazine

8. Nitroanilines
    Benefin   Fluchloralin
    Butralin   Isopropalin
    Chlornidine   Nitralin

Dinitramine   Oryzalin
Dipropalin   Trifluralin

9. Phenols and Phenylethers
     Bromophenoxim   DMPA
     Dinophenate   DNOC
     Dinoprop   Etinofen
     Dinosam   Fluorodifen
     Dinoseb   Medinoterb-acetate
     Dinoseb-acetate   M0338, M0500
     Dinoterb-acetate   PCP
                               Nitrofen

10. Phenoxys
     Dichlorprop   2,4–D
     Erbon   2,4–DB
     MCPA   2,4–DEB
     MCPB   2,4–DEP
     MCPES   2,4–DES
     Mecoprop   2,4,5–T
     Sesone   2,4,5–TES
     Silvex

11. Pyridazones
     Brompyrazon   Norflurazone
     Chlorazon   Oxapyrazon
     Dimethazone   Pyrazon

12. Thiocarbamates
     Benthiocarb   Metham
     Butylate   Molinate
     CDEC   Pebulate
     Diallate   Triallate
     EPTC   Vernolate

13. Triazines
     Ametryne   Prometone
     Atratone   Prometryne
     Atrazine   Propazine
     Aziprotryn   Sebuthylazine
     Cyanazine   Simazine
     Cyprozine   Simetone
     Desmetryne   Simetryne
     Dipropetryn   Sumital
     Ipazine   Terbuthylazine
     Methometon   Terbutryn
     Methoprotryn   Trietazine
     Metribuzin
     Norazine

14. Triazoles

    Amitrole   Amitrole–T

15. Uracils

    Bromacil   Terbacil
    Lenacil

16. Ureas

Anisuron	Isonoruron
Benzomarc	Karburylate
Benzthiazuron	Linuron
Buturon	Methabenzthiazuron
Chlorbromuron	Methiuron
Chloroxuron	Metobromuron
Chlortoluron	Metoxuron
Cycluron	Monolinuron
Difenoxuron	Monuron
Diuron	Monuron-TCA
Fenuron	Neburon
Fenuron-TCA	Siduron
Fluometuron	Tebuthiuron
	Trimeturon

17. Unclassified Herbicides

Banair	Fenac
Bandane	Flumezin
Benazolin	Flurenol
Benoxazole	Fluromidine
Bensulide	Glyphosate
Bentazon	Haloxidine
Bentranil	Methazole
Benzazin	MH
Chlorflurazol	NOA
Chlorfluorenol	Nortran
Dazomet	Nortron
DCPA	Oxadiazon
Decazolin	Picloram
Destun	PMA
Dichlone	Rhizobitoxine
Dimexan	TCBC
Endothall	TH–1568A
EXD	Tri-PE
	Vorlex

Herbicide Persistence in Irrigated Soils
by
S. R. Radosevich, C. L. Elmore, and W. B. McHenry

The following table was developed from a variety of sources and reflects what we believe to be a *minimum* time period a herbicide might be expected to carry-over in soil *under ideal conditions*. The material in the following table should *not* be used as a replacement for label suggestions on planting a subsequent crop.

Appendix Table 3.
Relative Persistence of Certain Herbicides in Agricultural Soils
Values Based on Phytotoxicity to Susceptible Plants.

Herbicide	Rate (1b/A)	Persistence* (weeks)
phenol:		
PCP (pentachlorophenol)	18–27	2–5
DNBP (dinitro)	1–10	2–5
phenoxy:		
2,4–D	1–4	2–5
2,4–DB	1–4	3–6
MCPA	1–4	3–10
mecoprop (MCPP)	1–4	4–6
2,4,5–T	1–4	4–8
silvex	1–4	2–6
organic arsenicals:		
DSMA	2–4	None Elemental ar-
MSMA	2–4	None senic compon- ent will remain in treated soils.
cacodyllic acid	3–4	1–2
bipyridylium:		
diquat	.5–1	None Herbicide
paraquat	.5–1	None inactivated by adsorption to soil particles but herbicide may not be degraded.
aliphatic acid:		
TCA	4–30	8–12
dalapon	5–10	2–6

*Values may vary according to differences in soil type, soil moisture, and organic matter.

aryl carbamate:

IPC	4–8	3–6
CIPC	2–8	4–8
CIPC + PPG-124 (Furloe®)	2–8	6–12
barban (Carbyne®)	.25–1	2–3

thiocarbamates:

EPTC (Eptam®)	2–6	6–8
butylate (Sutan®)	3–4	4–6
vernolate(Vernam®)	2–4	4–8
pebulate (Tillam®)	4–6	4–8
cycloate(Ro-Neet®)	3–6	6–12
diallate (Avadex®)	1–2	6–8
triallate (Avadex BW®)	1–1.5	4–8
CDEC (Vegadex®)	3–6	4–6

acetanilide:

aachlor (Lasso®)	1–4	6–10
propachlor (Ramrod®)	3–6	4–8

others:

amitrole (Amino triazole®)	2–10	2–6
bromoxynil (Brominal®)	.5–1	1–4
nitrofen (Tok®)	2–6	5–10
fluorodifen (Preforan®)	2–4	4–8
endothall (Endothal®)	1–6	4–8
glyphosate (Roundup®)	2–8	1–3

Herbicide	Rate (1b/A)	Persistence* (months)

aryl aliphatic acids:

dicamba (Banvel®)	1	1½–2
	4	6–8
2,3,6–TBA (Benzac®, Trysben®)	4	4–6
	20	18–24
fenac (Fenac®)	4	8–12
	20	18–24
chloramben (Amiben®)	2–4	1½–2

substituted amides:

diphenamid (Enide®, Dymid®)	4–6	3–6
Napropamide (Devrinol®)	1–2	2–4

nitroanilines:

trifluralin (Treflan®)	.75	8–12
	3	18–24

*Values may vary according to differences in soil type, soil moisture, and organic matter.

Herbicide	Rate (1b/A)	Persistence* (months)
benefin (Balan®)	.75	3–5
	3	8–10
nitralin (Planavin®)	.75	6–8
	3	17–18
butralin (Amex 820®)	.75	2–3
	3	6–8
dinitramine (Cobex®)	.75	3–5
	3	12–16
profluralin (Tolban®)	.75	6–8
	3	15–16
oryzalin (Surflan®)	.75	6–8
	3	14–16
isopropalin (Paarlan®)	.75	5–6
	3	10–12
ureas:		
linuron (Lorox®)	1–3	3–4
diuron (Karmex®)	1–3	6–8
	5–6	12–18
monuron (Telvar®)	1–3	6–8
	5–6	12–18
chlorbromuron (Maloran®)	1	1.5–2
	4	3–4
chloroxuron (Tenoran®)	2	2–3
	8	4–6
fluometuron (Cotoran®)	1	3–4
	4	12
siduron (Tupersan®)	2	1–2
	8	4–6
triazines:		
atrazine (Aatrex®)	1	6–8
	4	15–18
simazine (Princep®)	1	8–10
	4	18–20
propazine (Milogard®)	1	6–8
	4	18–20
prometone (Pramitol®)	1	10–12
	4	18–24
prometryne (Caparol®)	1	1–2
	4	3–5
ametryne (Evik®)	1	1–2
	4	5–6

*Values may vary according to differences in soil type, soil moisture, and organic matter.

terbutryn (Igran®)	1	3–4
	4	8–12
GS–14254 (Sumitol®)	1	5–6
	4	15–18
cyanazine (Bladex®)	1	1–2
	4	3–4
cyprazine (Fox–4®)	1	5–6
	4	3–4

uracils:

bromacil (Hyvar–X®)	1	5–6
	4	20–24
terbacil (Sinbar®)	1	5–6
	4	20–24

others:

pyrazon (Pyramin®)	1	1
	4	2–3
benusulide (Betasan®)	4–6	6–8
	10–15	10–16
picloram (Tordon®)	.5–3	18–24

*Values may vary according to differences in soil type, soil moisture, and organic matter.

AUTHOR INDEX

Numbers in italic indicate bibliographic references.

INDEX